The Machine Age

The Machine Age

An Idea, a History, a Warning

ROBERT SKIDELSKY

ALLEN LANE
an imprint of
PENGUIN BOOKS

ALLEN LANE

UK | USA | Canada | Ireland | Australia
India | New Zealand | South Africa

Allen Lane is part of the Penguin Random House group of companies
whose addresses can be found at global.penguinrandomhouse.com.

First published by Allen Lane 2023
001

Copyright © Robert Skidelsky, 2023

The moral right of the author has been asserted

Set in 12/14.75pt Dante MT Std
Typeset by Jouve (UK), Milton Keynes
Printed and bound in Great Britain by Clays Ltd, Elcograf S.p.A.

The authorized representative in the EEA is Penguin Random House Ireland,
Morrison Chambers, 32 Nassau Street, Dublin D02 YH68

A CIP catalogue record for this book is available from the British Library

ISBN: 978-0-241-24461-6

To my grandchildren

Contents

Contents

Preface

This book tells three stories about the impact of machines on the human condition: on the way we work, on the way we live and on our possible future. The stories follow in order, since they relate the growing intrusion of machines into our lives over time; but they are linked together by both history and anticipation, from the first simple machines to the complex technology of our own day, in which interconnected systems of machines colonize an increasing range of activities of hand and brain. Each story brings us nearer to the cliff edge at which every increase in our own freedom to choose our circumstances seems to increase the power of technology to control those circumstances. Each story contains within it a vision of heaven and hell: the promise of freedom from necessity, from religious dogma and from natural disaster confronts its opposite in the spectre of uselessness, of algorithmic dictatorship and of physical extinction. The resistance of humans to schemes for improving their conditions of life is one of the constants, and paradoxes, of all three stories. It has rarely led technologists and social engineers to conclude that their schemes might affront some basic requirement of human flourishing, preferring to attribute resistance to obstinacy, stupidity, ignorance and superstition.

Its inspiration was a short essay by John Maynard Keynes, 'Economic Possibilities for Our Grandchildren' (1930). Extrapolating from the progress of technology in his own lifetime, Keynes predicted that his putative grandchildren would have to work only three hours a day 'to satisfy the old Adam in us'. The theological reference was explicit: machines would do most of our work for us, making possible a return to Paradise, where 'neither Adam delved nor Eve span'. Keynes's prediction was rooted in the very old idea that, once the material needs of humanity had been met, a space would be opened up for the 'good' life. Efficiency in production was not good in itself, but the means to the good, and only insofar as it was the means. Keynes did not say that individuals, freed from work, would necessarily choose to lead a good life; rather that this choice would be open to them. Machines were simply a means to an end.

The idea came to me of updating Keynes's essay in prophecy, taking into account not just what has happened since 1930, but factors which Keynes might have taken into account in 1930. This makes for a much longer composition than Keynes's, but perhaps not longer than his would have been had he not intended to write a *jeu d'esprit* to cheer people up at a time of economic depression.

It turned out that Keynes's prognostication was only partly right. Since 1930 technological progress *has* lifted average real income per head in rich countries roughly five times from $5,000 to $25,000 (in 1990 dollars), much in line with Keynes's expectation, but average weekly hours of full-time work in these countries have fallen by only about 20 per cent, from about 50 to 40 hours, far less than Keynes envisaged. He seems to have got three things wrong.

He ignored the distinction between needs and wants, leading him to neglect the possibility that insatiability might corrupt our Adam, making him not a lover of the good and beautiful, but a slave to junk. It is insatiability, natural and deliberately created, which keeps machines in business, by ensuring that the material requisites of happiness remain permanently scarce. Secondly, Keynes treated work purely as a *cost*, or as economists call it, a *disutility*, whereas it is both a curse *and* the condition of a meaningful life. People weigh the cost of living against the pleasure of work. Thirdly, Keynes ignored the question of distribution, and therefore the question of power. He implicitly assumed that the gains from efficiency improvements would go to everyone, not just to the few. But there is no automatic mechanism to ensure this, and since the ascendancy of neoliberal economics in the last forty years, the social mechanisms for securing real wage growth have weakened or gone into reverse. While some people have reduced their hours of work because they can afford to, many others are compelled to work longer than they want to in a desperate effort to hold on to what they have already got.¹ For this reason the *economic* future facing our own grandchildren is much less rosy than it seemed to Keynes in 1930.

But this isn't the end of the discussion. Like Marx, Keynes believed that the reduction of necessity would automatically lead to an increase in freedom: indeed his economics of full employment was designed to get us over the hump of necessity as quickly as possible. He was curiously blind to the possibility that the machines which freed us from work might colonize our lives. In retrospect the entanglement of actual machines with ideas about how to organize the machinery of living seems inevitable once science took control of both departments. It led to what I call the 'torment of modernity'. In his classic *The Road to Serfdom*, Friedrich Hayek warned against 'the uncritical transfer to the problems of society of the habits of thought of the natural scientist and the engineer'.² But it was precisely the engineering ambition of making society as efficient as the factory or the office that built the modern world and turned Keynes's realm of freedom into Weber's 'iron cage of bondage'. My second story, then, is about the relationship between technology and freedom. It asks the question: is machinery the agent of liberation or entrapment?

The wider possibilities of technology were dramatically visualised in Jeremy Bentham's famous design for a *Panopticon* in 1786. This was an ideal prison system, in which the prison governor could shine a light on the surrounding prison cells from a central watchtower, while himself remaining unseen.³ This would in principle abolish the need for actual prison guards, since the prisoners, aware of being continually surveilled, would voluntarily obey the prison rules. Bentham's ambitions for his invention stretched beyond the prison walls, to schools, hospitals and workplaces. His was a vision of society as an ideal prison, governed by self-policing impersonal rules applicable to all. His key methodology was the one-way information flow: the governor would know all about the prisoners but would himself be invisible.

Bentham's world is coming to pass. Today's digital control systems operate not through watchtowers but through computers with electronic tracking devices, and voice and facial recognition systems. We enter Bentham's prison voluntarily, oblivious to its snares. But once inside, it is increasingly difficult to escape. Platforms and governments can direct the flow of their online communications to us through our devices, while at the same time 'mining' the data about our own tastes and habits. Who gets the better of the bargain is moot.

Keynes was, of course, aware of the malign uses to which surveillance technology was being put in his own time, notably in Nazi Germany and Soviet Russia. But he seems to have been thrown off guard by his belief that free societies provided sufficient safeguards against an Orwellian outcome.[4] He was insensitive to the possibility that surveillance might creep up, unobserved, and even unintended, until it was too late to reverse. So we must alert our grandchildren to the potential malignity of the machinery they take for granted.

'Assuming no important wars and no important increase in population . . .' With these words Keynes briskly dismissed the most obvious impediments to the realization of his utopia. It seems extraordinary that he should have done so at that particular time. Europe had just been through the most destructive war in its history, and in his book *The Economic Consequences of the Peace* (1919) Keynes himself had predicted, accurately as it turned out, that 'vengeance will not limp'; in the same book, he had also attributed the Bolshevik Revolution to the 'disruptive powers of excessive national fecundity'.[5] The possibility that such events might repeat themselves on an ever more horrific scale was not allowed to cloud the sunny prospect he unfolded for his grandchildren. Did he suppose that the First World War had been a sufficient 'wake-up' call? Such abstraction from existential challenges is not possible today. They have become too urgent and encompassing. My third story, therefore, is about the destructive power of uncontrolled technology.

Our planet has always been threatened by natural disasters – the dinosaurs were probably extinguished 60 million years ago by an asteroid hitting the earth. However, for the first time, life on earth is being threatened with anthropogenic disasters – disasters caused, directly or indirectly, by our own activity. Nuclear war, global warming, biologically engineered pandemics now hasten to end not just hopes of a better life but life itself. Men, wrote H. G. Wells, must either become like gods or perish. Some scientists and philosophers conceive of the new God as a super-intelligent machine able to rescue humanity from the flaws of purely *human* intelligence. But how can we be sure that our new God will be benevolent? It is a sign of the times that no one pays much attention to what the old God might have advised in these circumstances.

The consensus view today is that the march of the machines is unstoppable: they will only get more and more powerful and could well spin out of control. Hence the demand, which has migrated from science fiction to science and philosophy, to equip them with moral rules before they go 'rogue'. The problem is to find agreement on moral rules adequate to the task in face of the epistemological nihilism of western societies, and the resurgence of geopolitical conflict between the democracies and autocracies.

So what should we advise our grandchildren? There are basically two alternatives. We can either urge them to seek technical solutions for the variety of life-threatening risks which present technology will bequeath them or we can urge them to reduce their dependence on machines. In writing this book I have come to believe that the first endeavour, while it might salvage fragments of human life, will destroy everything that gives value to it. The second alternative is the only one that makes human sense, but it requires the recovery of a framework of thought , in which religion and science both play their part in directing human life. Einstein put the case with exemplary lucidity: 'science without religion is lame; religion without science is blind'. Such a recovery on a sufficient scale to affect the course of events in time seems to me inconceivable. The arguments of the book, therefore, lead to a sombre conclusion. In biblical terms, a plague of locusts is a necessary prelude to the Second Coming.

The book is over-ambitious. It is primarily about how western civilization came to be captured by the dream of utopia through science and about the successive stages by which this dream turned sour. Based on my own academic grounding in history and economics, it nevertheless trespasses on highly specialized fields of study and is open to the criticisms that scholars usually level against intruders into their protected domains. Each topic dealt with in this book has accumulated a vast specialized literature, much of which I have only been able to scratch the surface of. As Steven Shapin has noted, the interdisciplinary environment is an 'endangered habitat'.[6] My only defence is that the relationship between humans and machines has become the most urgent problem of our time, and that its treatment is properly philosophical, not in the sense of philosophy as a discipline, but in the traditional sense of thinking about the meaning of human life. I have preferred to pursue this inquiry in ordinary language, which invites memories of an earlier language in which such matters were talked about.

I would like to thank the Centre for Global Studies, which supported research for this book. I am especially grateful to my son Edward Skidelsky for the time and effort he took with the manuscript. It is much better as a result. Meghnad Desai and Rodion Garshin have read all or most of the manuscript. They, together with Ewa Atanassow, Massimillano Bolondi, Harold Lind, Edward Luttwak, Michael Mertes, Heinrich Petzold, Peter Radford, Max Skidelsky, Allan Strong, Lanxin Xiang and Junqing Wu have all offered insights from which I have benefited.

My thanks go to Alex Bagenal, Nan Craig, Michael Davies, Rachel Kay, Jack Perraudin, Erik Schurkus, Leanne Stickland, Jessica Tomlinson and Thomas Tozer for their help in research. Special thanks go to Alex Bagenal. Alex's philosophical acumen has been of inestimable help. His contributions, and those of Nan Craig, go beyond the normal work of research assistants. I am grateful to my editor, Ben Sinyor, for many helpful suggestions which have greatly improved the book's structure and style. Needless to say, I remain responsible for the form this book has finally taken, its contents and its faults.

Finally, my thanks go to my wife, Augusta, for her support in my struggle against age and time.

June 2023

Introduction

For most of their history humans used tools and machines. But they did not live in a machine age. That is to say, machines did not determine their conditions of life. Today, we live in a machine age. We humans are 'wired up' parts of a complex technological system. We depend on this system for the way we fight, the way we work, the way we live, the way we think.

The arrival of the 'age of machinery' was announced in 1829 by Thomas Carlyle.[1] As he saw it, humanity had, for the first time, crossed over into a machine civilization composed of four elements: a mechanical philosophy, new practical or industrial arts, the systematic division of labour, and impersonal bureaucracy. Carlyle's elements would come to be united in what Lewis Mumford, a century later, called the 'technological complex'. In the age of machinery, it is the interaction between humans and machines, not between humans and nature, which sets the terms of human existence.

Carlyle's framework offers a helpful way of thinking about how humans have reached this point. He put first 'mechanical philosophy' – the view of the world as a machine (or, as it was then thought, a clock wound up by God). In this view humans were to be understood as mechanisms for the production of value; the scientific method would enable laws of human behaviour to be established, just like the laws of physics. Knowledge of these laws could be used to build a better society. In this book I use the word 'technology' to describe the application of the mechanical philosophy, first to the organization of work and then to the organization of life.

Second came the 'new practical or industrial arts'. This was technology in its narrow sense of applying scientific knowledge to the production of useful things, thus obliterating the classical distinction between *episteme* (knowledge) and *techne* (know-how). The history of machinery had hitherto been one of 'tinkering with tools', based on experience and local knowledge. With the Industrial Revolution came, for the first time, the application of scientific knowledge to production, which, by the nineteenth century, was making possible an unprecedented increase in material wealth that would only accelerate in the twentieth century.

Third was the division of labour. The age of machinery marked a fundamental shift from the practice of a single person making the whole (or the major part of an) object (like the potter at his wheel) to breaking up the different tasks involved in its manufacture into discrete bits, as in Adam Smith's pin factory. This greatly increased the efficiency of production. Specialization of tasks was not just for individuals but for nations: a 'world economy' was born, with nations trading in goods and services for which they were thought to be specially advantaged by climate or aptitude. More and more human tasks have been 'optimized' in this way, leading to the conception of humans as interchangeable 'bits' in national and global supply chains. Specialization in the production of ideas was an important aspect of the division of labour. Fields of study became 'disciplines' with their own hierarchies. Scholars and academics became specialists in small bits of thought, with no idea how these bits linked up with other bits to give shape and meaning to the whole product.

Carlyle's fourth element, 'impersonal bureaucracy', denotes obedience to rules without regard for persons. It is what Weber would call 'rationalization' – the process by which conduct based on custom or emotion is transformed into conduct based on the rational adaptation of means to ends. Weber saw it as the inevitable outcome of the 'death of God'. It is particularly important for understanding modern techniques of control. Today we are governed by digital bureaucrats, whose directions are justified by their scientific rationality and are therefore beyond the affections, compromises and animosities of religion, politics, or personal relationships. With the spread of computer networks the limited possibilities of intrusion by traditional bureaucracies into everyday life are overcome, and their vice of unaccountability is magnified.

Whereas champions of the mechanical philosophy emphasized the benefits of machines in making economic and social processes more rational and therefore efficient, Carlyle offered the key distinction between the inhuman and the inhumane. He contrasted the often *inhumane* conditions of pre-industrial life with the *inhuman* sovereignty of impersonal rules. I try to show how this disharmony between being human and humanity explains the torment of modernity. I also claim that this is a uniquely *western* disharmony, exported to the non-European world by western science and western guns.

The book is structured round the application of the mechanical philosophy first to work and then to society. The modern age is dominated by machine-builders of both types, engineers of the body and engineers of the soul, and by the persistent opposition to both by poets, writers, artists.

The first half of this book is principally about the effect of machines on work. The Prologue on robotic hype, ancient and modern, introduces the important mythological idea of the automaton, inanimate matter brought to life by hidden powers, from which today's hype around artificial intelligence ultimately derives. The persistence of such archetypes as humankind moves forward from myth to science is a key feature of our relationship with machines.

Successive chapters discuss the rise of machine civilization, its material and cultural context, its material promises, the emergence of Britain as the 'first industrial nation' and the resistance to forced industrialization. The protest and fate of the Luddites, the doomed handloom weavers of early industrial Britain, sets the scene for the current debates about the 'future of work' and the meaning of 'upskilling'. A crucial discussion point is about whether our future is determined by the technology we use.

The following questions dominate today's discussion. Will human job holders be entirely replaced by machines or only partly replaced? Will humans want to reduce their hours of work or consume more? What social arrangements best ensure that the fruits of productivity gains are fairly distributed? What account should the drive to optimize production take of the moral value of work? We will encounter in this discussion the crucial issue of the costs of learning to 'race with the machines', and whether these involve the sacrifice of what it is to be human.

As Carlyle already noticed in 1829, machinery was not just affecting particular industries 'but altering the very fabric of society through the internalisation of mechanical axioms'. The effect of the mechanical axioms was to internalize (make as if our own) a set of norms of behaviour externally prescribed by the engineers of the soul. We would obey Big Brother not because he wielded a big stick, not even because we loved him, but because he talked to us in an irresistibly rational way.

The implications of the rise of the 'mechanical philosophy' have been neatly, if unwittingly, summed up in a question by Rick Fernandez, Google's head of Learning and Development: 'As we optimize our technology, how can we optimize our lives, so we can be our best selves?' The idea of optimizing 'our lives' is very seductive. But it confuses process with purpose. An optimal state of affairs from the point of view of the criminal or the state may be very far from what is optimal from the point of view of society. The second half of the book takes on the implications of attempts to 'optimize our lives'.

One does not, of course, need any special hypothesis to explain the quest of rulers for optimal obedience from their subjects. Spying is, with prostitution, the oldest profession. However, the purposes of control have expanded in line with the promise of science to improve the human condition. Systems of control based on the incorrigibility of human behaviour have yielded to those based on the idea of perfecting it. Since the doctrine of progress took hold in eighteenth-century Europe, social reformers have attempted to correct not specific faults or causes of discontent, but to build societies in which such imperfections are impossible. The social and psychological sciences treat humans as works in progress. The chief example of the radical social engineering project in our time was Soviet communism. It is information technology which has made such 'scaling-up' of control feasible. This was the message of the three great twentieth-century dystopian novels by Yevgeny Zamyatin, Aldous Huxley and George Orwell.

Successive chapters follow the utopian trail from Plato to the Enlightenment, with Christianity offering a contrapuntal theme, in which the Platonic dream of the ideal republic came up against the implacable Augustinian doctrine of original sin. We meet the thinkers of the Enlightenment who impatiently swept aside the Christian obstacle to building an earthly paradise, and attend to the much-debated subject of the relationship between science and religion. Are they opposing principles, as many of the protagonists of both sides thought (and still think), or are they complementary forms of knowledge, and, if so, what might be the terms of their co-existence? The chapter 'The Devil in the Machine' identifies the moment at the end of the eighteenth century when philosophers and writers first started to take account of the disruptive power of technology in their visions of the future. I then go on to describe the political revolt against the 'mechanical philosophy', centred, in my reading, on the German version of Romanticism, and culminating in the barbarism of the Nazis; take stock of the important interwar debate on the 'question of technics'; and survey the passage from utopia to dystopia in the imaginative writing of the nineteenth and early twentieth centuries. Dominating the discussions of Part II is the question of whether the constructivist approach to building society is compatible with what Bertrand Russell called 'the pursuit of truth, with love, with art, with spontaneous delight, with every ideal that men have hitherto cherished.'[2]

Finally, we come to the question of the future to which our technology has led us. At the end of his life, in 1945, H. G. Wells thought that humanity could go either up or down, a thought echoed by contemporary transhumanists. Part III of this book tells of the rise of the computer from its humble beginnings in counting and calculating to the project of creating an artificial intelligence, which I interpret as a deliberate attempt to rescue the quest for perfectibility from the destructive blows inflicted on it by purely *human* intelligence. Natural science, social science and military science have all been heavily

invested in this transformative project, mostly funded by governments and visionary entrepreneurs. The question overshadowing this
part of the book is whether AI will free us finally from the tragic
cycles which have marked human history or whether it is the royal
road to spiritual and physical extinction.

Today it is possible to imagine five pathways to the future. The
first is bullish. Arnold Toynbee extolled the benefits of machines
taking over the mundane tasks of life: 'the transfer of energy . . .
from some lower sphere of being or of action to a higher'.[3] He is in
a long line of technological optimists which includes Karl Marx,
John Stuart Mill, Lewis Mumford and John Maynard Keynes. These
and many others have looked to science and technology to free the
mind from mundane clutter, investing it with higher and ampler
possibilities, a hope which is still alive and well, despite the blows
inflicted on it by the events of the twentieth century.

A second prognosis is optimistic but conditional. One version is
that a better future crucially depends on the replacement of capitalism by socialism. This is the Marxist tradition. Unlike Keynes, who
believed that capitalism would end automatically once it had 'done
its job' of supplying the world with capital goods, Marxists have
argued that the end of capitalism has to be brought about by deliberate political action, otherwise it would continue to put utopia
beyond reach. The other school of conditional optimists are the
technological utopians who believe that the realization of humanity's
'best self' depends on developing super-intelligent machines.

A third possible future is spiritual extinction. This is the grand
theme of dystopian thinking as it emerged at the start of the twentieth century. Science and technology have rendered humans not
superhuman, but subhuman. In Aldous Huxley's *Brave New World*
(1932) human freedom is removed by chemical and psychological
treatment. Huxley said in a 1961 lecture that:

> There will be, in the next generation or so, a pharmacological
> method of making people love their servitude, and producing dicta-
> torship without tears, so to speak, producing a kind of painless

concentration camp for entire societies, so that people will in fact have their liberties taken away from them, but will rather enjoy it, because they will be distracted from any desire to rebel by propaganda or brainwashing, or brainwashing enhanced by pharmacological methods. And this seems to be the final revolution.[4]

A fourth future is apocalyptic. Almost daily, tech experts warn that technology could lead to the extinction of humanity.[5] Technology is the modern Beast of the Apocalypse. Either it precipitates a disaster – a nuclear or ecological holocaust – or it stops working, leaving humans without the means of livelihood. Both these versions of dystopian prophecy imply the destruction of a large part of the human population and the reversion of the 'saved' to a simpler form of life. Mary Shelley's *Frankenstein; or, The Modern Prometheus* (1818) is a prefigurement of technology run amok; E. M. Forster's short story 'The Machine Stops' (1909) imagines what happens when the system of machinery on which we have come to depend seizes up. Films like *The Day the Earth Caught Fire* (1961) picture nuclear explosions precipitating extreme climatic events. At the heart of apocalyptic prophecy is the ancient idea of *hubris*, of man seeking to usurp the place of the gods, and the gods taking their revenge.

Dostoevsky's *Notes from Underground* (1864) opens up a fifth way of casting the net. To the claims of the technician, his narrator responds:

> You . . . want to cure men of their old habits and reform their will in accordance with science and good sense. But how do you know, not only that it is possible, but also that it is *desirable* to reform man in that way? And what leads you to the conclusion that man's inclinations *need* reforming? In short, how do you know that such a reformation will be a benefit to man . . . It may be the law of logic, but not the law of humanity.[6]

Dostoevsky raises the fundamental question of what it is to be a person. His is a lament for the world of choice we have lost – and the world which we might yet regain through religion and simple things. It also points the way to a non-western future for humanity.

Is a non-western humanism possible? The questions unfolded above are questions which have tormented western thinkers since the big technological acceleration in the eighteenth century. My justification for the neglect of eastern thought on these matters is that Carlyle's 'mechanical philosophy' is a western invention, which has been spread round the world by western example, success and conquest. But if this version no longer offers an assured pathway to human liberation, but rather carries a strong risk of destruction, one needs a parallel history of non-western civilizations to get a proper sense of the possible futures facing our planet. In chapter 5 I offer the briefest sketch of such a history, with a few salient reference points for contrast. It remains to be seen whether a technology with meaningful 'Chinese' or 'Indian' characteristics is possible.

The purpose of this book will have been accomplished if it dents the hubris of the engineers of the soul. As St Augustine wrote of the Neoplatonist philosophers of his day: 'They think of themselves as exalted and brilliant with the stars' but end up 'lost in their own ideas'. The book's message is that these ideas will destroy the world we know.

Glossary for the Technologically Challenged

Work, Jobs, Employment

Work is using up energy: a human 'works'; so does a machine. If a
human or a machine does not 'work' it 'runs down'.

Jobs are specific work assignments. They result from the division of
labour into separate tasks. Today they usually involve 'going out
to work' for set periods of time, as in a factory or office. But they
can be done at home. Today the word 'job' normally means paid
employment.

Employment usually means having an employer – someone who
'hires' you to work for them for wages. But there is also self-
employment, which means working for oneself. Today the terms
jobs, work, labour, employment are generally (and imprecisely)
used synonymously.

Leisure and idleness. Leisure is the condition of not having to work for
a living, equivalent to having 'free time'. *Idleness* is doing nothing
at all. The two are therefore not the same, though they are popu-
larly conflated.

Tools, Machines, Robots, Automatons

A *tool* is any object which can be used to make a task easier. The
most important characteristic of the primitive tool is that it is set
to work by muscles, human or animal.

A *machine* is a tool which has been constructed with internal parts,
such as levers, wheels, pulleys, which are 'set in motion' by human
or natural force. Thus a hammer is a tool, an electric drill is a

machine. At what point a tool becomes a machine is fuzzy: is a clock or a watermill a tool or a machine?

Robot (also automaton). The term *robot* was first used to describe a human-looking machine, which performed tasks unthinkingly. It was actually coined by Karel Čapek, the Czech writer, from the word *robota*, which means forced labour or drudgery. A robot is a machine that mimics human functions with limited instructions to perform specific repetitive tasks, e.g. a robotic arm used in car manufacture, or a robotic vacuum cleaner. However, robots are extremely specialized in their tasks, and therefore the tasks for which they can actually replace human activity are still quite limited. We are far from having reached a position where a robot could beat Federer at tennis.

An *automaton (also robot, avatar)* is an archaic version of a robot. They were a mechanism, often in human or animal form, which appears to move spontaneously. Often used for illusions and party tricks. Today we use the word *mechanization* to describe the replacement of physical labour by machines, and *automation* to describe the replacement of routine, repetitive physical and mental tasks by computers.

Computers, Semiconductors, Moore's Law

Computers are literally calculators, or devices for 'adding up' and communicating information and instructions at speed. They date from the Second World War, when electrical calculators started to replace desktop calculators. Today the word 'computer' refers almost always to the digital computer, which operates by logical rules on a string of digits, generally on the binary scale. The importance of the modern digital computer is its ability to carry out computations involving many steps – often millions – at high speed without human intervention. Super-computers are networks of computers used by scientists and engineers to solve calculations that would take humans many thousands of hours to complete.[1] Computers come in different sizes and types, including desktops, laptops, tablets and smartphones.

Semiconductors are the building blocks of computer chips. They allow electricity to pass through them in only one direction. The correct placement of semiconductors on a computer chip creates logic gates allowing electricity and therefore information to cascade through the computer chip, thereby creating the underlying structure the computer needs to speak in its binary language.

Moore's Law, the prediction by the American engineer George Moore in 1965, that the number of transistors per silicon chip will double every year. This was based on the steadily shrinking size of transistors (electronic conductors of information). The higher the density of transistors, the greater the flow of information.

Hardware, Software, Algorithms, Apps, Social Media, Internet

Hardware is the physical object like your desktop, laptop or smartphone.

Software consists of the instructions given to the hardware to find or retrieve the data stored in it. It is the interface between the user and the hardware.

Algorithms are 'procedures or sets of rules used in calculation and problem-solving'.[2] They are used as the base language for all computer programs and apps. Tasks such as 'open Google', 'select that picture', 'play that video-game' are all accomplished with algorithms giving the instructions to the computer.

Apps (applications) are programs for specific retrieval tasks such as making Excel spreadsheets or business accounts or playing your favourite music.

Social media (platforms) are used by people to communicate online. The main platforms are Facebook, Twitter, Instagram and TikTok.

The internet (as defined by ChatGPT): 'The Internet is a global network of connected computers and devices that communicate with each other using a standard set of communication protocols. It enables users to share information and communicate with other users across the world, regardless of their physical location. The Internet is made up of numerous interconnected networks that use a variety of technologies, including wired and wireless connections, to enable the transfer of data between devices.'

Technology, Information Technology, Digitization

Technology is the application of natural science to objects, with the aim of improving their functions. It is the general term for a system of interrelated fixed components (e.g. computers) programmed to perform prescribed tasks in a regular way.

Information Technology (IT) is the study of computers, software and hardware.

Digitization is converting information or instructions into electronic form. Newspapers are now mostly available online: they can be accessed through the internet, using a computer or smartphone. Many companies these days are going through a digitization programme, trying to convert their communications and workflows from analogue to digital.

Artificial Intelligence, Natural Language Processing, Machine Learning, Big Data, Deep Learning, Super-Intelligence

Artificial intelligence (AI) 'is now used to refer to a heterogeneous network of technologies – including machine learning, natural language processing, expert systems, deep learning, computer vision and robotics – which have in common the automation of functions of the human brain'.[3] Researchers distinguish between 'narrow' AI and 'general purpose' AI, depending on whether the AIs are limited to specific tasks or whether they can perform a variety of tasks. 'In contrast to previous technological innovations, AI is a feedback technology, reacting to user input in a non-linear fashion and creating additional decision points in social network'.[4]

Natural language processing (NLP) uses AI to understand the written and spoken word.

Machine learning is a field that trains computers with Big Data.

Big Data is a large quantity of data analysing trends in the economy or social media, used to understand human behaviour. 'Billions of individuals are being minutely tracked from cradle to grave' by information they provide about themselves on social media.[5]

Deep learning is taking machine learning to the next level. It does so by mimicking the human brain's method of analysis. Instead of giving the computer many detailed instructions, it is using an artificial neural network to replicate the functions of the human brain. This allows for far faster and 'smarter' analysis of data than a normal computer.

Super-intelligence is an advanced form of AI in which machines exceed human performance in all tasks. This is as yet only in contemplation, but if realized, it carries obvious risks of AIs enslaving or destroying the merely intelligent.

Metaverse, Virtual Reality, Augmented Reality, Gamification

Metaverse is at the core of the discussions at the moment about the future of the internet. In simple terms it is a vision of the real world brought to life online conjured up by Meta, the company formerly known as Facebook. It is supposed to bring us closer together, help us to learn more and work more efficiently.

Virtual reality is the technology that enables access to the Metaverse. Goggles with LCD screens as lenses can be worn to see the virtual reality right in front of your eyes. While sitting down you have a 360° view of a new surroundings. Imagine not just watching your character act out things in a video game, but becoming the character and seeing the virtual world as they would. A familiar way of describing this experience is that you are *immersed* in the game.

Augmented reality is similar to virtual reality, but the key difference is that you don't lose track of the real world around you. Augmented reality blends both the real world and the virtual reality, overlaying the former with the latter. Imagine looking at your sitting room through the camera and screen of your smartphone and seeing a virtual sofa projected into the space that you can manipulate and move around the room by swiping left or right with your hand. Neither VR nor AR have many practical uses as of yet, but industry leaders hope it will revolutionize the workplace through immersive virtual meetings and increased productivity. Reliance on hardware will be reduced.

Gamification refers to the use of game mechanics in a traditionally non-gaming environment, like a website, the workplace or in schools. It works by engaging the reward system in the brain to make interactions more involving and enjoyable with clients, students or co-workers.

Cybernetics, Neuroscience, Nanotech, Biotech, Cognotech

Cybernetics derives from Greek *kybernetes*, steersman of the ship. Cyberneticians study the ways 'complex systems – whether brains, organisations, swarms of insects or computer networks – are brought under control'.[6]

Neuroscience is the general name for the attempt to link human behaviour to the structure of the brain. It aims to understand the circuits and patterns of neural activity that give rise to mental processes and behaviour. It is estimated that the brain contains 100 billion neurons.

Nanotech is the use of extremely small parts and building blocks to create technology invisible to the human eye. One of its uses in brain research started with a talk entitled 'There's Plenty of Room at the Bottom' by physicist Richard Feynman in 1959. An example of its use given by Gerald Yonas, vice-president and principal scientist of Sandia National Laboratories, New Mexico, is to make it feasible to use brain implants to modify behaviour or brain function.

Biotech is an area of biology which aims to modify living organisms, either by bioengineering or by bioenhancement. The science of both developed rapidly after the decoding of human DNA (deoxyribonucleic acid) in the 1950s as the basic building block of the human body. Having learned the language of the human body, scientists could start changing words or perhaps entire phrases in the book that is our body. This new field is called *bioengineering*. It aims to improve the function of plants and animals by such techniques as tissue engineering, biopharmaceutics and genetic engineering. According to Jose Delgado, 'the ultimate objective of this research [into remote control of several species of animals] is to provide . . . a practical system suitable for human application'. The Human Brain Project aims to fully map the human brain. By doing this we could potentially be able to 'download' our brain and to then 'upload' it onto a computer. This would mean immortality, at least for our minds. Elon Musk's latest brainchild 'Neuralink' aims to implant a chip into our brain to increase the mind–machine interaction. Why wait for our clunky meat sacks to do something when our minds could accomplish the task in milliseconds?

Cognotech arises from a convergence of information technology, nanotech and biotech. 'The interface between nano-, bio-, info- and cognotech is where the exciting discoveries are occurring,' enthuses one scientist. At its heart is *predictive analytics*, which focuses on remote monitoring of brain signals to reveal the search intent of internet users. It can be used, e.g., to discover an intention to blow up a bridge or rob a bank. Biotech and cognotech are the main stuff of current dystopian imagination, having superseded nuclear technology as the focus of disaster narratives.

A *cyborg* is a hypothetical being with both organic and electromechanical parts. So far they exist only in the imagination. The most famous filmic cyborg is played by Arnold Schwarzenegger in *The Terminator*.

Prologue: Robotic Hype, Old and New

'All things are full of gods.'

Thales of Miletus, pre-Socratic Greek philosopher (*c.*626–*c.*545 BCE)

The human relationship with machines has always been a mixture of the practical and magical: humans have found them useful but also mysterious. Today hardly any more people understand how computers work than in the past they understood how natural forces worked. They use them without comprehending them, and this is as much a source of power to their controllers as it once was to priests, magicians, shamans and witch doctors.

In all ancient mythologies the powers of nature were seen as gods. They were masters of human fate, the arbiters of luck, and needed to be kept on side by worship and sacrifice. We read that the

> people [of the Aztec empire] worshipped Quetzalcoatl, the god of light and air, who rescued humanity after the fourth sun had been destroyed by Tezcatlipoca, god of judgement, darkness, and sorcery. In order to appease Tezcatlipoca, he had to be paid off and nourished with the blood of human sacrifice. If this was not sufficient, he would turn the sun black, the world would be rent asunder in a violent earthquake, and Tztzimitl, the goddess of the stars, would slay all of humanity.[1]

The Greeks had a word, *hubris,* for the attempt by humans to usurp the place of the gods in the scheme of life, a presumption which was inevitably followed by *nemesis.* It was exemplified in the legend of Icarus, whose wings melted because he flew too close to the sun. The ancients also built 'automata', or artificial humans, which moved, blinked and spoke automatically.

Pre-modern Hype

The Chinese have a story called 'A Marvellous Automaton', dating from the fifth century BCE, told by the Taoist philosopher Lie Yukou in his *Lieh Tzu*. An artificer, Yen Shih, presented a human-looking contrivance to King Mu and his concubines:

> 'Who is that man accompanying you?' asked the king.
>
> 'That, Sir,' replied Yen Shih, 'is my own handiwork. He can sing and he can act.' The king stared at the figure in astonishment. It walked with rapid strides, moving its head up and down, so that anyone would have taken it for a live human being. The artificer touched its chin, and it began singing, perfectly in tune. He touched its hand and it began posturing, keeping perfect time . . . As the performance was drawing to an end, the robot winked its eye, and made advances to the ladies in attendance.

Taken apart, it was found that all the internal organs were complete, all of them artificial. 'The king tried the effect of taking away the heart, and found that the mouth could no longer speak; he took away the liver and the eyes could no longer see; he took away the kidneys and the legs lost their power of locomotion.'[2]

Ancient automata were frauds, in the sense that they pretended to powers they did not have in order to deceive. This is the basis of all hype. Thus, the statue of the Egyptian god Re was made to speak through a tube connecting its mouth to a hidden priest. Because the observers of this demonstration knew nothing of its hidden mechanisms, they assumed the statue was speaking directly to its worshippers. Artificers in Hellenistic and Roman times also made puppets to amuse. Ancient automata were thus both tools and toys: tools of priestly control and playthings. The effect of both depended, as they still do, on an apprehension of the uncanny, of hidden and unsettling forces pulling the strings behind the scenes. But might it not be possible for science to get these lifeless forms to move genuinely, for 'what', wondered Hobbes centuries later, 'is the heart but a spring; and the nerves, but so many strings; and the joints, but so many wheels, giving motion to the whole body'? The idea of artificial humans was born, and with it the question of what they might be capable of, and whether they were a benefit or a threat.

The ancients sought divine help for four main purposes. The most important was victory in battle. The ancient world was heavily populated by prodigiously powerful fighting gods like Skanda (Hindu), Ares and Athena (Greek) and Thor (Norse). This is not surprising. Pre-moderns spent more time at war than at peace. Bravery was especially highly prized; soldiers craved the assurance of success. Military competition has been history's principal driver of technological innovation. Without it we would hardly have developed the technology we now have. The Greeks imagined bronze warriors like Talos who heated up to repel enemies, dragons' teeth which could sprout into fully formed warriors and eagles who picked out Prometheus' liver. Today's eagles are military drones enhanced with computers and sensors.

The second big preoccupation of pre-modern life was, as it has continued to be, with health. Soma was the main Hindu god of healing, and Apollo counted medicine and healing in his bulging portfolio. Priests, holy men, shamans were the earliest doctors. One apparently incurable condition was death, and, in ancient legend, demigods provided the link between mortality and eternity. Today rejuvenation researchers and transhumanists believe that science can make death optional.

A third context, not surprisingly, was sexual. Female fertility and male prowess were highly prized. Aphrodite and Athena were goddesses of love; Priapus and Shiva were depicted with huge erect phalluses. Pygmalion makes love with an ivory maiden he has sculpted, 'one of the first female android sexual partners in western history', and they have a child. Ancient paraphilia prefigured 'robotophilia'.[3]

Fourth were the gods who brought abundance, like the Hindu Lakshmi or the Roman Pluto (who was also god of the underworld). Hindu worshippers sacrificed to the gods in order to receive cattle, horses and gold. Good fortune was a gift of the gods, not the result of hard work. In Greek mythology only one of the gods was associated with work. He was Hephaestus, the blacksmith or craftsman god, whose crippled body testified to his lowly status in the Olympian hierarchy. Nevertheless, Hephaestus was also the patron of craftsmen and artificers, boosting their social standing. In this lay the promise of a democratic future.

The gift of fire bestowed on humanity by Prometheus to redress his brother Epimetheus' failure to give humans foresight may be read as the first scheme of human improvement. But with it comes the misfortunes decreed by Zeus as punishment for Prometheus' theft, in the form of Pandora, the temptress. Delusion pops out of Pandora's box, with a crooked smile, luring men to their doom. Following the ancient trail of animating matter into the Renaissance and beyond, Victoria Nelson points to the enduring appeal of the uncanny, the feeling that there are worlds which science cannot explain.[4] The Magus – magician, sorcerer, trickster – a devilish figure with 'animating' powers who emerged in late mediaeval times as a shadowy fourth figure in a quartet of theologian, philosopher and alchemist – inspired the Faustian legend of the scientist who sells his soul to the devil in return for power. With Mary Shelley's *Frankenstein*, the 'mad scientist' became a familiar figure of Victorian horror stories.

Thus the imaginative ground for thinking about robots and artificial intelligence had been laid well before the present explosion of robotic hype. Whether singing statues, mobile servants, mechanical ducks and puppets deserve to be considered genuine precursors of invention or scientific hoaxes is less relevant for our purposes than their testimony to the perennial human urge to transcend the human.

Modern Hype

Today's technological hype is driven by the same exaggerated or fraudulent prospectus. The worlds of science fiction and scientific promise have drawn closer together, each stimulating the other, both drawing on ancient imagination. Here is a typical pronouncement in modern business-mission speak:

> AI has moved from the age of discovery to the age of implementation, and the biggest opportunities are in businesses where AI and automation can deliver significant efficiencies and cost savings . . . We have companies in our portfolios developing AI solutions to personalize and gamify [*sic*] math learning, to improve English pronunciation, and even to grade exams and homework. This promises to free teachers from routine tasks, allowing them to spend time building inspirational and stimulating connections with the next generations.
>
> In health care, we have companies combining deep learning and generative chemistry to shorten the drug-discovery time by a factor of three or four. We have also invested in a company that uses AI and big data to optimize supply chains, reducing medication shortages for more than 150 million people living in rural China. I feel particularly confident that AI education and health-care applications are evolving in ways that will benefit current and future generations at scale.[5]

As Simon Colton writes:

> The hype is understandable: technology leaders have to hugely overstate the life-changing power of their AI systems to have any chance of gaining venture capital these days; journalists have to overstate the strength of results from AI projects, to compete in a click-bait environment; and in order to make a name for themselves, politicians and philosophers need to take an extreme and short-term view of AI in order for it to appear relevant and timely.[6]

Behind the hype lies the competitive scramble for money: the taller the story the more money you might succeed in getting behind it. The promise of machines that kill and cure are as fundable today as they were in ancient times. Christian Brose, chief strategy officer of Anduril Industries, a venture-backed defence technology company, and author of the book *The Kill Chain* (2020), is a tireless advocate of revolutionary technologies for war. Prospective weapons are to be controlled by 'neural signals directly from the brain', making it possible for humans to 'direct and oversee the operations of drones and other robotic military systems purely with their thoughts'. It is a promise entirely in line with classical budget-enhancement strategies, predicated on the 'egregious exaggeration of a prospective opponent's capabilities'. China cannot yet manufacture its own advanced integrated circuits, imports of which were blocked by President Trump, but is deemed to be racing ahead in the development of drones. Brose's proposal for overcoming resistance to his reforms is to enlist the support of defence industry lobbyists with promises that their clients will make just as much money with the new as with existing procurement programmes.[7]

The promise of medical improvements has always been a prolific source of hype. The Covid-19 pandemic of 2020–23 predictably turbocharged the insatiable quest for miracle cures. Advocates of AI believe that we are experiencing 'just the start of a revolution in drug discovery that will harness growth in biological and chemical data, computing power and smarter algorithms that can reduce soaring health care bills and create treatments for conditions where we have none'.[8]

The ancients dreamed of immortality. Today immortality research is guaranteed massive funding from high-tech billionaires, who understandably attach high value to their own survival. Twenty-five million people in the USA have paid for indwelling devices (joints, lenses, valves, pacemakers, stents, neural implants, artificial organs) which claim to prolong and improve life. And beyond mere 'Methuselarity' stretches eternity. Famous performers of stage and screen can be brought back to life as avatars. And cosmic immortality might be achieved by firing 'digital minds' into space.

Hype can easily slide into fraud. Theranos, a Silicon Valley biotech start-up, claimed to have developed a portable desktop technology which could diagnose hundreds of diseases with a single drop of blood. In 2023, its charismatic founder and CEO, Elisabeth Holmes, was sentenced to eleven years in jail for defrauding investors and misleading millions of users with her fake technology.[9] Sam Bankman-Fried's 'church of benevolence' became a huge cryptoscam, and he faces a total of 155 years in jail.[10]

The Mad Max of the AI world is the South African tech magnate Elon Musk. The richest person in the world (net worth end of 2021 almost $300 billion), Musk's career started in the 1990s, when he founded the company which would later become PayPal. Now he is known as the man behind many of Silicon Valley's best-advertised ventures. Musk's electric-car company Tesla has developed technology that can, apparently safely, entirely automate the process of driving; his 'Boring Company' is working on plans to create an underground network of 'hyperloop' tunnels in order to solve Los Angeles's traffic problems; and his company SpaceX promises to establish a colony on Mars to 'preserve the light of consciousness'.

In late August 2020, Musk held a public demonstration of a pig – Gertrude – into the brain of which had been implanted a computer chip the size of a coin. The stunt was the first public unveiling of so-called 'brain–machine interface' technology, developed by one of Musk's technology ventures, Neuralink, that would theoretically allow the brain to be manipulated by electrical signals produced by a chip sitting just below the skull. When Gertrude sniffed at the straw in her sty or ate food given to her by a handler, a graph tracking her neural activity registered the action. The immediate hope for the technology is medical: if it can be safely implanted in humans, it could be used to cure neurological disorders ranging from addiction to anxiety and blindness. In the long term, Musk's ambitions for Neuralink are stratospheric: brain 'augmentation' technologies will, he hopes, usher in an era of 'superhuman cognition', in which computer chips to optimize mental functions will be easily and cheaply available. The procedure to implant them will be fully automated and minimally invasive – something you could do during your lunch break. And every few years, as the technology improves, the chip could be taken out and replaced with a new model, just as consumers buy the latest iPhone. If this sounds like something lifted from science fiction, it is: Musk admits that his interest in brain augmentation came from reading Iain Banks' series of novels the *Culture*.[11] Dream or nightmare? It is so far above all a PR stunt: in reality, Musk is nowhere near mastering the human (or indeed any other) brain.

Elon Musk's augmented human is a cyborg – a brain–computer interface. Another line of hype promises super-intelligent machines. In 2005, the techno-utopian Ray Kurzweil predicted the emergence of 'conscious robots' in 2045. At this surprisingly precise moment would come a 'technological singularity' or 'tipping point', after which the further development of technology would be taken over by the machines themselves, and technological progress would speed up exponentially. The premise is that machines as intelligent as the most intelligent humans would be able to develop super-intelligent versions of themselves far more quickly than the flickering intelligences of humans would allow. Kurzweil thought that this super-intelligence could retain some inheritances of human intelligence, but for all intents and purposes would represent something truly new, better, posthuman. Following the singularity, Kurzweil divined, this intelligence could 'radiate outwards' from the earth in the form of tiny, self-replicating probes crewed by nanorobots, first into the solar system, then interstellar space, then the galaxies and so on, until the entire universe was suffused with intelligent, albeit synthetic, life. Echoing Kant, Kurzweil refers to this process as the universe 'waking up'.[12] There is an appealing mysticism to Kurzweil's prophecy which belies the poverty of his thinking.

The single event that put AI on front pages the world over was IBM Deep Blue's victory over the world chess champion, Garry Kasparov, in six matches in May 1997. It was twenty-one years after psychology professor Eliot Hearst of Indiana University declared that the only way for a computer program to win a single game against a professional 'would be for the master, perhaps in a drunken stupor . . . to commit some once-in-a-year blunder'. Today, there are separate chess tournaments for computers because humans can no longer compete with them on equal terms. However, it turned out that computers plus humans could beat humans or computers on their own. This has suggested to optimists that over a wide range of cognitive tasks, computers would not replace humans but complement them.

Deep Blue was mainly an input-output machine, consuming information from multiple systems and mechanically applying it to the problem at hand. A further step came in 2016 when Google's DeepMind program AlphaGo defeated Lee Sedol, the world's top player, over five games of Go, the most complex board game in the world. A year later, AlphaGo itself was defeated in 100 straight games by an improved version of itself, AlphaZero. The novelty of AlphaGo was that it 'learned for itself' over hundreds of millions of games. It was given not a program, but a task, and told to get on with it. In producing something that wasn't inside the data, Alpha-Go foreshadowed a higher level of artificial intelligence. The only human input was to set the task: no humans were needed for the operation itself.

The last few years have seen a torrent of wild extrapolation from computer achievement in the closed world of board games to the open game of life. If computers can play chess better than humans, why could they not write better novels or music? The ambition of Demis Hassabis, former chess master, whose brainchild DeepMind was, is to 'solve intelligence' and then 'use it to solve everything else', by building a 'general learning' AI system. The latest claim for DeepMind is that it has 'cracked the machinery of life'. By working out the 'true structure' of the proteins which make up living things, it will enable us to produce 'drugs and enzymes and all the additional tools we need to improve the human condition'.[13] In their sober moments, scientists know such enabling discoveries are only in prospect and, if feasible, might be weaponized by states or terrorists to destroy human life. Yet they are tempted by power and research grants and, like Icarus, they are in love with the sun.

Elon Musk, Ray Kurzweil, Demis Hassabis *et hoc genus omne* represent the latest iteration of a story which uniquely combines scientific ambition, the quest for power and greed for money. It must always have been thus.

We have inherited two contrasting stories about humans and machines. Science tells us that a machine cannot be anything other than a slave of our purposes, since we alone supply it with the directives which cause its activity. By contrast, the animist tradition endows it with sources of action independent of us, and hence the potential to intervene in our lives on behalf of a higher power, for good or evil. Today's vision of transhuman intelligence seems to owe something to both traditions. Science tells us that we cannot create such a being – or at least its creation is so far off as to be not worth thinking about. And yet predictions of its imminent arrival, whether in the form of souped-up augmented biology or supercharged machinery, or a mixture of the two, tap deep pockets of credulity and money.

PART I

The Mechanization of Work

The Coming of Machines

'Technology outwits Nature.'

Friedrich Klemm

Why did technology take so long in coming; to put it another way, why did it take so long for humans to get from tools to machines? In the famous scene at the start of Kubrick's film *2001: A Space Odyssey*, one of our fur-covered ancestors picks up a bone from a skeleton lying on the ground and realizes that it can be used to fight off enemies. Having killed the leader of a marauding group, this humanoid throws the bone up in the air in triumph, where it transforms before our eyes into a slender spaceship speeding towards Jupiter. The message is clear: man's technological odyssey is wired into his brain. 'It is the intrinsic dynamic of humankind,' writes Norbert Elias, 'from which ultimately the successful striving for ever faster means of transport, motor cars, aeroplanes and spacecraft derived its force.'[1]

However, this take-off story encounters a big problem. It took several hundred thousand years for the bone to become the spaceship. Perhaps the human brain was not yet fully developed. But ten thousand years ago, and with the start of settled agriculture, our brains were fully formed. Yet it still took thousands of years to get from bows and arrows to machine guns. Anyone who believes that technological progress is hard-wired into human nature will need to confront the fact that there were long periods, lasting thousands of years, when there was almost no technological progress at all. And this is true of all civilizations. Further, it started in one part of the world – north-west Europe – and spread from there to others. There was no technological dynamism elsewhere, and none to this day in the few human societies which the West has not yet reached. Dynamism cannot be dormant: it is either there or not. Certain things, it seems, have to happen or have to change, for societies to be set on a technological path.

Here is the puzzle of stagnation as it appeared to Keynes in 1930:

> From the earliest times of which we have record – back, say to two thousand years before Christ – down to the beginning of the eighteenth century, there was no very great change in the standard of life of the average man living in the civilised centres of the earth. Ups and downs certainly. Visitations of plague, famine, and war. Golden intervals. But no progressive, violent change. Some periods perhaps 50 per cent better than others – at the utmost 100 per cent better – in the four thousand years which ended (say) in A.D. 1700 . . . Almost everything which really matters and which the world possessed at the commencement of the modern age was already known to man at the dawn of history. Language, fire, the same domestic animals which we have today, wheat, barley, the vine and the olive, the plough, the wheel, the oar, the sail, leather, linen and cloth, bricks and pots, gold and silver, copper, tin, and lead – and iron was added to the list before 1000 B.C. – banking, statecraft, mathematics, astronomy, and religion.

The lack of progress, Keynes thought, was caused by two things: 'the remarkable absence of important technical improvements and . . . the failure of capital to accumulate'.[2] But his essay provides no explanation of these facts. Why did the inventive fire, supposedly hard-wired into the human brain, flicker so feebly for so long? And why did it then suddenly burst into flame? The places to look for an answer are in attitudes to nature and attitudes to property.

Attitude to Nature

In the pre-modern world there was much more acceptance of things as they were. The natural environment was determining, and work was fitted to its requirements. The Greeks distinguished *techne* and *episteme*, skill and knowledge. *Techne* was acquired from experience of nature, whereas *episteme* was knowledge of how nature worked. The eventual union of *techne* and *episteme* opened the way to the technological momentum of our day.

Skill was learned from nature. The pre-Socratic philosopher Democritus believed that we learned our most important technical skills by *mimesis*, or copying animals: 'spinning and mending from the spider, housebuilding from the swallow'. Roger Bacon, the thirteenth-century monk known as the 'Doctor Mirabilis', anticipated 'flying machines . . . in which a man . . . may beat the air with wings like a bird'.[3]

In the seventeenth and eighteenth centuries CE, the idea of learning from nature was gradually replaced by the idea of mastering nature. This was made feasible by the development of seeing and hearing machines like telescopes, microscopes, spectacles and clocks. The sixteenth-century Spanish educator Juan Luis Vives (1493–1540) was already entreating scholars to 'enter into the workshops and factories, and ask questions of the artisans'.[4] Such a prescription would have been unthinkable a few centuries earlier. Likewise, the character of the polymath or Renaissance man, typified by Leonardo da Vinci or Galileo, whose expertise comfortably straddled the liberal and mechanical arts, was made possible only by the newly raised status of technical knowledge.

Roger Bacon's seventeenth-century namesake, Francis Bacon, offered a brilliant rationale for the new attitude: Proteus, he wrote, was 'forced by art to do that which without art would not be done'.[5] Nature ceased to set a conceptual or moral limit to human ingenuity; rather it became, in Heidegger's phrase, a 'standing reserve' to be exploited at will. However, technics did not really become technology in the modern sense until the advent of electronics and atomic energy in the late nineteenth and early twentieth centuries. It was only when technical innovation became institutionalized in research laboratories and corporations, and transport and communication costs fell dramatically, that technology reached a point when it was constantly revolutionizing itself. It is scientifically based technology rather than pure science which defines the way we now think about our world. All mythological and religious understandings of our relationship with nature have fallen by the wayside and continue to exist, if at all, outside the walls of our scientific civilization.

Technology has lost all contact with imitating nature. Non-western societies learned their technology from imitating western technology. All of us are now expected to learn it from imitating computers.

Capitalism

In the pre-modern world, wealth was largely disconnected from work. It was inherited, acquired by conquest or plunder, and spent on politics, war, grand buildings and lavish display. It was only in the sixteenth and seventeenth centuries that control of wealth started to pass to a new class of 'capitalists', private property owners for whom wealth was the reward of work, and its continuous increase a sign of virtue. The concentration of wealth in this class provided capitalism's 'start-up' fund. The bourgeoisie, wrote Karl Marx, 'cannot exist without constantly revolutionizing the means of production'.[6]

The scientific revolution, with its promise to reveal nature's secrets and the idea that wealth was to be accumulated rather than spent, jointly created the technological dynamism of the modern world. Its impact on living standards, the prevention and cure of disease, and military technology has been colossal. It has also exposed us to huge dangers. We are left with the question: is technology now irreversible? Are our futures determined by the machines we now use?

Determinisms

Technological determinism is the theory that our lives are determined by our tools and techniques. The conventional wisdom is that our way of living has come to depend on continual technological innovation. Technology produces social structures which then require the continuation of technology. The technological system, that is, has become fully autonomous. Whatever caused it in the first place, once it has achieved a certain momentum, it creates its own draught. Moreover, it is global: all parts of the world, European and non-European, are locked into the same automatism. This is the view of Jacques Ellul, for whom technique fills the void created by the 'erasure of substantive ends'.[7] By contrast Langdon Winner argues that technology remains subject to political choice.[8] As always, the truth lies somewhere in between. There are many intermediate positions, ranging from 'soft' determinism to the claim that different cultures retain some freedom to decide their future.

Technological determinism today comes in two packages, 'hard' and 'soft'. The claim of the 'hard' determinists is encapsulated in the guidebook of the Chicago World Fair of 1933: 'Science finds – Industry applies – Man conforms'.[9] In this account, technology became unstoppable once science started to direct it. Many who are not knowingly determinists cannot imagine a future which is not determined by computer science.

At present, belief in 'hard' technological determinism is not tenable. Machines today do not determine anything. Without human animators, machines are just collections of lifeless parts. Someone, somewhere builds and sets the machines in motion. However, if we think in terms of a technological 'system' made up of interacting human and machine parts, the question of who controls which part, while still important, is secondary. It is the logic of the system itself which determines the behaviour of controllers and users alike.

Much more plausible today is 'soft' determinism. The 'soft' determinist argument is that our technology does not determine our choices, but sets the 'frame of necessities' or 'constraints' within which our power of choice operates. Our choices are shaped by what we have and what we would lose by not having it; and what we have is a technologically based infrastructure of living which carries the expectation of continuing improvement.[10] Contemporary society has put all its eggs in the scientific-technological basket; it is 'path dependent'. Exit to the Stone Age or even Middle Ages is not a voluntary social choice: it can only be compelled by catastrophe. We operate within the limits set by our dependence on machinery.

The *cost* of giving up technology was dramatically brought home to policymakers when they were presented in 1944 with the Morgenthau Plan for pastoralizing Germany after the Second World War. They abandoned the idea when it was pointed out that, if it were implemented, half of the German population would starve to death.[11] For such reasons a *voluntary* choice for a less technologically intensive future cannot happen, except for small or less-developed communities. This conclusion does not exclude the possibility that the 'frame of necessities' may change.

However, even 'soft' determinism' may be questioned. There is no single science, but different branches of science which ask different questions, have different theoretical frameworks and suggest different applications. As a journalist put it: 'We might say yes to penicillin, electricity, and mains drinking water and no to nuclear bombs, intercontinental commercial flight and disposable plastic.'[12] In practice this lacks plausibility. It presupposes the existence of a universal standard by which to judge the value of different kinds of technology. In a value-relative world, this will be exceedingly hard to come by.

More plausible is the claim that technology is unstoppable because we cannot unlearn what we already know. To this there are two answers. The first is that it conflates discovery with application. We may not be able to command what science discovers (though totalitarians try to do just this), but application depends on demand for that particular technology at that particular time and for that particular purpose. There are many examples in history of lines of application which have been blocked, eugenics being one example. What appears in retrospect as the determined outcomes of cumulative processes may be the result of choices which might have gone the other way, or simple luck. That something is irreversible after it has happened is not the same as saying it was determined in advance.

The second answer is that it ignores the possibility that knowledge can be destroyed. This has already happened several times in history, by accident or deliberately. The great fire of the library of Alexandria in Roman times destroyed much of the accumulated knowledge of the ancient world. With the post-Roman fracture of the Mediterranean into Christian and Muslim realms, knowledge of Greek philosophy disappeared in Europe, except for some texts of Aristotle. Nor is knowledge electronically stored in the cloud safe from the burning or banning of books. In his dystopian novel *A Canticle for Leibowitz* (1959), the author, Walter Miller, imagines a nuclear holocaust ushering in a new dark age, in which science is preserved only in a remote monastery. If our own system of electronic storage stops functioning, by accident or design, knowledge is destroyed. Knowledge depends on access: knowledge without access does not exist.

Technical stagnation over a period of several thousand years should alert us to the possibility that the technological momentum of the last 250 years, while being a crucial episode in the history of our species, may be a 'blip', a consideration reinforced by the fact that the changed attitudes to nature and to wealth outlined above were European exports to the non-European world, rather than being indigenous growths in the latter. Telling against the idea of the blip is the competitive dynamic released by Europe's overseas expansion. Those like Marx and Keynes who envisaged a post-technological utopia did not take into account the dynamics of a highly competitive world system able to recreate scarcity on an increasingly colossal scale. So the question of the future of technology, and with it humanity's future, remains open. Determinism cannot be proved, but neither can it be falsified.

The golden thread running through this discussion is attitudes to work. Machines replace, enhance or reduce the need for human labour. Attitudes to them will vary depending on whether work is considered a curse or a blessing. Two very broad currents run through this history, the Classical and the Christian. The first is marked by the contempt of work, the second by the duty of work. The first leads to the ideal of not *having* to work. This is the aristocratic ideal, and the view of Keynes and others was really a democratic version of it. Machinery here overcomes or conquers nature; capitalism is the most efficient means of filling up the world with machinery. Against the contempt for work, Christianity proclaimed it as a calling. Emerging from the monasteries of medieval Christianity, work became part of the bourgeois ideal of the moral life, with wealth not as something one inherited, but something one had to work for and spend carefully and productively. In a complicated way the two sets of attitudes, the contempt for work and the duty to work fused to create the technological age. It is this matrix that we will aim to explore in the following chapters. Our method is not to bury it in historical detail but, as Karl Jaspers suggested, to 'make a circuit through history in order to find out what our own opportunities are'.[13]

2.

Natural Obstacles

'Is nature a gigantic cat? If so, who strokes it?'

Nikola Tesla as a child

The history of science and technology is dominated by the idea of blockages, natural or customary, to the progress of the mind. There is nothing wrong in discussing the advance of science and technology in these terms, provided one remembers that what the Enlightenment thought of as fetters were forged, in part, to protect humans from *hubris*.

One such blockage might have been scarcity of genius. The world had to fill up with enough people before the requisite number of geniuses to support continuous invention became possible.[1] However, the answer is wrong. There was no shortage of genius in the thousands of years when technology was relatively sleepy. One obvious example is the enormous flowering of thought in what Karl Jaspers has called the Axial Age, running 500–300 BCE, which produced Plato, Socrates, Moses, Buddha and Confucius, among others.[2] Round these outstanding thinkers were genuine 'clusters' of followers and colleagues capable of taking their work forward. Plato's famous Academy in Athens (the world's first university), which existed for 800 years, might have become the scientific laboratory of its day. It was not so much that pre-modern civilizations lacked genius as that the attention of their worlds was on other things. They produced philosophers, not scientists, who were more interested in cultivating the soul than the soil, in dialectics than discovery, in religion than in economics. Why this was so is a puzzle. Why did Plato think that the treatment of bodily ailments was much less important than the pursuit of the good? If told that such an attitude was a hindrance to the advance of medical science, he would surely have replied that the health of the body was much less important than the health of the soul.

Challenge and Response

External environments set all species and societies a challenge. Their survival depends on the effectiveness of their response. In western mythology, expulsion from the Garden of Eden set humans their first environmental challenge. 'It was only *after* Adam and Eve had been expelled from their Eden Lotus-land that their descendants set about inventing agriculture, metallurgy and musical instruments'. With these words, the historian and polymath Arnold Toynbee unrolls his famous theory of 'Challenge and Response'.[3] 'Man achieves civilization', he wrote in his monumental *A Study of History*, 'not as a result of superior biological endowment or geographical environment, but as a response to a challenge in a situation of special difficulty, which rouses him to make a hitherto unprecedented effort'.[4] Societies are, he writes, 'confronted in the course of [their] li[ves] by a succession of problems which each [society] has to solve for itself as best it can'. The emergence of each problem is a 'challenge to undergo an ordeal', and through this series of ordeals societies 'progressively differentiate themselves from one another',[5] into evolutionary successes and failures.

As we can see, Toynbee is applying the Darwinian theory of the 'survival of the fittest' to cultural history: 'adapt or perish' is the common logic of species and civilizations. In Toynbee's version it is not the fittest genes but the 'fittest' cultures which survive. In Darwinian theory, the successful responses to environmental challenges are triggered by mutation. The Toynbean equivalent is cultural adaptation. Toynbee then goes on to elaborate the cultural mechanisms that make the difference between survival and extinction,

Toynbee identified five fundamental 'ordeals': a hard ('difficult') habitat; a new habitat; epic military defeats; continuous military pressure on the frontier; and enslavement and persecution. It is greatly to Toynbee's credit that he refuses to reduce the mental to the physical, as today's neuroscientists do. The challenge is external, but the response, for humans, is always mediated by the mind. '[As if] the great human adventure that we know as Hellenism [can] be reduced to a kind epiphenomenal by-product of the Balkan plateaux!' he writes.[6] Toynbee acknowledged that some challenges may be too severe to overcome by the thinking and technology of the time: our ancestors were powerless against natural disasters which we can now avert or mitigate. He writes: 'of the twenty-one civilizations that have been born alive and have proceeded to grow, thirteen are dead and buried; seven of the remaining eight are apparently in decline; and the eighth, which is our own, may also have passed its zenith for all that we as yet know'.[7]

The most common challenge which has faced humans over time is the imbalance between population and resources. The trigger may be population growing faster than available land, over-hunting, over-grazing or climate change. Toynbee gives the following account of the reaction of a population to the growing desertification of the Sahara following the end of the Ice Age around 11,000 BCE. The original foragers now had three choices: (1) to follow their animal prey to still forested lands; (2) to remain where they were without changing their habits, eking out an increasingly miserable existence; (3) to stay more or less where they were but start domesticating animals and growing crops. In a rare 'double reaction', some hunter-gatherers changed both their habitat and their way of life. Their migration to a new habitat and transition to pastoral and arable farming created Egyptian and Sumeric civilization: 'the wantonness of nature was subdued by the works of man; the formless jungle-swamp made way for a pattern of ditches and embankments and fields; the lands of Egypt and Shinar were reclaimed from the wilderness and the Egyptiac and Sumeric societies started on their great adventures'.[8]

Some civilizations never made the 'efficient' response to the 'challenge' they faced and are presumed to have perished. Why did they not all 'optimize'? Toynbee offers four answers which, in his view, apply to all civilizations.

First, the nature of the response is shaped by institutions. Different kinds of political system will produce different responses. For despotisms, protection against coups or revolts may be more important than protection against foreign enemies. This may explain why imperial China restricted the use of gunpowder. Or sectional rivalries may, if strong enough, obstruct any collective attempt to develop a coherent response to a military challenge: the old kingdom of Poland suffered extinction because of the *liberum veto*. On the other hand, 'Greek fire' – an incendiary hurled at attacking ships by catapults – kept Constantinople safe from the Arabs for several hundred years.

Second, even where a challenge is recognized, institutional conservatism – what economists call 'sunk costs' – may delay the efficient response to the new situation. The Mughals of India were blinded to the superior power of artillery by their loyalty to the horse, the instrument by which the Mongols had achieved world empire under Genghis Khan. 'A culture of horse-riding nobility continued to prevail until the Europeans came.'[9] In the First World War the prestige of cavalry as the aristocratic mode of fighting undoubtedly delayed the deployment of the tank. The historian of science Thomas Kuhn recognized that 'sunk costs' can explain the institutional conservatism even of communities of scientists, ostensibly dedicated to the search for truth.[10]

Third, the response to a challenge depends on prevailing ideas of efficacy. If divine intervention is considered a possibility, a turn to religion may be considered a more efficacious response to starvation than three-field crop rotation. Thus challenging circumstances may produce a 'flight to religion' rather than the invention of new tools. Toynbee gives examples of the spread of monasticism, which helpfully emphasized celibacy, at the end of the Roman empire, and of Buddhism in China in the period of the breakdown of the Han dynasty.

Finally, different groups perceive the same environment differently. The anthropologist Mary Douglas gives the example of two neighbouring tribes in Africa, who live in the same climate, but one of them sees it as hot, the other cold. Beliefs about the environment, she says, 'relate to social systems and values, not only to facts, and . . . one can confront people with the same facts about the environment and find them coming to diametrically different conclusions'.[11] In short, societies respond to challenges in ways shaped by stories they tell about themselves.

Geography

Geography is an important subset of the challenge and response story. For most of human history, mountain ranges and oceans were almost impassable barriers to transport and communication, so commerce was restricted, and invention was inevitably local, isolated and easily lost. Societies were also largely powerless against extreme climatic events, like droughts and floods, plague and pestilence. Such diffusion of technology as occurred was along big rivers and hazardous trade routes.[12] Conversely, the mechanization of transport and communication since the steam engine and telegraph has helped make technology self-reinforcing by breaking down geographical barriers.

Geographical explanations of differences in human ability go back thousands of years: 'In the majority of cases, you will find that the human body and character vary in accordance with the nature of the country.' This is from a Greek fifth-century BCE work entitled *Influences of Atmosphere, Water and Situation*.[13] The 'Teutonic hypothesis' of nineteenth-century historians was a favourite explanation for the entrepreneurial vigour displayed by northern Europeans and Protestant Americans, in contrast to the 'physical and mental torpor' found in the 'colonial peoples'.[14] With the discovery, in the nineteenth century, of genes as the units of heredity came the language of 'scientific' racism. The 'mental torpor' which European ethnologists detected in 'colonial peoples' might well be the result of an inferior genetic stock determined by an adverse climate.[15]

Less distasteful to modern eyes would be analyses, also dating from the eighteenth and nineteenth centuries, which emphasize the impact of the physical landscape on a society's political and cultural landscape. For example, Montesquieu believed that the need to control the flooding of Asia's big rivers determined a despotic form of rule, a theme famously taken up by Karl Wittfogel. (see pp. 81–2)

Geography was also put to work explaining international relations. 'Geopolitics' achieved academic recognition following the publication of US Admiral Mahan's *The Influence of Sea Power upon History* in 1890 and a celebrated lecture in 1904 by the geographer Halford Mackinder entitled 'The Geographical Pivot of History'. In this lecture, Mackinder claimed that the 'physical features of the world . . . have been most coercive of human action'.[16] Thus the roots of Europe's 'world empire' were to be found in its possibilities for maritime expansion; in contrast, extensive plains spreading out from great rivers produced settled empires and geographically adjacent client states. The idea that their geographical location determines the constitutions of states (democracies or dictatorships) has been taken up by international relations theorist Kenneth Waltz.[17]

Mackinder's intervention was intended to warn the West that, unless it reinvigorated itself, eastern landpower, fortified by western technology, was about to strike back against western seapower. In his own words: 'Who rules eastern Europe commands the Heartland; who rules the Heartland commands the World-Island; who rules the World-Island commands the world.'[18] Hitler was duly impressed by this resounding assertion.

The standing of geographical explanations declined in the twentieth century with a shift in the nature of the study of geography. The 'old geography' taught schoolchildren that the physical environment shaped the human environment. The 'new' ('human') geography, which came of age in the 1960s and 1970s, emphasized the ways humans shaped and altered the physical environment for their own purposes. The Industrial Revolution is said to have marked the start of the Anthropocene – the age in which human activity started to reshape the climate and environment, rather than be shaped by them.

Today we are paying for our lack of homage to geography. With nature taking its revenge on human presumption in the form of pandemics, resource shortages and extreme climate events, the 'old' geography, and with it a 'soft' determinist theory, is back. This is most apparent in recognition of the impact of contagious or enervating diseases. At the same time, geographical location continues to illuminate the tensions of international politics: Putin's war on Ukraine cannot be understood without reference to the gigantic sprawl of Russian dominions across Eurasia, which obstructs the establishment of settled frontiers. Fashions in scholarly explanation change, and we are now more inclined to believe that, while the human species as a whole may have the same potential for progress, the 'manner of its realization' is profoundly affected by geography.

Jared Diamond's *Collapse: How Societies Choose to Fail or Succeed* (2005) echoes Toynbee's treatment: societies can succumb to climate change, environmental damage, hostile neighbours. In his earlier *Guns, Germs, and Steel* (1997) Diamond claimed that those who came to dominate others did so because of advantages given to them by their natural endowments. This included the presence of versatile animals, like horses, that can be domesticated for fighting, farming and transport. Diamond's principal claim is that, because of similarities in climate, technology diffuses more readily latitudinally than longitudinally. That is why technologies spread along the temperate climate of Eurasia, but not up and down Africa and South America, bisected as they were by disease-infested tropical forests. Europeans in particular were best placed to exploit natural resources, which brought them their higher living standards. They may now be shielded from the worst effects of the climate crisis their activities have brought about.

One big question raised by the geographical interpretation is whether empires or nation-states are most conducive to techno-logical development. Empires can confer conditions of peace over a large territory and thus foster the exchange of knowledge, ideas, techniques. Up to the fifteenth century, the Arab, Indian and Chinese empires were probably ahead of Europe in science and technology. Under the Mongols the whole Eurasian landmass became briefly a single empire, united by a system of highways connecting China, Persia and Russia. One could call this lucky geography. After that point, their size seemed to turn against them: the empires disinte-grated or could only be held together by oppressive and rent-seeking bureaucracies, which left them vulnerable to external challenges. In contrast, Europe established a competitive dynamic. It benefited from the fact that mountains and valleys prevented a concentration of power in one place. Monarchs were eager to encourage technical innovation as a means of enhancing competitive national power; and cities and merchants always had independent wealth and com-peted with each other.[19]

What is the relevance of geography for the further development of technology? Some would claim that global transport systems, supply chains and 'virtual networks' have abolished the importance of locations and borders. This is a claim too far. Political borders have become increasingly porous, but are still intact. States, which exist in geographical locations, can close down electronic networks and have already done so in the name of national security; there is thus always a possibility of politically induced technological regres-sion. Against this, some strategists, both American and Chinese, envisage a new era of geopolitical conflict in space, with mastery going to the nation which can first tap the limitless resources of the cosmos.

Geography provides a 'frame of necessities' within which insti-tutional choices are made. It advantages some institutional arrangements over others; the institutions then start to shape the responses to the challenges thrown up by the location – and much else.

3.

The Rise of Capitalism

'The hand-mill gives you society with the feudal lord; the steam-mill society with the industrial capitalist.'

Karl Marx

Today's technological momentum started with the advent of the property system we call capitalism. Capital must be distinguished from wealth. Wealth is simply valuable possessions. Previous societies had been wealthy: why did they not 'accumulate' capital? The standard answer, as we have seen, is that wealth was separated from work and was used for religion, politics and luxurious living not for investment. Marcus Licinius Crassus may have been the first tycoon of the ancient world but to him wealth was simply a means to power.[1] Wealth had to pass into the hands of an aspiring bourgeois class before it could become 'saved up' in the form of machines capable of producing more wealth. Only in north-west Europe, initially in Holland, then in Britain, did this happen. The question of why it happened there and not elsewhere is one of the enduring puzzles of history.

Karl Marx's important insight was that the technical possibilities of an era – what he called the level of the productive forces – determine a particular kind of property system (the relations of production), which in turn stifles or prompts further technical developments. He identified three main property regimes – ancient, feudal and bourgeois – which dominated successive European 'stages' of development, as well as a more nebulous Asiatic 'mode of production' which stood apart from these. In the first of these (slavery), masters owned labour; in the second (serfdom) they owned the work of labour, and in the third (bourgeois) they hired labour. While each property regime 'exploited' labour, the first two limited exploitation by enabling each class of producer – master–slave, serf – to reproduce itself at its accustomed standard of life. They were thus both a product of the existing technology and, in Marx's view, a break on its further development. It was only when wealth was freed of its customary obligations to labour that investment in machines became possible. As Eric Roll tells it: 'Under the stimulus of competition, every capitalist tries to be first in the field with an improvement in the productivity of labour, because so long as that improvement has not become general, his individual surplus value will increase.'[2] This explains why technology came with a rush with the onset of the 'capitalist' mode of production.

Powerful though Marx's insight is, it is limited by its insistence on the property basis of all social and intellectual relationships. He failed to distinguish between the class of private proprietors and the priestly and professional class, treating the second as simply providing an 'ideal' cover for the power of the first. As a result he failed to identify an independent role for the intellectual elite and state bureaucracy in technological change. Inattention to the role of ideas and lack of a theory of the state are the main weaknesses in the Marxist account of technical innovation. It seemed to Marx a waste of intellectual energy to pay undue attention to shadows when the reality of the class struggle beckoned so strongly.

Hunter-gatherers

Innumerable origin myths start with a Golden Age when no one had to work, God or the gods providing all the necessities. For one reason or another, this enchanted existence came to an end; from that point dates the world's misfortunes. The Genesis myth of expulsion from Eden is the familiar western version, but other cultures have similar stories to tell. For example, in the first era, the

Satya Yuga (often referred to as the 'Golden Age'), described by the *Mahabharata*, a Vedic epic, 'there were no poor and no rich; there was no need to labour, because all could attain to the "supreme blessedness" by power of will.'[3] Each successive *yuga* sees a degradation in humanity's physical and moral condition until it is totally contaminated by evil. A historical pattern in which happiness and misfortune follow in endlessly recurring cycles is common to all mythologies. Secular cyclical theory has inherited mythical cycles. The Malthusian cycle is a secular upgrade of the myth of Persephone and Hades. Business cycles of varying length have been a regular feature of human experience.

The hunter-gatherer way of life has been reconstructed by some anthropologists as one of 'original affluence'.[4] Hunter-gatherers didn't have to work much, it is claimed, because they 'had enough' for their needs. A few simple tools and weapons – choppers, hand axes, spears, bows and arrows – sufficed and they harnessed the first of the classical elements, fire, to make them.[5] Work (hunting) was playful rather than burdensome, free from the curse of regular hours, and it left ample time to create art on the walls of caves. The hunter-gatherers' condition was one of original anarchy: a communitarian utopia, without a state or private property, held together by natural bonds of fidelity. Eighteenth-century travellers' tales from South Pacific paradises such as Tahiti reinforced the idea of an original innocence and state of plenty ravaged by civilization. Rousseau thought the hunter-gatherer life was the happiest age of man.

But, averred Hobbes, life in the forest was bound to be 'solitary, poor, nasty, brutish, and short'. Carlo Cippola agrees:

> Such a state of affairs cannot have been very comfortable. Man spent all his time and energy in the search for food, relying mainly on good luck and his ability to kill wild animals and other men. Starvation was a constant threat, forcing people to infanticide and cannibalism. Furthermore, since man had not yet learned to domesticate animals and knew no other source of energy, his muscles were the only mechanical power he could command.[6]

Clearly some hunter-gatherers had it easier than others. Few today are inclined to idealize the material conditions of the foragers, but hunter-gatherer societies get high marks for freedom and equality.

The story of the hunter-gatherers is an anthropological version of the biblical paradise lost. Foundation myths may well have been idealized memories of distant natural/historical events; but through their influence on memory, they continue to play a part in shaping the future. The appeal of the forager or nomad as a 'free spirit' (as opposed to the modern urban dweller imprisoned by his mortgage payments) has been enduring. As we shall see, the myth of the forest was hugely important in late nineteenth-century German Romanticism, with baleful political effects. Today's secular mythology sometimes romanticizes the past in this kind of way (the happy peasant) but more insistently looks forward to a new Golden Age brought about by the machine.[7]

Agriculture

In the standard histories of technology, it was the start of farming about 10,000 BCE – probably in response to population growth or climate change or both – which marks the start of civilization. Animals, previously hunted, started to be domesticated, and fertile lands farmed rather than trampled over. Put simply, the shift meant more food per unit of land. Farming could support up to a hundred times more people than foraging.[8] A surplus of 'rude' produce over survival enabled villages to grow into towns, towns to turn into cities, and cities to become centres of empire. Urbanization created a demand for artefacts which ignited the instinct for workmanship: metals were mined and masons, carpenters and other craftsmen supplied the demand. There could be no 'turning back'. At the same time foraging, together with the celebration of the nomadic lifestyle, coexisted with settled agriculture for millennia. The Mughals of India were nomads turned empire-builders; seafaring seventeenth-century Europeans 'hunted' for fresh lands. 'Hunting, shooting, fishing' are contemporary residues of earlier mainstream activities, both practical and therapeutic.

Harari describes the agricultural revolution as 'history's biggest fraud'.[9] Rousseau thought of it as a fall from original grace, the sin being private property, and with it came the state to defend it, the division of labour and the 'war of all against all' which Hobbes wrongly supposed to be the product of the 'state of nature'. For Thorstein Veblen, too, settled agriculture marked the start of the 'predatory' stage of human history.[10] David Graeber regarded the disappearance of the hunter-gatherer way of life as history's great wrong turning.[11] According to climate-change campaigner George Monbiot farming was 'the most destructive force ever to have been unleashed by humans'.[12] These protests leave obscure the question of how the human species could have survived natural disasters of the kind described by Toynbee without the mental leap into farming. Nevertheless, the huge material and intellectual gains of settled agriculture were offset by two losses. First, the fruits of the earth now increasingly went to private proprietors; second, the more complex technology, like writing, which settled societies needed to function, inevitably led to the concentration of power in the hands of the priestly class: Latin, Sanskrit and Mandarin were languages of power, in contrast to the vernacular, or local, languages of the largely illiterate peasants.

Slavery

Slavery is one of history's oldest property systems, in which not just the labour of others is owned, but their bodies too. In the Marxist scheme, it is the first *historical* relationship of production – the one that evolves from primitive peasant settlements. Its origins lie in war, and the realization that it was more useful to put captives to work than to kill them.

It was the economic basis of Roman civilization, lasting from 500 BCE to 500 CE, with slaves at their peak constituting about one-third of the population of the Roman empire; they were also common at this time in China and India. Arable land in Italy was relatively unproductive, so Roman conquests fulfilled both the need for land and a large captive labour force. Cities like Rome were great slave markets, with captives being bought and sold – alongside those born into slavery, sold into slavery as children in order to pay parental debts or made slaves as punishment for crimes. As well as tilling the soil, they worked in households, workshops and mining, and there were different grades of slavery, where some took charge of teams of other slaves, or had more complicated administrative responsibilities. Marcus Tullius Tiro, Cicero's secretary (and the narrator in Robert Harris's fictional Cicero trilogy), was a famous historical slave, whom Cicero manumitted. Slave labour, not exceptional technology, built the famous Roman aqueducts and roads.

Slavery is classically associated with imperial rule, because empires are engines of conquest, and an economic system that relies on conquest has to be governed autocratically. But slavery carries its own nemesis. Slave populations are acquired and replenished in periods of conquest; they die out when conquest stops, since slaves have little incentive to reproduce. The doom of classical slavery sounded as early as 14 CE, when Augustus fixed the boundaries of the Roman empire at the Rhine, dividing Europe into its Mediterranean and Germanic parts. Fewer military conquests meant fewer fresh slaves, and the supply of slaves depended increasingly on the inadequate fertility of the slave population.

The slave 'mode of production' survived the passing of classical civilization, as Arabs, and much later Europeans, discovered new sources of slaves in Eurasia and Africa, as well as in their own prisoner populations: the Trans-Siberian railway was largely built by convicts. In the eighteenth and nineteenth centuries the plantation owners of the West Indies and the southern states of the United States enjoyed the sumptuous lifestyles made possible by African slaves, much like the Roman aristocracy of old. The relative technological backwardness of these regions even as their neighbours industrialized is explained by the persistence of slavery.

The hypothesis is that 'the supply of slave labour rendered it unnecessary to introduce costly labour-saving machinery'.[13] Slaves, it is claimed, were sufficiently cheap to make innovation unnecessary, especially as the installation costs of slaves (conquest) were not individually attributable. They enabled the Romans to ignore such productivity-improving devices as the water mill and reaping machine, both invented in the first century CE. It was only as the philosopher of a class dependent on servile labour that Plato could belittle medical science as providing no answer to 'diseases . . . of the soul'.[14] Aristotle imagined that, someday, human slaves would be replaced by mechanical ones. But for his time and place, there was no need of mechanical slaves, because there was no shortage of human ones.

However, the fact that the aristocratic ideal of life long survived the demise of slavery as an institution suggests that slavery reflected as well as caused the aristocratic contempt for work. The 'work' of the aristocracies of antiquity was to fight and govern, and they found personal fulfilment in heroic deeds. As the importance of fighting waned, the aristocratic ideal was increasingly transformed into the ideal of a leisured, as distinguished from an idle, class whose 'work' was to cultivate the art of living, and for whom political leadership was an extension of estate management.[15] This is the form in which Keynes inherited it in his essay of 1930. He thought that machinery would make the aristocratic lifestyle available to all. He neglected to consider that the aristocratic ideal of leisure might be inherently scarce, inasmuch as the good life for the few may depend on the servitude of the many.[16]

The popular version of the aristocratic ideal is idleness, because it is at the opposite extreme of the burdensome work which most people for most of history have been compelled to do. The dream that no one would *need* to work is what lies behind the utopian fable of the Land of Cockayne, dating from the thirteenth century. Work is forbidden. Everything needed for life is to hand with minimal effort required: the rivers flow with oil, milk, honey and wine, the trees are abundant in low-lying fruit, and the body is freed for the delights of love. This is how the Garden of Eden has always been imagined. Hence the promise of machines. Machines would liberate sex from its bondage and make the rivers flow with Coca-Cola: a vision which ran all the way from classical times to the Freudian Marxists of the 1960s.

As with all institutional explanations, slavery poses the question of causation. Did the availability of a cheap and pliant labour force to do the dirty work inspire the classical ideals of the noble life and contempt for work? Or did the supreme value attached to heroism and gracious living inspire the search for slaves? There is no clear answer to this conundrum. What is clear is that at some point classical antiquity ran out of slaves, and this led to a radical change in the property and governmental systems.

Feudalism

Serfdom is routinely slotted into the history of property systems as the bottom rung of feudalism, that system of reciprocal obligations stretching from the lowest to the highest ranks of society which flourished in Europe for about a thousand years following the demise of classical slavery. But this is an incomplete depiction. Serfdom had a specific economic taproot in the inadequate reproduction rate of Roman slave populations, and the decay of the money economy of the empire. Population in the Roman empire fell from a peak of about 75 million in 200 CE to 50 million by the fifth century. Trade declined, the money economy shrank. Serfdom can be seen as an 'efficient' economic response to this situation. Shortage of manpower was met by paying for labour services by grants of land rather than in cash or produce. Serfdom came before feudalism and outlasted it.

Feudalism had a different root. As its name suggests, its core value was 'fidelity': the fidelity of followers to their chief. This was the nomadic, and specifically Germanic, input into the Roman world. The invaders from the steppes introduced two sentiments into

European civilization unknown in Roman times: 'love of liberty' and 'military clientship' – the bond between warriors which gave rise to the aristocratic organization of feudalism.[17] It became a Europe-wide response to extreme political disorder following the breakdown of the Carolingian empire in the tenth century. Europe was swept first by Scandinavian and then by Islamic invasions. In consequence, the ancient supply chains were broken: both production and protection were localized. It was the fusion of serfdom and military vassalage which gave feudalism its specific character as a politico-economic organization, with serfdom as the lowest rung in a system of recip-rocal obligations, and conditional property rights stretching from the bottom to the top of society. At no level of society was land held in fee simple: all cultivated land was 'encumbered' by obligations.

Looked at from the civilized heights of nineteenth-century Europe, the feudal era seemed an age of barely licensed barbarism. 'Almost everywhere the lord of the manor [is] a brutal and rapa-cious cut-throat; he goes to war, fights at tournaments, spends his peacetime hunting, ruins himself with extravagance, oppresses the peasants, practises extortion on his neighbourhoods and plunders the property of the church.'[18] Modern institutional history is more appreciative, seeing feudalism as incubating a political structure of pluralism favourable in the long run to the development of individ-ual freedom, private enterprise and markets. Medieval Europe was much more than fragments of the hitherto unified Roman world. It incorporated the German and Slav lands in the north and east, hith-erto the homes of the 'barbarians', in a decentralized, but common Christian culture, in aggregate richer and more variegated than the imperial civilizations of the past. Its mix of weak monarchies, armed aristocracies with juridical functions, a powerful independent Church and 'free' cities was the foundation of the constitutional state. The Church's claim to exercise a co-equal authority with the secular power ('Render unto Caesar the things which are Caesar's and unto God the things that are God's') was a crucial contribution to the idea of a 'balance of power'. For Guizot, the distinctiveness of Europe's political organization lay precisely in its 'pluralism'.

Modern historians have followed him in regarding this pluralism as marking a fundamental divergence from the 'Asiatic' type of despotic rule, in which imperial, not aristocratic, government was the norm. Montesquieu likened Europe's intermediate feudal institutions to the 'weeds and pebbles' that lie scattered along the shore obstructing the otherwise overflowing tide of autocracy.[19] The incubation of liberalism in Christianity is the most important claim of Larry Siedentop's history of medieval thought.[20]

At the heart of feudalism was the 'manorial system'. Manors had a similar structure to the Greek *oikos* and the Roman *villa*, but, as they had to be fortified, they were communities rather than households, with a high degree of self-sufficiency, and structured around one landlord (himself a feudatory of a greater lord) who commanded the labour on his estate in return for protection. Manors typically consisted of at least two areas, the *demesne*, which was land for the landlord and his family, and 'serf' land, which was rented out to peasants for their own use, in exchange for working part of the time on the lord's land. The demesne land was the source of aristocratic revenues, producing crops and other goods that could be sold or traded. At the centre of most manorial estates was the castle, with the castellar system at its height between the tenth and eleventh centuries, following the break-up of the Carolingian empire.

All political and economic relationships were fixed. All were secure in their 'livings' in return for services rendered. Vassals rendered military and juridical services; serfs had a right to part of the produce of the manors; artisans' skills and jobs were preserved from competition by the guild system; the Church offered the security of the afterlife. In the perennial conflict between innovation and security, feudalism represented the choice for the latter.

Au fond, such a property system would seem hostile to technical innovation. Everyone possessed land, but no one owned it, since even noble land was held 'in fief' from the sovereign. No one, therefore, had any incentive permanently to increase the output of the land. Likewise, because the urban guild system reserved occupations to licensed merchants and craftsmen, machines or work practices which undercut established prices were seen as a threat.

The feudal system broke down over several centuries between the thirteenth and sixteenth centuries. Its political-juridical basis ended with the gradual re-centralization of power in the hands of strong monarchies, but its economic basis migrated from western to eastern Europe, and especially to Russia, where serfdom was abolished only in 1861. A form of serfdom known as indentured labour lingered on even in England until the twentieth century.

Different causes are adduced for the decline and fall of feudalism, including the spread of commerce, which led to the growth of free cities, and the declining cost of protection, as barbarian invasions ceased, and gunpowder shifted the comparative advantage to monarchies, thus ending the castellar system, and leading to the creation of national markets.[21] The decisive event, though, is reckoned to be the bubonic plague, known as the Black Death, which destroyed between a third and a half of Europe's population. It originated in central Asia along the Eurasian Silk Road, reaching Genoa in 1347 and much of the rest of the world in 1348: a classic apocalypse. 'The entire inhabited world changed,' wrote the Arab scholar Ibn Khaldun. The plague 'devastated nations and caused populations to vanish. Cities and buildings were laid waste, roads were obliterated, settlements and mansions became empty, dynasties and tribes grew weak.'

According to David Landes, the Black Death 'compelled the propertied classes to offer substantial inducements to attract and hold the manpower needed to work their estates'.[22] This marked the end of serfdom as a 'mode of production'. Obligations in kind were converted into cash rentals at highly unfavourable rates; the 'manorial' system of feudalism gave way to a system of landlords, tenants and agricultural labourers. Further, the Black Death, by diminishing aristocratic revenues, provided the impetus to the 'voyages of discovery' in search of new lands to exploit and thus led to the emergence, for the first time, of European 'world empires'. In what Karl Polanyi called the 'great transformation', the three 'factors' of production, land, capital and labour, gradually became mobile within a framework of laws protecting private property. This released the pursuit of wealth from the restrictions of feudal 'overlappingness'.

The transition to capitalism unfolded over centuries not decades. It took a succession of big wars to establish the modern form of competitive European statehood. It took centuries for serfs to be converted into peasant proprietors and 'wage slaves'. Throughout Europe economic life continued to be based on the household and the small workshop, and thus on the habits and skills of the small farmer and artisan: even in Britain, the heart of the Industrial Revolution, the numbers employed in non-mechanized industries in 1850 (especially servants) were more than three times larger than those in the mechanized ones.[23] The 'putting out' system was a long intermediate stage between the feudal manorial economy and the capitalist factory system, a form of 'remote working', in which merchant-employers 'put out' raw materials to rural producers who worked them up in their homes or workshops into textiles, clothes, shoes, glassware and other artefacts. It combined cottage-industry manufacture with grazing sheep on common land and paid agricultural labour. Women and girls were often the family members carrying out this work, while men concentrated on agricultural work and sometimes took over traditional 'women's work' such as cooking and childcare, while the women were engaged in craft work. This was a stable system of home working using limited technology.

The Spirit of Capitalism

Capitalism is not just a property system, but also an attitude to life. This attitude started in the monasteries and then came out into the world in the sixteenth century in the character-type of the worldly ascetic. Serfdom was not the only type of labour contract in the feudal order. Church land stood apart from feudal tenancy arrangements. Monasteries with their 'working monks' brought with them a Christian attitude to life and work completely different from the philosophy of slavery. God's command that 'by the sweat of your brow you shall eat bread' denied the aristocratic ideal of leisure: it was the degradation of leisure from a noble to an ignoble pursuit which led Nietzsche to call Christianity a 'slaves' religion'. 'Happy is he who earns his bread by the work of his hands,' declared John Chrysostom in the second half of the fourth century. Two centuries earlier, disgusted by the decadence of his time, Theophilus of Antioch inveighed against 'sloth and levity . . . repugnant in the eyes of God'. In attributing to Christianity the decline in the martial spirit which sustained the Roman empire, Edward Gibbon paid it a backhanded compliment.

From the start, work was an important element of monastic life. It was praised by John Cassian in the *Institutes* (*c.*400), and then St Benedict in his *Regula* (*c.*500). The *Regula* of St Benedict not only laid down the rules for organizing and governing a monastery, but also a strict schedule of activities to be undertaken day and night. In his *Regula,* we read that 'Leisure is the enemy of the soul, and for this reason the brothers must spend a certain amount of time in doing manual work as well as the time spent in divine reading.'[24] Work was a moral discipline, a protection against sloth, and even worse, vice. Through such 'canonical hours' the Benedictine rule stressed the close relationship between manual and spiritual work, summed up in the injunction *ora et labora*, or 'pray and work'. The routine labours of daily life, the very fact of their tedium, were moralized.

The approbation of work did not necessarily extend to technics. Properly understood, God's punishment for the original sin of Adam and Eve was not to make humanity work but to make work painful. Nevertheless, the idea of the duty to work did stimulate interest in technical innovation. This was for two reasons. Technics might discover new ways of getting closer to God: Franciscan monks were especially interested in 'decoding nature' for this purpose, and one of their order was probably the inventor of spectacles.

A second motive came from the desire to free up time for prayer. The tension between work and prayer in Christian thought can be seen in the New Testament story of the sisters Martha and Mary – Martha, the hard-working one, took exception to her sister Mary, who sat listening to Christ's stories instead of working. She complained that Mary should help her, but Christ chided Martha that her sister had chosen correctly.

Through their interest in the mechanical arts monasteries became medieval Europe's major inventors. Mechanical clocks for time-keeping and spectacles for reading both came out of the monasteries. Lewis Mumford praised the fact that monks turned over only boring work to machines, while keeping the rewarding, thoughtful types of work – such as illuminating manuscripts or carving – for themselves.[25] If the ideal type of the classical world was the gentleman of leisure, the medieval world exalted the 'working saint'.

Thus Christian attitudes to work, combining economic with moral necessity, helped break down the classical contempt for work. The fruits of the earth which God provided had to be garnered by toil. Christian life helped transform the labour of slaves into the work of the righteous. By making time scarce, it paved the way for the capitalist work ethic. However, the notion of work as a divine requirement limited the interest in easing its burden. It was only when work became both dignified *and* secular that a strong motive developed to improve productivity. 'Working saints' had to be re-imagined as 'saintly workers', suitably disciplined to the demands of the factory system. This was the achievement of Calvinism.

In his introduction to Weber's *The Protestant Ethic and the Spirit of Capitalism* (1905), R. H. Tawney pointed out that capitalism was created by parvenus. The tonic that braced them for conflict with the established order was a new conception of religion which taught that the pursuit of wealth was a duty.[26] Weber denied that individuals are maximizers by nature. In traditional society 'a man does not "by nature" wish to make more and more money; but simply to live as he is accustomed to and to earn as much as is necessary for this purpose'.[27] It was Protestantism, in its particular form of Calvinism, which turned greed into a virtue. In so doing it legitimized the capitalist and his works, by turning a predator into a benefactor.

Weber's argument is easy to misinterpret. The 'spirit of capitalism' entered history at a particular time (sixteenth century) and place (north-western Europe), and for a particular reason. It was the unintended consequence of the Calvinist belief in predestination, the doctrine that God had divided people into the saved and damned, and no religious observances, however devout, could influence His selection, because God's will cannot be subject to human influence. The complete elimination of salvation through the intercession of the Church and the Sacraments imposed on Calvinist man an unprecedented need for reassurance that one was not damned. Reassurance might come about in two ways: through intense and continuous activity – 'it and it alone disperses religious doubts and gives the certainty of grace' – and secondly, through the piling up of objective results: wealth accumulated over a lifetime was a sign of a job well done. In short, Puritanism took monastic asceticism and its methodical habits out of the monastery and placed them at the service of active life in the world.[28] In Weber's view it was the 'permanent intrinsic character' of their religious beliefs which explains the different aptitudes of Protestantism and Catholicism for capitalist activity.[29] Whereas traditional religion offered consolation for suffering and indulgences for sin, the new worldly asceticism provided both a moral conviction and a 'method' for business success based on rational calculation. What came to be identified as the Puritan work ethic – punctuality, reliability, frugality in personal habits, sexual chastity, efficient use of time ('time is money') and avoidance of debt – was the moral foundation and justification for the accumulation of capital. Catholicism had tried to hold in equilibrium the tension between work and play: work in the service of God was interrupted by 'feasts of misrule, licensed orgies, and so on'.[30] Puritanism abolished the festive character of religious life. It was all work, no play: every Christian has to be a monk all his life. This 'worldly asceticism' turned the Calvinist diaspora in Holland, Britain and America into the capitalist economy.[31]

The 'Weber thesis' is central to the history of technology for two reasons. First, because it explains how the duty to work came out of the medieval monastery into ordinary life, expelling the classical contempt for work; second, because it offers a psychological account of the capitalist character, who sought wealth not for pleasure but for the health of his soul and the improvement of the world. Both offer non-Marxist accounts of the 'origins of capitalism'. Economic historians have mainly been interested in the second because of its attention to the psychology of 'saving'. They ignore the other leg of the thesis, the duty to work, which is a moral claim on the individual independent of self-interest. This leads them to minimize the legitimacy of capitalism and the psychological anxiety created by the prospect of the 'end of work'.

It is important to be clear about what Weber was claiming. He did not see the worldly asceticism of the Puritan as the only possible source of capital accumulation, only as the form capital accumulation took in societies and communities heavily influenced by Calvinism: in principle, a rationally motivated bureaucracy could set aside the same resources for long-term economic development. Rather, Weber saw the Puritan character-type, together with competitive markets, as the psychological and institutional foundation of a liberal economy. He used this analysis to explain why effective checks to bureaucracy developed in Britain and the United States but not in Germany, where capitalism was yoked to bureaucracy from the start. In the anglophone world the pursuit of gain was sufficiently separated from the pursuit of power to prevent a fusion of the two. And it was this separation which helped capitalism gain a moral legitimacy absent from pure calculations of power.

Economists and Luddites

'About 1760 a wave of gadgets swept over England.'

Schoolboy howler

Why Was Britain First?

The technological age was ushered in by Britain with the mechanization of spinning and then spread first to the rest of Europe, then round the world via trade, migration, finance and empire. Within the larger question of why Europe took the technological lead is the question of why Britain was the first industrial nation.

The schoolboy 'howler' cited above was once the favoured explanation. The industrial age starts with a stream of British inventions: Watt's steam engine of 1763, Crompton's mule of 1779, Cartwright's power loom of 1787, Henry Cort's puddling furnaces for the production of wrought iron of 1784, etc. It was power-driven machinery which enabled the Industrial Revolution to 'take off' and, starting with textiles, inaugurated the factory and system and mass production. The 'gadget' theory still has advocates. Joel Mokyr argues that most of the inventions between 1750 and 1830 were made by theory-free 'mechanically talented amateurs'.[1]

Some homage is paid to 'lucky' geography: Britain's island location, the density of its natural sources of power (wood, coal, water and iron ore), perhaps also diet (beer and tea).[2] But the 'new economic history' of the 1980s downplays the 'gadget' theory. There was no sudden 'take-off' into a technological future. Rather, Britain was the first society 'that interposed relatively few institutional barriers' to fundamental technical innovation.[3] Although 'enclosure' of the commons was widespread in Europe from the sixteenth century onwards (leading to peasant revolt across the continent), the dissolution of the monasteries by Henry VIII between 1536 and 1541 gave Britain a decisive start in developing capitalistic forms of agriculture. The improvements in agricultural productivity which it enabled forced redundant labour into the towns, where it was cheaply available for manufacture. Long before the Industrial Revolution, England was much more urbanized than France and other continental countries, with London in the late seventeenth century being the most populous and opulent city in Europe, enriched by its global trading connections, new industries and immigrants.[4] The English revolution of 1649 had also clipped the wings of its monarchy, forcing it to bargain with landlords and merchants for revenue, and initiating a naval competition with the Dutch for commercial mastery which led to the first British empire overseas in North America.

Economic historian Douglass North compares Britain and Spain to illustrate the property hypothesis. The modernization of property rights in Britain set it on its path to growth, by making it possible for 'improving' landlords to capture the profits of their improvements. By contrast, in Spain, the Crown failed to curtail the right of the *mesta* (the shepherds' guild) to drive their sheep across the land wherever they wanted. 'A landlord who carefully prepared and grew a crop might expect at any moment to have it eaten or trampled by flocks of migrating sheep.' The owner lacked exclusive rights to his land, so the private rate of return fell short of the social rate. Enclosure or privatization of the commons made this possible in England.[5] This example makes vivid the costs and gains of capitalism, setting the destruction of age-old ways of life against improvements in economic efficiency. North gives a straightforward explanation for the difference in the two countries' economic performance: it was the tax revenue Spanish monarchs received from the *mesta* which made them reluctant to abrogate the latter's rights. His handy formula can be applied generally: the predations

70

of the state can have the same effect as those of the *mesta* in retard-
ing innovation.[6] He briefly mentions the doctrine of the 'just price'
as an obstacle to efficiency, but ignores the fact that this was central
to scholastic – and later to Catholic – social teaching.

According to neoclassical economic historians the institutional
change most pertinent to technological innovation was the establishment of 'intellectual property rights', normally secured by
patents, by which governments grant inventors temporary monopolies over the products, processes and techniques they have created.
This was the only way of avoiding that great disincentive to innovation known as the 'free-rider problem', the inability of an inventor
to profit personally from their invention because knowledge is a
public good. In Britain, guarantee of private property in inventions
dates from the Statute of Monopolies in 1624, which abolished existing monopolies and limited the Crown's right to grant patents or
temporary monoplies to 'first inventors'.[7] The guarantee provided
an incentive to innovate cost-saving technology. But it was not the
only such stimulus. Between the mid-eighteenth and mid-nineteenth
centuries, Britain's Royal Society of Arts awarded over 2,000 innovation 'prizes' in the form of medals and money. Whether by way of
patents or prizes, the 'private rate of return' from an innovation
was slowly equated to 'the social rate of return'.[8]

Private property rights went together with the rule of law, independent central banks and the reliance of rulers on parliaments to
supply them with funds. In all of this Britain was the pioneer. For
capitalism to flourish, the state had to be strong enough to protect
individual owners against predators, but not so strong as to become
predator in chief. Such a constitutional or limited state was achieved
in Britain in the seventeenth century. Social contract theorists of the
state understood the importance of opening this 'corridor' for individual initiative between autocracy and baronial disorder. 'An
unlimited despotism', wrote David Hume, 'effectively puts a stop to
all improvement, and keeps men from attaining knowledge'.[9] Or, as
Michael Ignatieff has put it, 'If you create a state that protects everyone, sooner or later you have to protect the individual against the

state.'[10] Compound interest was built into the liberal institutional structure.

The problem with this account is that it reduces the role of the state to that of nightwatchman. In fact, it was the symbiosis between capitalism and state which made economies dynamic. This was true of eighteenth-century Britain and even truer of subsequent economic catch-up strategies in which governments have always played a leading role. The magic – and potentially destructive – secret of technological dynamism lies in the harnessing of capitalist interests to competitive state missions.

Ironically, Britain, the 'first industrial nation', started to fall behind in integrating science and technology, largely because of the low social esteem attached to 'engineers'. There is, after all, something in the idea that the Industrial Revolution was started by tinkerers, and that the British continued backyard tinkering long after the Germans and Americans, and many nations since, had entrusted their futures to state-funded research laboratories.

Luddites

As Britain's Industrial Revolution got under way, the costs and benefits of installing machines were fiercely debated on the streets, in Parliament and by the leading thinkers of the time. The earliest victims were the handloom weavers. 'The spinning mills came first to supply the self-employed home-working artisan weavers. Later came the weaving shed that usurped the very people who had been the earliest beneficiaries of manufactured yarn.'[11] In 1811, groups of English weavers known as the Luddites started smashing factory machinery – wide knitting frames and power looms. The movement spread from Nottingham to other centres of the textile industry. It was put down by the military in 1812, and the Luddite leaders hanged or transported to Australia. The poet Byron made an eloquent speech in their defence in the House of Lords in 1812: 'The perseverance of these miserable men in their proceedings, tends to prove that nothing but absolute want could have driven a large and once honest and industrious body of the people into the commission of excesses so hazardous to themselves, their families, and the community.'

Unexpectedly the Luddites found a scientific defender. David Ricardo, one of the founding fathers of classical economics, thought the Luddites had a point. In the first edition of his *Principles of Political Economy and Taxation* (1817), he had argued that the introduction of machines benefited all classes, since all would enjoy a rise in real incomes. A key assumption was that the demand for 'dress, equipage, and household furniture' being limitless, rising real incomes would automatically create new jobs.[12] The increase in demand created by machines, that is, would serve to offset the decline which would follow from extending production to less fertile land.

But in chapter 31 of the revised edition of the same book, 'On Machinery', Ricardo retracted. He now believed 'that the substitution of machinery for human labour was often very injurious to the interests of the class of labourers'. He gave this example: 'If I employed 100 men on my farm, and if I found that food given to 50 of them could be diverted to support of horses, and afford me a greater return of raw produce (after allowing for interest to be paid for buying the horses) it would pay me to substitute horses for men. But this would not be for the interest of the men, and unless the income I obtained was so much increased as to enable me to employ the men as well as the horses, it is evident that the population would become redundant.'[13] Here Ricardo raised the fundamental issue of distribution: introducing machinery would only be in the interest of the workers if it increased their income as well as the income of the master.

Two conclusions from chapter 31 captured the attention of all students of political economy and have been debated ever since: first, 'that the opinion prevailing in the labouring class, that the employment of machinery is frequently detrimental to their interests, is not founded on prejudice and error, but is conformable to the correct principles of political economy';[14] second, that to the extent this opinion is true, 'there will necessarily be a diminution in the demand for labour, population will become redundant, and the situation of the labouring classes will be that of distress and poverty'.[15]

However, Ricardo thought this true only in the short term; in the long run, machinery would raise everyone's real income, and employment would be maintained. He suffered from what Schumpeter called the 'Ricardian Vice' of abstracting from his analysis all processes as they unfolded over time. As he explained: 'I fix my whole attention on the *permanent state of things* which will result from [these disturbances]'. This method of reasoning abolishes all *lived* experience, which includes memory and anticipation. Ricardo's 'vice' became the standard method of economists in thinking about machines and work. Together with physics, from which it drew much of its inspiration, economics exemplified what Carlyle called the 'mechanical philosophy'.

Ricardo's friend the Reverend Thomas Malthus famously argued that wages would be held to subsistence by the pressure of population on resources. Population, driven by sexual passion, increases geometrically, while food supply increases only arithmetically. If every couple has four children, the population is bound to double each generation, outstripping food supply. Population almost doubled in Britain in the eighteenth century, from 6 to 10 million, but cultivable land increased by only a small fraction of this and, according to Ricardo, was subject not to constant but to diminishing returns, meaning that each extra unit of land produced less food than the preceding one. According to Malthus, a population catastrophe, like that of the fourteenth century, was inevitable in the absence of 'moral checks'. These two 'natural' checks to general prosperity – rampant fertility and declining marginal productivity – beckoned a bleak future. No wonder economics came to be known as the dismal science. However, machines which *artificially* increased production might offer an escape from famine and pauperization by enabling a humane rather than catastrophic path to an equilibrium of population and resources. The Industrial Revolution was crucial in detaching society from the land and turning the Enlightenment dream of abundance into a feasible economic prospectus.[16]

Later economic discussion added little of importance to the ground rules laid down early in the nineteenth century. Distribution of the gains of machine production dropped out of the picture. Ricardo's rejection of the inevitable 'redundancy of population' was formalized as the theory of compensation: the idea that the working class would be compensated for temporary 'redundancy' by favourable indirect effects on demand. Rising aggregate real incomes would create new consumer demands, the meeting of which would absorb the workers displaced by machines. The neo-classical economist of the twentieth century would argue confidently that, provided wages and prices were flexible, the 'elasticity of substitution' would ensure permanent full employment.

Economics produced two powerful dissenters, Karl Marx and John Maynard Keynes. Marx rejected the Malthusian assertion that land was naturally scarce relative to population. It was the disproportion between population and land in *private* ownership not between population and 'resources' which created the so-called Malthusian problem. He also argued that making capital or tools artificially scarce left labour with nothing to sell but its 'labour power'. This opened it to its almost limitless exploitation. There is no compensatory mechanism; *all* companies are compelled to compete with each other to cut labour costs. So the introduction of machinery would be accompanied, not by any compensatory growth of new jobs, but by mass pauperization. Marx wrote that mechanization threw labourers on the scrap heap.[17] Keynes also denied the efficacy of compensating effects. Unless government took deliberate steps to keep up total demand for goods and services, the introduction of labour-saving machinery would cut aggregate spending *before* any reallocation of labour to alternative jobs took place: hence the possibility of 'underemployment equilibrium'.

The benefits of industrialization took a long time in coming. Economic historians like Eric Hobsbawm believed that the initial gains in Britain accrued entirely to the capitalists and that its costs were borne by the working class, whose standard of living declined from 1780 to 1840.[18] Improvements in constructing cost of living indices have now provided a 'best guess' that real wages rose slightly per year for all blue-colour workers between 1780 and 1850[19] but that substantial real wage growth came only in the third quarter of the nineteenth century – a 'transition' of nearly 100 years.

The effects of machinery must also be distinguished from those of expanded acreage. Between 1870 and 1913, 15 per cent of Britain's population emigrated.[20] Globally, the European colonization of sparsely inhabited lands in the Americas, Australasia, Africa and eastern Europe increased the ratio of land to population from 24 acres per European in 1500 to 148 acres by 1900. This helped solve the Malthusian problem, with the Irish potato famine of the 1840s a serious bump on the way. But emigration itself does not explain rising income per head. For this, machinery must be given the credit.

Such quantitative measures cannot tell us about changes in the quality of working life. Three were most important. First was the replacement of the household by the factory as the unit of production. Working-class men and women now 'went out' to work; homes became exclusively domestic spaces. Division of labour now more sharply separated the middle class from the working class: the middle-class ideal was that of the 'non-working' woman, whose increasingly constricted clothes, in Veblen's sardonic phrase, signified their 'exemption from useful activity'. Second, workers lost control of their time. They now work for fixed days and hours, and at the pace set by machines. Time wasted on the job was money lost to the employer. The result was an increase in the labour intensity of work. Finally, workers were separated or 'alienated' from what they produced. For many, the increase in real incomes, when it came, was bought at the cost of a sharp deterioration in conditions of work.

The factory system polarized articulate opinion. Factories were sometimes seen as miraculous cathedrals to modernity; but they were also William Blake's 'dark, satanic mills', belching black smoke.

'From this foul drain', wrote Tocqueville of Manchester in 1835, 'the greatest stream of human industry flows out to fertilise the whole world.'[21]

The unspeakable conditions of work and life in the factories and sweatshops of industrial Britain gave birth to the movement for social reform. Especially influential was Sir James Kay-Shuttleworth, a doctor who reported on the health of Manchester mill workers. On the effects of working alongside machines he wrote, 'Whilst the engine runs the people must work – men, women and children are yoked together with iron and steam. The animal machine – breakable in the best case, subject to a thousand sources of suffering – is chained fast to the iron machine, which knows no suffering and no weariness.'[22] Similarly, the Victorian 'social novel' was a response to the drastic change in workers' living conditions. Elizabeth Gaskell's *Mary Barton* (1848) and *North and South* (1854) described the miseries of mill workers in Manchester.[23] The utopian socialists hoped that cooperation, mutual aid and self-sufficiency could allow workers to escape the worst effects of the factory. Of those, the industrialist Robert Owen was the most practical and effective, buying a partnership in the mills of New Lanark in Scotland, which he ran along utopian lines, with good housing, education and more limited working hours. Though his other attempts at utopian communities failed, he successfully showed that it was possible to run a profitable business without inflicting long hours, low wages and horrible conditions on workers.

So what happened to the handloom weavers? Miriam Cherry has offered a counterfactual sketch of the world in 2500 CE – had the Luddites succeeded in ridding it not of machines *per se* but of the appalling conditions of their use.[24] The Luddites peacefully take over the factories, start a political movement and get parliamentary approval for a mixed form of ownership by capitalists and workers' collectives, the former owners being properly compensated. Thereafter, the Luddite Councils decide technological goals and resource allocation. To be implemented, all proposed new technologies have to pass the test of being for the common good. Miriam Cherry goes on to describe the emergence of an economic doctrine called Sustainomics dedicated to Human Flourishing. Priority in technological development is given to agriculture, food distribution, health and nutrition. Labour-saving gains are distributed as dividends to the 'cadres' of workers. Schools of engineering and technology are established to teach children how to construct 'new and better industrial machines'. Lots of beneficial inventions – including a cure for cancer and chromosomic disorders – follow. Workloads fall, and citizens spend their spare time with their families, on hobbies and civil pursuits. In the new doctrine, principles come before property, sustainability supersedes planned obsolescence and respect for human life and the environment trump market logic.

However, as we know, Ricardo was right 'in the long run'. From about the middle of the nineteenth century the indicators of wealth started to move sharply upwards. Europe's population (minus the Russian empire) grew from 179 million to 340 million between 1820 and 1913.[25] Over the same period, real income per head in the same area grew from $1,870 to $5,000 (in 1990 dollars)[26] – income, that is, grew faster than population. Average annual hours of work in western Europe and the USA fell from just under 3,000 in 1870 to 2500 in 1913 and 2,000 in 1950.[27] Levels of unemployment fluctuated with the business cycle, but there was no evidence of any growth in 'technological unemployment'.

None of this did anything for the handloom weavers. Whereas spinning had already been mechanized in factories by Hargreaves's spinning jenny, weavers mainly used handlooms on a domestic basis until after the Napoleonic wars, that is, they still owned their means of production. Wages in weaving were high, as it was a skilled craft. It was not until the early 1840s that the number of power looms exceeded the number of handloom weavers.

The spread of the powerloom in the 1820s and 1830s concentrated the weaving side of cotton production in the factories, displacing the handloom weavers and destroying the wages they had received. This led to severe distress and starvation amongst the weavers and contributed to a general economic depression which lasted for several decades.

In 1800, the wages of handloom weavers were about 19 shillings per week (standard for a skilled artisan of the time). In 1830, the artisan was earning about 23 shillings, while the wages of the handloom weavers had fallen to 6 shillings, 3 pence per week.[28] Their wages kept falling until they and their trade were extinguished. Nassau Senior's icy advice was that 'they should get out of that branch of production'. They did: 240,000 handloom jobs disappeared between 1829 and 1860 as power looms surged ahead.[29] The Industrial Revolution opened up fissures between work and jobs, work and play, employment and unemployment, the private and the public, men's work and women's work and, in politics, between capitalism and socialism. These wounds only started to be healed during and after the two world wars of the twentieth century, when the efforts of social reformers and the advent of political democracy led to the welfare state.

The Luddite resistance to the power looms that destroyed their craft is still a key reference for the current debate about jobs at risk. The terms of the debate have scarcely changed; nor have its memories faded. But it has been made more urgent by the spread of automation.

5.

Why Europe and Not Asia?

'Oh East is East and West is West and never the twain shall meet.'

Rudyard Kipling

The story the three previous chapters has tried to tell has been about the causes of the West's technological achievement. Now we turn the question round: why was there no autonomous techno-logical miracle outside Europe? The Marxist answer starts, and in fact ends, with property relations. Marx wrote to Engels on 2 June 1853: 'the basic form of all phenomena in the East . . . is to be found in the fact that *no private property in land existed'*.[1] This lack, he thought, enabled 'Oriental despotism' to siphon off the whole of the surpluses of peasant communities for its grandiose building projects, leaving nothing for capital accumulation. The static binary relationship between peasant and despot meant that the motor of history, the class struggle, never got going, so Asia exhibited a pre-mature senility. The function of the British conquest of India was to get the class war under way.[2]

The Sinologist Karl Wittfogel (1896–1988) set out to explain the persistence of the Asian form of rule he too called Oriental despot-ism. An arid environment isolated from 'strong centres of rainfall agriculture' fixed a certain level of technique and 'specific hydraulic way of life'. The reason was that the 'technical task' of moving water was such that it had to be solved by mass labour or not at all. In such societies, the conditions of life required manipulation of large bodies of water to guard against rivers flooding and to irrigate parched regions. These problems were especially acute in those civilizations based around the Nile, Tigris and Euphrates in the Middle East, the Ganges in India and the Yellow River (and Yangtze) in China – areas containing two-thirds of the world's population. Water could only be distributed as required by large-scale protective or irrigation works, which required the mobilization of labour under despotic leadership. Government-managed water works placed a large-scale feeding apparatus in the hands of the state, and government-managed construction works made the state undisputed master of the largest part of economic activity. (Wittfogel thought Soviet communism was simply an application of these principles to industry.)

Wittfogel used these 'requirements' of climate and geography to explain the divergent paths followed by the economic and political systems of Asia and Europe. The absence in Asia of effective private property rights stymied both economic growth and political pluralism – joint explanations of the technological dynamism of the West. Not just obstacles to inheritance, but confiscation in the form of heavy taxes was the source of revenue for the centre. So land could not be used to augment the wealth of private proprietors and thus become the base of an independent nobility and church. The crucial nexus in such societies was the ruler and the bureaucracy. 'The despot establishes horizontal checks by giving equal authority to two or more officials. He maintains vertical checks by a multiple system of reporting and supervising.'[3] 'Nowhere', Wittfogel writes, 'did internal forces succeed in transforming any single-centred agro-managerial society into a multi-centred society of the western type.'[4]

Marx and Wittfogel are in a long line of western commentators on the East who believed that what needed to be explained about Asia was its 'backwardness', whether economic (Marx) or political (Wittfogel). Early eighteenth-century thinkers like Montesquieu had shown considerable respect for Asian, and especially Chinese, civilization. But by Adam Smith's time it was Asia's 'stagnation' which attracted attention. The question then asked was why Asia was so conspicuously 'lagging behind' in the growth of wealth.

The lag is not in dispute. Round about 1000 CE, the whole world had roughly the same GDP per head ($453 in 1990 dollars) By 1820, Europe's had shot up to $1,940, while Asia's was around $600. In fact, west Asia, India and China had remained stuck at between $550 and $600 per head for 300 years.[5] The big debate is about when exactly western Europe started to forge ahead, and why. The consensus is that the divergence started after 1500. Angus Maddison came to believe that it started earlier – from the fourteenth century.[6]

After about 1750, the non-European world drops out of the history of technology. There was no indigenous technological momentum in the Middle East, India or China. Since progress is commonly measured by standards set by western science, this fact was a huge blow to the self-respect of non-western societies, evoking two inconsistent reactions: the first, that their technological trajectories were cut off by European intrusion (the post-colonial theory); the second, that their civilizations were equal or superior to Europe's if judged by non-European standards.

The post-colonial thesis currently dominates western historiography. It has rediscovered the prosperity and ground-breaking advances made in architecture, mathematics and metalworking by Indian, Chinese, and African armament. The huge flaw in such post-colonial accounts is their failure to acknowledge that the Europeans must have already had a big technological advantage to be able to intrude successfully. As Aristotle put it, 'superior power is only found where there is a superior excellence of some kind'.[7] Whatever the moral value of their respective civilizations, European armament was already way ahead of Indian and Chinese by the end of the fifteenth century.

On the other hand, the civilizational judgement in favour of Asia deserves great respect. To believe that what needs to be explained about Asian society is its 'retardation' is to judge the performance of non-European societies by European standards. From a non-European standpoint, the problem to be explained is not any retardation of Asian civilization, but the aggressive, imperialistic and predatory character of European civilization. It was Europe which forced capitalism on the non-European world and thereby exported its own torment. Now a civilizational reversal may be happening, whose outcome is uncertain.

We can obtain a historically richer flavour of what Marx called the 'Asiatic mode of production' by briefly considering the roadblocks to science, technology and political pluralism put in place by Islamic, Indian and Chinese cultures,[8] while remembering that the ground is heavily contested.

The Arab World

The 'dark' European Middle Ages is often contrasted with the glittering Arab Golden Age which flowered in the Pax Islamica. Between the ninth and twelfth centuries, the Arab-Islamic world was more scientifically and technologically advanced than the Christian West. The contributions of Arab astronomers, physicians, alchemists and mathematicians had a lasting impact upon scientific knowledge. The replacement of Roman numerals by Arab numerals was decisive in creating a mathematically based science. Many of the more empirically minded Christian Scholastics were inspired by the experimental work of Arab physicians, astronomers and physicists like Avicenna and Alhazen. Some of the earliest foundations of science thus came to Europe from the East. Techniques of crop cultivation, food processing, metallurgy, irrigation and navigation were invented or discovered in China and then imported, refined and put to more extensive and significant use in the Islamic world. Improved rigging for ships, later used in the European voyages of discovery, came from Arab seafarers. Knowledge of the compass was shared between Europeans and Arabs in the twelfth and thirteenth centuries.[9]

This efflorescence is not surprising, since the Arabs were at the centre of a worldwide trading empire stretching from the western Mediterranean to south-east Asia, with all the advantages accruing from freedom of trade, extensive transport networks, circulation of

ideas and the division of labour, at a time when much of Europe was
sunk in barbarian stupor. Then the Arab world went into decline.
The reason might seem obvious: the 'barbarians from the steppes'
shifted their attention from Europe to Asia. The Mongols and their
descendants seized Baghdad in 1258, India in 1526, China in 1644. The
Turks, another nomadic people from central Asia, seized Constantinople in 1453. A century later, another lot of 'barbarians', this time,
the Europeans, invaded Asia from the sea: the East India Company
was founded in 1600. These Toynbean 'ordeals' were perhaps
enough to bring the Arab, as well as other Asian, golden ages to an
end. But this raises the Toynbean question: why did the rich and brilliant Arab civilization succumb to the external challenges it faced?
Two specific questions involve technology. Why did the Arabs not
develop the military muscle (the equivalent of 'Greek fire') which
enabled the Byzantine empire to fight off its challengers for centuries? And why had not the gains from trade produced enough capital
accumulation to kick-start a technological revolution?

The property system takes pride of place in economic explanations of Arab-Islamic 'retardation'. 'Islamic systems of land tenure,
in combination with the Islamic law of inheritance which led to the
fragmentation of estates, and the practice of establishing the *awkwaf*
or religious trusts, controlled by lawyers, discouraged the owners of
land from themselves making improvements and inducing the culti-
vators to adopt superior methods'.[10] This is, as we have seen, the
standard neoclassical explanation of economic retardation. And there
is a lot to be said for it. One can argue, in the spirit of Douglass North,
that a tax system which favoured camel owners 'led to the disappearance of wheeled transport throughout the Middle East'.[11] However,
there is a deeper question. Why was there no 'Enlightenment' in the
Arab world, corresponding to what the West experienced?

The answer may well be that, in Islamic thought, politics was
viewed as an extension of religion, and political life remained closely
woven together with ideas of religious obligation. With some
exceptions, the Muslim *ummah* (community), as an ideal type, is
ruled by a caliph – a politico-religious successor to the prophet

Muhammad. This left less room for scientific, technical and political freedom from religious authority. Significantly, Arab Islam rejected the printing press and remained until 1800 a world of oral and manuscript – that is, priestly – communication. Whilst in Europe a corridor of intellectual freedom was opened up for philosophers, scientists, technicians and inventors, in the Muslim world the Koran and the Imams were unchallenged.

Indo-Islamism

The India of the Mughals had been one of the world's most advanced economic regions. It was a hybrid civilization, which André Wink calls Indo-Islamic, resulting from a fusion of Hindu and Muslim peoples (or in Wink's telling of 'settled' and 'mobile' societies) and lasted until the eighteenth century, when it was overcome by the superior armaments of the European traders and colonialists.

The data show a slow population growth between 1500 and 1700, from 110 million to 165 million, and GDP per head stationary at $550 (in 1990 US dollars). This was the 'Hindu equilibrium'. Historians have debated whether this was a static or dynamic equilibrium. Traditionally, British historians have typically tended to see it as one of 'stasis and misrule'; revisionists, both Indian and British, have preferred to look for signs of dynamism in the Indian economy which British interference aborted. Specifically, post-colonialist theory identifies a period of 'proto-industrialization' and urban growth, especially in Bengal, which was cut short by the deliberate British destruction of Indian textile manufactures. These accounts produce different, often opposing, answers to the same question: why did India 'fall behind' Europe scientifically and technologically? But perhaps the question should be: what caused parts of Europe to deviate so strikingly from the *habitus* of most of the rest of the world and then seize control of its future?

The traditional view of the Mughal empire was that it was an 'insatiable leviathan', extracting the entire peasant surplus for the unproductive spending of its governing elite; consequently Smithian [market-led] growth was stifled. [12] A counter-view is that royal ownership was only notional. Standing between the predatory state and peasant villages was a class of Hindu nobles called the Zamindar, and they collected taxes, taking 10 per cent for themselves. This is all laid out in court historian Abul-Fazl's contemporary (late sixteenth-century) book on Mughal administration under Emperor Akbar (1542–1605): 'All land belonged to the peasant families, the Zamindar, and the king. This communal ownership fostered the development of canals, common grazing grounds and so on. It also helped in developing trade and commerce in village and society.'[13] However, this was not private ownership: Zamindars were representative of the village communes rather than private owners. This was like the 'overlappingness' of the European feudal system.

Nothing in India's internal development seems to have been able to disrupt this feudal aspect of its economic life. India, as is well known, had castes not classes. In his book *The Hindu Equilibrium* Deepak Lal greatly annoyed Indian scholars by treating India's economic stagnation as the result of its Brahmin-dominated caste system. The consolidation of classes into rigid, hierarchical castes was, in his view, the response to three Toynbean 'challenges': endemic warfare, the need to secure a stable labour supply and the problem of monsoon-based irregularity in agriculture. Once put in place 2,000 years before the coming of the West, the caste system, which ranked the merchant caste (Vaichnyas) third, well below Brahmins (the priestly and government caste), produced a 'Hindu' rate of growth, i.e., no growth at all.[14] If anything the caste system became more rigid as time went on.

Revisionists like Jack Goody resist attempts to primitivize the pre-colonial Indian economy. 'There was much more than shoots of mercantile "capitalism",' he writes.[15] Much of the revenue seized by the centre was redistributed back to local interests and there were thriving regional and, for some goods, national markets. Central control was weak in many areas, and the proportion of the gross agricultural produce actually collected was significantly less than claimed by the Oriental despotism school.

Supporting the idea of a pre-colonial proto-capitalism is that India ran a large balance of trade surplus with Europe, exporting textiles, jewellery, spices, wine, and receiving gold in return. (European military intrusion was based on real panic about outflow of gold to Asia.) However, the diversion of luxury production to export raised the domestic price of luxury goods to their main consumer, the imperial court, and therefore increased the tax rate it imposed on the peasant cultivator. Trade surpluses were thus 'paid for' in increased taxes.[16] As important is that most of the gold gained from export was hoarded or used for decoration not applied to stimulate trade. 'India', noted the nineteenth-century economist W. Stanley Jevons, echoing Pliny 2,000 years earlier, 'is the sink of the precious metals.' Unstable climate probably explains the well-known Indian propensity to hoard: with floods and monsoons regular events, peasants needed to keep wealth in portable form. Hindus prayed to the gods to grant them cows, horses and gold.

With few exceptions, accounts of Indian 'retardation' are purely materialist. Yet no student of Indian history can fail to be struck by the importance of belief systems in explaining Indian political and economic behaviour. Religion had a profound influence on the way Indo-Islamism was organized politically. Neither Hindus nor Muslims recognized an institutional separation between church and state. The Hindus had no tradition of monotheism which brought with it a single sacred text like the Bible or the Koran; no thinker from whom everything flows like Jesus, Mohammed or Confucius. Hinduism was more a cluster of beliefs and practices, broad enough to incorporate Buddhism.[17] 'It used to be said [at Harvard] that every Sanskrit word means itself, its opposite, a name of god, and a position in sexual intercourse.'[18]

The polytheistic character of Hinduism produced an attitude to nature completely at odds with the European view of it as a force to be conquered and bent to human will. Non-violence, simple living, simple tools – these are legacies of Hinduism. For all its failings in the material sphere, Hinduism did not produce the morbidity of western civilization.

Islam, which *was* monotheistic and universalist, accepted religious pluralism as a condition of governing India. The third Mughal emperor, Akbar (1556–1605) tried to synthesize Hinduism and Islam, hosting 'a series of multireligious theological salons'. In the end he decided that all religions were equally true or equally illusory.[19] However, neither Muslim nor Hindu leaders renounced religion as a tool of governing. The syncretic character of Indian beliefs shielded them from the assault of the rationalists. It was the Europeans who brought atheism to India.

The conclusion of historian M. Athar Ali is sensible:

One need not be a follower of Marx's theory of the unchangeableness of traditional Indian society to accept the fact that there was no conscious spirit of technological innovation (and scientific enquiry) here and in the Islamic East to match the spirit already motivating a large part of European society in the seventeenth century . . . The pace [of Indian innovation] was certainly slow and the scope severely limited. This is manifested above all by the utter absence in the literature of India of any satisfactory descriptions of even the most important products of Europe's new technology, e.g. the clock, the telescope, and the flintlock.[20]

The Case of China

Already by 1776, Adam Smith noticed that China 'seems . . . to have been long stationary', having, centuries before, 'acquired that full complement of riches which the nature of its laws and institutions permits it to acquire. But this complement may be much inferior to what, with other laws and institutions, the nature of its soil, climate, and situation might admit of.'[21] According to economic statistician Angus Maddison, China was the world's leading economy in terms of per capita income until the fifteenth century, outperforming

Europe in levels of technology, the intensity with which it used its natural resources and capacity for administering a huge territorial empire. However, Chinese income per capita barely shifted from $600 between 1500 and 1870, while the UK's quadrupled from $714 to $3,190 in the same period, and even Spain's doubled.[22] This is the statistical basis of the notion of a 'Chinese equilibrium' disrupted by the West.[23]

China's population grew from about 100 million in 1500 to 300 million in 1800, starting with population movement from the north to the Yangtze delta from the eighth to thirteenth centuries. The Yangtze region had been a swampy, lightly settled area, but with irrigation and early-ripening seeds, it provided an ideal opportunity for the massive development of rice cultivation. Since the land produced more rice per acre than wheat had, southern expansion enabled China both to support more people at the same standard of living and to delay the onset of diminishing marginal returns.

The comparative data are full of holes, but most of them endorse Adam Smith's finding about the stationary character of the Chinese economy: Mokyr writes that 'by 1800 a decisive technological gap had opened up and the European effort had gathered a momentum that would not find an equivalent in the Asian world until after 1970'.[24] This prompts the famous 'Needham question': why had modern science not developed in China?[25]

A revelatory moment was the Chinese emperor's reply to Lord Macartney, the British emissary who had come to Beijing in 1793 with three shiploads of British wares to negotiate the opening of north Chinese ports to British trade. 'As your Ambassador can see for himself,' the Emperor told him, 'we possess all things. I set no value on objects strange or ingenious, and have no use for your country's manufactures.'[26] The Emperor's incuriosity about the world outside was picked up by the great historian of China, Joseph Needham, who counted twenty-six Chinese inventions which came to the West and only three which went from the West to China. Often the lags were several centuries.[27] China was, in the Emperor's eyes, a prosperous, well-governed empire that had nothing to learn from others and needed only to apply its own historic knowledge, stored in its rituals and gigantic encyclopedias, to the management of its affairs.[28] There was no need for curiosity about how things were done elsewhere; they were almost certain to be done worse; and if they were done as well, this was because foreigners had copied the Chinese. This Chinese complacency can be contrasted with the Promethean striving of post-Renaissance Europeans.

Two pivotal moments in China's 'withdrawal' were the dismantling of its navy in 1525 and the expulsion of the Jesuits (and all westerners) by the Ming between 1723 and 1744. Headrick comments on the first that 'China turned inward, leaving the oceans to foreigners'. The reason is 'still a mystery'.[29] Goodrich thinks the decision 'unquestionably changed the course of history', by isolating China just when the Europeans were about to penetrate every corner of the earth.[30] Today's China is determined not to repeat the mistake.[31] The expulsion of the Jesuits may be interpreted as an attempt to protect Chinese culture from western missionary zeal.[32]

The favoured answer to the puzzle of China's stagnation remains that most entrenched of economic beliefs: that a large bureaucracy stifles technological innovation, whereas a small bureaucracy (together with private property) encourages it. The immense size of the Chinese administration might be explained either as a requirement of geography, as Wittfogel did, in terms of the political purpose of keeping China's empire together; either way, the bureaucracy swallowed up the public revenues.[33] The fact that, for thousands of years, China was run by tens, and eventually hundreds, of thousands of officials, is sufficient, therefore, for most to explain its technological somnolence.

This is too simple. Bureaucracy was responsible for some of China's most permanent accomplishments. It was seen to its best advantage in agriculture. It enabled the state to squeeze a surplus in the form of taxes and compulsory levies to finance a collective agricultural system of great complexity. It enabled the diffusion of best-practice techniques by widespread distribution of illustrated agricultural handbooks. It settled farmers, often compulsorily, in promising new regions. It built a public granary system to mitigate famines. It promoted the introduction of new crops. Though it did not produce any great rise in living standards, it enabled the Malthusian population problem to be overcome while avoiding catastrophe.[34]

However, the bureaucratic system brought heavy costs. Most importantly it came at the expense of those intermediate institutions which in Europe encouraged and protected innovation. It prevented the fragmented jurisdictions which had characterized the feudal system: land was not parcelled out to military chiefs as in the feudal system, but was held and administered by *prebendaries* appointed by the emperor.[35] Despite plentiful talent for enterprise, China failed to produce an entrepreneurial class. As Maddison puts it,

> the bureaucracy and gentry of imperial China were quintessential rent-seekers. Their legal and customary privileges defined their status, lifestyle and attitudes . . . Entrepreneurial activity was insecure in a framework where legal protection for private activity was so exiguous. Any activity which promised to be lucrative was subject to bureaucratic squeeze. Larger undertakings were limited to state or publicly licensed monopolies. China's merchants, bankers and traders did not have the city charters and legal protection which merchants had in European cities. International trade and intellectual contacts were severely restricted.[36]

The bureaucracy, recruited by competitive examination, consumed not just China's political but also its intellectual life. This meritocratic system dated from the irrigation works started in 300 BCE. It was extended during the period of intense canal construction under the Sui and T'ang emperors in the sixth and seventh centuries CE and expanded still further under the Ming (1368–1644). Its reach was greatly extended by the invention of printing in 600 CE, which made possible the mass production of textbooks. 'Useful knowledge' for the administrators consisted of knowledge useful for running the state. Some of it was useful to ordinary business;

but much of it was useful only to the bureaucracy. The *mania bureaucratica* spawned an encyclopedia of 11,095 volumes, commissioned in 1403 and completed in 1408, which purported to contain all human knowledge up to that time. Selection according to ability produced a high level of administrative competence. But, whereas in Europe, churches, military forces, independent universities, the professions and trade provided lots of alternative careers for the elite, in China the 'brightest and best' were absorbed into the business of ruling the empire.

Running the examination system itself required a large bureaucracy. Much more important, the examination system shaped what was considered 'high learning'. Mastering the classics was not only a sign of a good upbringing, but also the ladder of ascent to the most prestigious class. 'Science' was largely despised as 'arts and techniques'. The examination system thus gave no encouragement to original thinking. From the Ming dynasty onwards, hostility hardened to intellectual dissent. Thus 'while in Europe the negative incentives for intellectual innovation were becoming weaker in the middle of the seventeenth century and had largely vanished a century later, they had become stronger in China at almost the same time'.[37]

Chinese historiography was either backward-looking – the Golden Age was in the past – or cyclical. Earlier efflorescences, it was thought, always led to negative feedback. Prosperity bred the very forces that would undermine it, particularly by attracting predators and parasites, external (tough horsemen) and internal (corrupt officials, rapacious rulers). These forces continually slaughtered the golden-egg-laying geese.[38] Since there was no Fall to be overcome, as in Christian Europe, the Chinese reversed the historical sequence: antiquity was the golden age, followed by a decline. A period like the Han empire, which coexisted in time with the Roman empire, set the standards of excellence to which future generations should aspire. The institutions for goodness and wealth did not have to be discovered but simply kept in good repair. The idea that all knowledge had already been discovered was a permanent restraint on Chinese speculation. That is why Chinese thought was incapable of setting an agenda for the future which was not a repetition of the best of the past. Chinese philosophers had to protect themselves from the charge of originality just when its value was gaining recognition in Europe. It is significant that whereas western political scientists and economists today talk about the 'emergence' of China, Chinese scholars speak about its 'restoration' to a former position of greatness and respect.

The reverential attitude to the past effectively eliminated the idea of progress. Students were taught to memorize linguistic taxonomies, derived from past observations of nature. As early as 100 BCE, Su-ma Ch'ien, the first known Chinese historian, could say: 'My narrative consists of no more than a systematization of the material that has been handed down to us. There is therefore no creation; only a faithful representation'.[39] The well-researched history of ancient Chinese inventions merely serves to underline the fundamental difference between inventions that remained ludic, ceremonial or served political and bureaucratic needs (paper-making, printing) and innovations that were actually applied to the economy. Thus the Chinese lodestone-and-plate compass in use by the third century BCE was superior to the lodestones of ancient Greek navigation, but mostly employed (till now) for Feng Shui geomancy in the form of the often heavily decorated south-pointing *luopan*. Western navigators by contrast used their compasses that may well have first arrived from China to sail all over the world, eventually reaching Chinese ports with it, while no antique Chinese navigator ever reached Portugal, the Netherlands or England. Much the same is true of the history of gunpowder in China, where gunpowder but – significantly, not guns – was first invented, centuries before it migrated to Europe.[40]

If religious belief is defined by faith in the existence of a supernatural deity, the Chinese had no religion. But in Confucianism, Taoism and Buddhism, China possessed three philosophical traditions which prescribed rules of life considered binding on their adherents. Confucianism taught how individuals should behave in order to lead a life worthy of respect; and about how they should behave in different social relationships. Taoism taught the unpredictability of natural and social forces. Buddhism maintained that worldly desires are an illusion, and that people can find tranquillity only when they realize this. Buddhism and Taoism spread in periods of imperial decay and were repressed when the empire was re-established, imperial officials objecting not to their specific teachings but to the perceived threat of an 'empire within an empire'. Elements of Buddhism and Taoism were, however, absorbed into a syncretic Neo-Confucianism that could serve state interests, while neutralizing any subversive content. Broadened in this way, Neo-Confucianism became *the* state religion.[41]

In place of divine law, against which western science eventually rebelled, the emperor's rule was legitimated by the Mandate of Heaven (*tianming*). A Confucian classic, *The Book of Odes* (*Shijing*), stated clearly that 'under the wide heaven, all is the king's land, all are the king's subjects'.[42] Thus the virtuous ruler, not the constitutional state, was the Confucian ideal. Ritual behaviour was the social cement of the Confucian polity; in Lanxin Xiang's pithy phrase, Chinese society was 'rites-based', not 'rights-based'; its good order depending on '*moeurs*', 'civilized usages', 'common decency', not on the law.[43] The only accountability mechanism was armed rebellion against a ruler who was deemed to have 'lost the mandate' by allowing natural or man-made disasters.

The political culture of China was the philosophy of an empire, its pillars the Mandate of Heaven and imperial bureaucracy. Autonomous powers were associated in China with 'warring kingdoms', the disruption of the irrigated economy and economic retrogression. Thus all political, economic and cultural institutions had to be aligned with the central aim of preserving the unity of the Chinese state.

To summarize: there was no room in Chinese thinking for the clash between church and state, religion and science, nature and nurture, the human and the animal world, or for the creative possibilities of political variety. In Chinese thought, the notion of

95

equilibrium in the relationship between humans and the relationship between society and nature was carried to the highest level; disturbance to the 'proper order' would lead to destructive events such as earthquakes, floods, eclipses and even epidemics.[44] In this equilibrium conception there was no place for the Fall of man and his possible earthly redemption, but a constant warning against hubris.

This chapter has travelled some distance from its predecessors, but for an important reason. It has shown that the European experience is neither universal nor inevitable. Its immediate purpose has been to explain why capitalism, and the technological dynamic it carries in it, did not take root outside the western world until Europeans brought it – and then only in a form which most western analysts consider despotic or corrupted. A wider purpose has been to argue that it makes no sense to see Asia's future in terms of Europe's past. Asia will find its own way into the future, taking from the West what is useful. Meghnad Desai's dictum 'The reformed Bengali was Westernized in his living room but otherwise Hindu in his bedroom and kitchen'[45] can be applied to all three civilizations considered above. They took from western technology what they wanted and kept their beliefs. They thus continue to offer a civilizational resource to augment the depleting western stock.

6.

Lovely and Lousy Jobs

'Work hard, have fun, make history.'

Jeff Bezos

Work and Labour

People work because they have to or because they want to. At one pole is work which is legally compelled, like slavery, serfdom or indentured labour, at the other is 'work which gives life meaning'. The two have given rise to two opposing theories of work. For economists, work is simply a disutility, the cost of living. If people could get the goods and services they wanted by working less, they would work less. For most social scientists, people work to be valued. If there was no work for people to do, their lives would lack meaning.

We use the terms 'work force' and 'labour force' interchangeably, but Hannah Arendt made a crucial distinction between them. Work is 'the act of creating something permanent outside ourselves'. Labour 'is the endless necessary work required to keep human life running smoothly'.[1] Automating work in the economist's sense would be to lighten the burden of toil; in Arendt's it would be to reduce it to labour. Fear of unemployment thus has two roots: fear of losing our means of livelihood and fear of uselessness. The American writer Studs Terkel sums this up well: 'It is about a search, too, for daily meaning as well as daily bread, for recognition as well as cash, for astonishment rather than torpor; in short for a sort of life rather than Monday through Friday sort of dying.

Perhaps immortality, too, is part of the quest'.[2] But Terkel was not an economist.

Both Marx and Keynes saw machinery as a way of reducing the amount of necessary labour, and thus creating space for 'higher-value' activities. They wanted to expand not idleness but productive leisure. Both hated capitalism. But whereas Keynes thought it would wither away naturally once it had filled up the world with capital goods, Marx thought that a kingdom of freedom would be possible only after capitalism had been politically destroyed. He was, that is, much more alert than Keynes to the power of capital to keep goods scarce.

This raises the central question of distribution. Can an economic system in which the means of production are largely privately owned ensure that the gains of productivity are shared sufficiently widely to enable the future that Marx and Keynes both wanted? Or is a socialist economy required for this? Until about 1980, trade union pressure and redistributive taxation were able to push up most incomes in most western countries in line with productivity. However, these forces have been in retreat since. Conspicuous beneficiaries of technological developments in recent years have been the tech titans; conspicuous losers have been those decanted into what the late David Graeber called 'bullshit jobs'.

Motives for Work

Economic theory treats all work as compelled, legally or not. It is the necessary cost of living. As Lenin put it with his customary brutality, 'he who does not work shall not eat'. The Bolshevik state would enforce the law of scarcity, the oldest law of nature. This is the secular version of God's curse on Adam and Eve. Behind the promise of shorter hours lies the dream of lifting the curse. But such an account of the motives for working is radically incomplete. We work both to live and to give meaning to our lives.

At one extreme of meaningful work is 'work for its own sake'. In this conception the 'intrinsic' motive for work, like the pursuit of knowledge or beauty, dominates over any thought of material reward. For Aristotle, 'what is worth pursuing for itself is more complete than what is worth pursuing because of something else . . . '[3] But he was able to say this because the 'something else' was mostly done by slaves. That is why work for its own sake is usually associated with not *having to* work for a living. It is the state of mind Keynes and others thought would come about when machines would satisfy all our material needs.

Between the two poles of compelled and voluntary work, there are all the hybrid motives for working. Most work is done both to earn money and to do something useful or worthwhile. Craftsmanship or workmanship is a typical hybrid form of joyful work, combining 'art for art's sake' with the creation of serviceable objects. Professional athletes and entertainers work both for money and to receive and convey pleasure. Which gives Roger Federer more satisfaction – the beauty of his shots or his pay cheque? In addition to the money we earn, we want to be able to value ourselves and be valued by our community. Money and status – the two are not the same – are the tangible expressions of group appreciation. In almost all our activities, intellectual as well as physical, we compete for recognition, acclaim and (in our diminished times) celebrity. Norbert Elias reminds us that 'without functions for others . . . a human life remains empty and meaningless'.[4] The idea of work as a service survives in the phrase the 'service economy', though this has long since shed its motivational connection with being 'of service'.

Most of us accept a moral obligation to work, because this is what others expect of us. 'Society doesn't owe you a living' is the standard response to those suspected of 'sponging'. The moral duty to work may have begun as a way of reinforcing economic necessity but has become an independent motive, especially as a defence against idleness and the vices which flowed from it. In Christian apologetics, idleness was portrayed as a moral affront to the Divine command to work 'in the sweat of thy brow'. The religious language spelled out that in a world in which God had made provisioning toilsome, there could be no place in heaven for non-contributors to the general effort. Calvinism, as we have seen, strengthened the compulsion to work and the sanctions against idleness.

Finally, there is the companionship of work. It is from minds, bodies, eyes and ears meeting and engaging that sociability arises, and in all cultures the workplace, whether located in home, field, factory or regiment, has been a primary locus of companionship. Tenacious coal-mining communities are legendary, as is the comradeship of the trenches. Much of the pleasure of working has always come from the feeling of camaraderie. Modern technology abolishes the spatial and temporal cohesion of work, replacing the concrete with the virtual. 'Remote working' ignores the appeal of sociability, teamwork and mutual recognition as well as offering increased scope for online surveillance.

People work, in other words, not just to eat, but to give them a sense of *eudaimonia* – of a fulfilled life, and its absence creates a sense of meaninglessness. Behind the fear of loss of income lies what Richard Sennet calls the 'spectre of uselessness'.

The Debate Today

Since the Industrial Revolution, the promise of machines has been of increased consumption, leisure and improved quality of life; the threat has been of degradation and redundancy. Optimism has dominated, validated both by theory and experience. However, the fear of the degradation of work and redundancy of a large fraction of the workforce – that is, its removal from any kind of gainful or meaningful employment – has never been absent. It surfaces whenever there is a burst of technological innovation. We are living through such a period now as automation spreads. Newspaper headlines tell of a continuous haemorrhage of jobs. From gas stations to supermarket check-out counters, service is being replaced by self-service. Bus conductors have gone; train conductors are clinging on by a thread. And the quality of work is being continually degraded as jobs themselves become ever more meaningless and precarious. So the old question is posed again, more urgently: are machines a threat or a promise?

Dispelling anxiety about automation has become a major part of business apologetics. Typical of the optimistic prospectus in both content and language is the title of one report: 'How New Technologies Can Create Huge Numbers of Meaningful Jobs'. 'Much has been made', we read, 'of the looming devastation that self-driving technology will have on the 3.5 million truck drivers in the US . . . The concern is misdirected.' The same might have been said when truck drivers replaced coachmen and postillions.[5] 'Augmented reality', which supplements what we see and hear with computer inputs, can create new jobs (as well as reducing the cost of travel) by bringing the workplace into the home. 'Upskill', an augmented reality company in the manufacturing and field services sectors, 'uses wearable technologies to provide step-by-step instructions to industrial workers . . . With the pace of technological progress only accelerating and with increasing specialisation becoming the norm in every industry, reducing the time necessary to retrain workers is pivotal to maintaining the competitiveness of industrialised economies'. There is no mention of the wages to be earned by these augmented workers, though it is presumed that they will be relocated to 'lower cost areas more in need of job creation'. Technology, the report finally acknowledges, 'is a force that has the potential to eliminate entire industries through robotics and automation, and for that we should be concerned'. But it also continues to be 'a catalyst for the creation of entirely new industries and opportunities, as well as a way for the economy to unlock inefficiencies in the market and create win-win opportunities for employers and employees alike'.[6]

Heir to arguments made throughout the twentieth century are the benefits of freeing up time for 'higher-value activities', especially of freeing women from the routine drudgery of home work, enabling them to lead more fulfilling lives, inside or outside the home. 'Work Less and Be More Creative' proclaims the headline of a recent article in the *Financial Times* advocating an 'alternative hedonism'.[7] The CEO of a retail clothes chain that had introduced automated merchandising assured buyers that 'freed of certain merchandising tasks, they [the sellers] could take on more high-value work . . . such as understanding younger customers' desires'.[8]

Medicine is a big pin-up for the benefits of new technology. 'How Automation Is Pushing the Boundaries of Drug Development', one headline tells you.[9] The gist is that automation drastically reduces the 'wasted' time it takes to develop new drugs and surgical procedures, e.g. testing and compliance costs. What seems to be on offer is a growing range of medical repairs for the increased stress of living in a speeded-up world.

Optimists

At the end of 2017, McKinsey Global Institute (MGI) published a report called 'Jobs Lost, Jobs Gained' in which they claimed that 50 per cent of working hours in the global economy could theoretically be automated. However, they suggested that the proportion was not likely to exceed 30 per cent in practice; and, in fact, as the mid-point between two plausible scenarios, the report settled on a prediction of 15 per cent. They estimated that less than 5 per cent of occupations could be *fully* automated, but that in 60 per cent of occupations, at least 30 per cent of work could be.[10]

The current consensus is that the people most at risk of redundancy from automation will be those working in routine office and research jobs and in low-paid, precarious jobs like shelf stackers. Back-office work will be handed over to software tools, as all the lower tiers of labour, those involving laborious routine, are automated. Machines would make all the calculations necessary for choice; managers would only be needed for the final decision. The potential haemorrhage of jobs that could result sounds alarming if unconstrained. Blockchain, the software that encrypts records across networks of computers, so they verify each other, will remove the need for most accountants and legions of middlemen in law and finance. Knowledge of several languages will no longer be necessary as voice recognition and AI-driven translation are perfected, so there will be no more need for interpreters. Nor indeed for drivers or pilots as driverless vehicles take control of roads, rail, seas and skies. Online shopping and automated cashiers will eliminate in-store shop assistants. The time for bringing new medicines to market will be cut from years or months to days as computers, equipped with big data, take over their testing, thus removing another layer of human technicians.[11]

Some human tasks will survive. Business models of the future allow for 'energized' strategic cadres working alongside chief executives to direct the labours of thousands of machines. As computers are unable to access subjective experiences, humans will continue to have the edge in the arts, expression, authenticity.[12] There will be increased demand for person-to-person jobs in the care sector as the population ages and becomes less healthy. It is assumed that jobs involving manual or human dexterity like bartenders will also survive, since robots are notoriously clumsy at pouring drinks. However, the computer scientist Stuart Russell doubted whether there would be enough such jobs. He tells of showing a colleague, Andrew McAfee, a video of a robot neatly folding a pile of laundry. 'Oh ****,' was the response, 'that's another 500 million jobs gone.' And there will always be a living for gurus, charlatans, frauds, consultants, experts, 'influencers'.

A prescient quotation from early in the Industrial Revolution captures the idea of humans as both unique and replaceable:

Man as motive power is weak and expensive, but he is equipped instead with intelligence, albeit this also is sometimes of a weak order. Thanks to his bodily form and thanks to his mind, he is a universal machine, capable of an infinite diversity of movement. He is a self-propelling motive power that can betake himself to the places of work, can at his pleasure start, interrupt or complete the work; and can deal with the many accidental disturbance and obstacles, so that there is a great variety of work in which he can be replaced by no other form of power. But human labour is and remains disadvantageous in those cases where (1) great power has to be developed and (2) when a high degree of uniformity is required in the work.[13]

In other words, humans can be replaced in all tasks which can be automated, but there will remain tasks for which they are indispensable.

The case for machines rests on the simple assertion that, in the long run, technological innovation increases real income per head and therefore reduces poverty. New technologies have, throughout history, eliminated repetitive and mundane jobs. As a result, livelihoods have evaporated, skills been made obsolete, humans compelled to adapt to new work. However, the pain is temporary: the benefits of new jobs at better wages and much-improved living conditions start to flow. This will be as true of our own third (or fourth) Industrial Revolution as of the first.

The simplest argument for machines goes as follows. For those manufacturers who introduce them, the incentive is, as it has always been, to reduce the cost of labour. Machines may cost a lot to develop and install, but they cost much less to run than the humans they replace. For example, human drivers account for two-thirds of the cost of an Uber taxi journey, so 'when there is no other dude in the car, the cost of taking an Uber anywhere is cheaper'.[14] Passengers benefit from the money saved from their taxi journeys by buying more of something else, like, say, pizza at a restaurant. The redundant Uber driver finds employment as a waiter. Technology offers a win-win situation for both producers and consumers.

Now take this argument a stage further. The waiters themselves have been replaced by robots, thus reducing the cost of pizzas. No matter. If human wants are as limitless as we suppose, or as advertisers can make them, the increased incomes of the pizza eaters will be spent on other wants hitherto unfulfilled or even unimagined, thus creating a new tier of jobs and tasks. And so it goes on, win-win to eternity.

The optimistic view rests on four technical arguments. The first is the theory of complements. This holds that a great deal of technology is potentially job-enabling rather than job-displacing: it improves productivity without causing job losses. What is important for employment is not jobs but tasks. Most jobs contain non-routine tasks, requiring social and emotional and higher cognitive skills which cannot be automated. With suitable education and training workers will be able to take on higher-level or 'value' tasks in any job, whilst the more menial tasks will be taken up by machines. As the spin for ChatGPT, the latest advance from OpenAI, puts it: 'Instead of replacing human workers, AI is being used to assist and enhance their abilities. By taking on the repetitive and mundane tasks, AI already allows humans to focus on more complex and creative endeavours. Additionally, AI can also generate new ideas and insights that humans may not have been able to come up with on their own.'[15]

The second argument is the 'bigger-pie effect': technology enables the pie to grow faster than the population, creating new jobs by enlarging demand.[16] For example, it is claimed that the number of tellers employed in American banks rose with the automation of their tasks by automated teller machines (ATMs), because banks were able to open more local branches as their labour costs fell.[17]

The third argument is that technology changes the nature of the pie, by producing a whole range of new goods and services unthought of in the past, which are the source of new pleasures and thus new jobs.[18] Specifically, the loss of manufacturing jobs through automation will be compensated by the expansion of service-sector jobs. Through one channel or another, technology enlarges incomes and choice while reducing hours of necessary work.

Finally, machines increase the choice people have between work and leisure. Economists distinguish between income effects and substitution effects. As people's incomes rise, the opportunity costs of leisure – that is, the wages forgone by not working – increase, and so people may work even more than before (the substitution effect). On the other hand, higher incomes increase the attraction of leisure and could encourage people to work less (the income effect). Historically, the substitution effect has dominated – real incomes have risen much more than hours of work have fallen. The important point here is that people's hours of work become a choice rather than a necessity.

The flavour of a typical optimistic assessment resting on such arguments is given by the following: 'There will be some bumps in the road, and there is no room for complacency on issues of workforce displacement and the ethics of smart machines. But with the right planning and development, cognitive technology could usher in a golden age of productivity, work satisfaction, and prosperity.'[19]

A huge bump in the road is smoothed over by the generous use of the word 'transition'. This issue was raised by Keynes in his 1930 essay with which this book started – and then evaded:

> We are being afflicted with a new disease . . . namely *technological unemployment*. This means unemployment due to our discovery of means of economising the use of labour outrunning the pace at which we can find new uses for labour. But this is only a temporary phase of maladjustment. All this means in the long run *that mankind is solving its economic problem*.[20]

The contemporary discourse echoes him. McKinsey claims that although there will be no net loss of jobs in the long run, the 'transition may include a period of higher unemployment and wage adjustments'. History shows that this 'transition period' may take 'decades, not years, and the rising prosperity may not be shared by all'.[21] Every translation machine that nets its owner $100,000 lowers the wages of human translators until they have to 'get out of the trade' like the handloom weavers and postillions. Where do workers transiting from one job to another go to? Often to poorly paid, precarious service jobs needed to clean up social media platform sites like Amazon and Google.[22] What is conclusive for the optimists is that, bumps in the road notwithstanding, history has shown them to be right. Mechanization has been the durable engine of productivity growth, wage growth and shorter working hours for the vast majority.

The economists line up pretty solidly on the optimistic side, as their discipline almost forces them to. Here are two examples. Paul Krugman argues that the increased premium commanded by highly skilled workers, while 'a key cause of the growth of earnings inequality in the United States as well as much of the rise in unemployment in Europe', is a passing phase. Humans will be in ever-shorter supply for such 'truly difficult occupations as gardening, house cleaning, and the thousands of other services that will receive an ever-growing share of our expenditure as mere consumer goods become steadily cheaper'. So their wages will rise relative to those of 'symbolic' (i.e., brain) workers. As a result, 'the current age of inequality will give way to a golden age of equality'.[23] This prediction, made in 1996, has not come to pass.

The economist William Baumol has offered a variation on Ricardo. There exists a class of goods – the so-called 'Baumol goods' – in which no productivity gains are possible. This has been much truer of services than manufactures. For example, it takes the same number of musicians to play a Beethoven string quartet today as it did in the nineteenth century. Similarly, education and health services can be automated only to a small extent: schools still need teachers, hospitals nurses, the elderly carers. As the service economy expands relative to the manufacturing sector, so the proportion of jobs which can be automated falls, thus offsetting redundancy and declining wages in manufacturing. The question then is how far service-sector employment can continue to be insulated from automation. Are there some tasks intrinsic to persons? Surely an automated performance of a Beethoven string quartet is impossible. Or is it? And what about call centres and banking services, where humans are being replaced by voice processing systems and online access for customers?

Through one channel or another, technology enlarges incomes and choice while reducing hours of necessary work. Theory is backed up by history. Over the ages, the cumulative saving of effort, time and cost wrought by technology has been colossal. In the Roman empire it took 9,000 hours of spinning to produce a posh toga. On the eve of the Industrial Revolution, it would have taken about a fortnight, using a state-of-the-art treadle spinning wheel, to make a sweater. Today machines turn out thousands of shirts an hour to the benefit of all. What is there to object to? Fears of mass redundancy and pauperization are surely groundless.

The material uplift produced by machines has been astounding. Between 1000 and 1700 world population doubled, from roughly 300 million to 600 million. World GDP per head in those 700 years hardly shifted, rising from $485 to $593. A larger population simply spread out over a larger area of land. Then came the acceleration. Since 1700, technology has not only enabled the planet to support more than ten times more people (600 million to 7.5 billion), but at ten times GDP per head ($593 to $5,700), with average world per capita income rising aggressively since 1950 by about 4.5 per cent a year.[24] With the general growth in prosperity has come all the benefits associated with it – decline in absolute poverty – greater longevity, less disease, advances in literacy.

Carl Frey makes the essential point that acceptance of technological change has depended heavily on the 'distribution of power'. During the Industrial Revolution of the nineteenth century, a dominant manufacturing class with the support of governments was able to push through mechanization in the face of sometimes violent opposition of groups of workers. In the social democratic phase of mid-twentieth capitalism fears of unemployment were dampened by the commitment to full employment, while strong trade unions were able to moderate the pace of technical change and negotiate a reasonable sharing of its gains. Since the 1980s, a resurgent capitalist class has forced through massive labour-saving restructuring of economies in Britain and elsewhere, indifferent to social breakage. This has provoked populist backlashes by the losers.

With creative destruction rather than cooperative adaptation hold-ing sway, the question inevitably arises whether the creation of so-called value is worth the destruction of jobs; and whether the destruction of jobs will lead to political disorder.

Pessimists

Today's pessimists have a new argument. Whatever may have been the case in the past, the current wave of automation differs from that of previous technological upheavals by automating mental work in addition to manual work. Not only does technology bite ever deeper into cognitive work, but it does so at an accelerating rate. This is said to mean that there will soon be almost no jobs that robots could not do as well as, or even better than, humans. There-fore, redundancies due to automation will inevitably exceed those caused by mechanization in the past; some new jobs may be cre-ated, but far fewer than those destroyed.[25] A prominent recent pessimist, Oxford economist Daniel Susskind, claims that there are fewer and fewer jobs which can 'only be performed by human beings'.[26] Jobs which require 'human' qualities will remain, but this class of employment is steadily shrinking.

It is automation, not mechanization, which underpins the gloomy forecast of Silicon Valley author and entrepreneur Martin Ford. His argument is that as the cost of information, and the dis-tributed machine intelligence which accompanies it, falls to zero, more and more firms will automate. 'As a result, emerging industries will rarely, if ever, be highly labor-intensive.' As creative destruction unfolds, the 'destruction' will fall primarily on labor-intensive busi-nesses in traditional areas like retail and food preparation, while the 'creation' will generate new businesses, and industries that simply don't hire that many people.[27] What will be left will be 'lovely jobs at the top and lousy jobs at the bottom'.[28]

Yuval Noah Harari oscillates between optimism and pessimism. General medical practitioners will be replaced by robots, but precisely because of this there will be more money for human-led research and development of new medicines and surgical procedures. Another possibility is that instead of competing with robots, humans could focus on servicing and leveraging them. Drones eliminate the jobs of some pilots, but create new opportunities in maintenance, remote control, data analysis and cyber security.[29] In chess, the combined efforts of humans and computers outperform both humans and computers separately. So the new job market in 2050 may well be characterized by computer–human cooperation, not competition. But these new jobs will not solve the job problems of unskilled labourers. Previous periods of mechanization allowed people to switch to jobs with adjacent skill-levels, thus limiting the need to retrain. But as robots take over cognitive work, the skills gap grows and with it the length of the transition.

Little of either the optimistic or the pessimistic forecasts are so far reflected in the data. Smaller companies (the vast majority) have shown little interest in introducing automated systems. *The Economist* of 11 June 2016 showed that in the UK only 5 per cent of jobs, 9 per cent of businesses and 7 per cent of output had been digitalized.[30] That progress has been slower than hoped or feared is not surprising. Many things have to be in place for productive systems made up of digitalized LEGO parts to work. It is only large, integrated corporates which can scale up automation sufficiently to realize the cost savings of using it.

Because automation has so far been restricted, there is little evidence of net job losses. There have certainly been technologically driven redundancies, but these seem to have been replaced in line with the general predictions. Measured unemployment, after peaking under Reagan and Thatcher in the 1980s, as part of the drive to reduce headcounts in government-subsidized industries, fell to average levels of about 5 per cent in advanced economies. This could be called the 'natural' rate of unemployment – a level not 'artificially' boosted by Keynesian demand-expansion policies. Before the Great Recession of 2008–9, unemployment in the UK stood at 4 per cent, and at the start of the Covid-19 pandemic it was the same.[31]

However, these comforting figures of healthy employment hide several worrying trends, in which new technology may well be playing a part. The first is the growth in underemployment: people who would like to work more hours but cannot. This is reckoned to be at least double measured unemployment.[32] Employers reduce their workers' hours as a prelude to sacking them. Second is the stagnation of mean wages, which suggests that the gains from automation accrue to a minority only. Third, there is the deterioration in conditions of work, measured by growth in numbers of working-aged people on precarious employment like zero-hour contracts, and in exploitative forms of self-employment. The growth of the 'precariat' may reflect a choice for more flexible employment, but in many cases results from a simple inability to find secure employment. Fourth, there has been a growth in the proportion of low-skilled to total jobs, especially in retail and hospitality, suggesting a transfer of labour to lower-paid jobs. Fifth is the growth in the number of public-sector jobs as the private sector sheds labour. Sixth is the increase in subsidized jobs as governments pay private companies to keep people working who would otherwise be made redundant. A seventh trend has been the growth of private debt, a measure of the inability of people to make a living from their earnings. An eighth indication of deteriorating labour-market conditions is the growth of 'over-employment', as more people are driven to work longer hours by the demands of the job or the need to make ends meet: in Marxist terms, a speed-up in the rate of exploitation. Stress-related breakdown is sometimes the result. Finally, there has been a growth in job surveillance as employers develop more powerful means of monitoring job performance.

The pessimists single out the stagnation of wages and growing inequality as portents of growing redundancy. Until the 1980s productivity gains led to income gains. Improvements in efficiency – both through technology and through better organization of work – made possible the employment of increasingly large populations at decent jobs. This no longer happens. Marx's forecast of widespread pauperization is no longer as far-fetched as it once seemed.

The Political Consequences of Automation

There is a cost to every improvement. There are good grounds for arguing that the benefits from mechanizing work have exceeded the losses. The Luddites were right for their own trade, but not for all trades taken together. However, there is no guarantee that this will remain true, and good reasons for doubting that it will. And neither the optimistic nor the pessimistic arguments consider at all carefully what effect the structure of employment in a country has on its political system. Thus, at the very minimum, one cannot take comfort from the argument that automation creates as many new jobs as it destroys, if it promotes a structure of occupations inimical to the survival of liberal democracy.

In the 1950s and 1960s, it was widely assumed that economic development would favour democracy by enlarging a managerial and professional class which would come to demand political rights.[33] This would dispel the spectre of 'mass society' ruled by populist dictators of the kind familiar to Latin America. Applied directly to developed nations, this 'embourgeoisement' thesis, while spelling death for the class struggle, promised a solid social basis for mid-century consensus politics. Now what we see is a reversal: a hollowing out of the middle class created by *mechanization*, as increasing numbers of so-called routine or 'white collar' jobs are *automated*. As a consequence, the expansion of the service economy has gone together with a decline in the premia attached to the jobs, earnings and status hitherto commanded by the middle class. This is the political meaning of the phrase 'Lovely jobs for those at the top, and lousy jobs for everyone else'.

The enthusiasts for automation are blind to the risks that this reversal poses for constitutional democracy. A society made up of resentful fragments and disappointed hopes is the classic recipe for populist dictatorship.

7.

Upskilling or Downskilling?

'You either automate or get automated'

Tech proverb

Mechanizing Humans

A big topic in the current discourse is the need to 'bridge the skills gap'. A recent document from the ILO sums up the current discussion in both mood and language:

> Policy debates are placing renewed emphasis on lifelong learning. This is based on the understanding that lifelong learning and skills development increase workers' and firms' capability to adapt to changes in the world of work. Lifelong learning can therefore foster productivity and innovation among enterprises and help workers transition to quality employment, in contexts where these are partly jeopardized or do not even exist to begin with.[1]

In short, humans have to 'up their game' to compete with the machines.

It is commonly said that the Covid-19 pandemic has accelerated the need to 'reskill workers for the new economy'. The tech giants are 'leading the way'. So say the tech giants. Microsoft has launched a 'global skills initiative'. Google will 'aid the recovery through our technologies, tools and training, so that local businesses, communities and people can grow strong, faster and more resilient'. Apple has an 'Everyone Can Code' initiative which focuses on economic growth, revival and transformation; work, wages and job creation; education, skills and lifelong learning; equity, inclusion and social justice.[2]

'Upskilling' promises to shorten the period of transition and ensure that humans will complement machines, not just be replaced by them. It is a partner of the claim that working with machines in and of itself raises the level of human intelligence. This is a version of 'learning by doing'. But it is also generally agreed that some threshold of knowledge is needed to shorten the time it takes to 'learn on the job'. Few are prepared to argue that one way to 'bridge the skills gap' is not by increasing workers' levels of digital skills but by reducing the number of jobs which require them.

At the core of the positive account of the relationship between humans and machines is the claim that machines will enhance human capacity. Thus computers have taught humans to play better chess. But John Thornhill warns that 'rather than augmenting human creativity, they may amplify human stupidity'.[3] What force is there in this warning? Imagine a worker receiving instructions on how to make a pair of shoes through augmented reality goggles. All the steps in the operation are precisely choreographed. Anyone of normal dexterity will be able to manufacture an acceptable pair of shoes from such instructions. Can we really say that they have been upskilled or enhanced? It would be odd to say that they *know* how to make a pair of shoes. They are simply following instructions.

The world of work in the machine age is a world of lost skills: invisible mending is no longer needed because we throw away clothes which have holes; handwriting has yielded to the typewriter, now typists have yielded to computers and predictive text software; doctors have become medical technicians, no longer required to 'know their patients', simply to be able to read computer printouts of their vital functions; London taxi drivers no longer have to 'do the knowledge' of the city's streets and buildings, but just use satellite navigation. However, it is also true that working with new technologies compels workers to learn new skills, skills which might be based on theoretical knowledge rather than just on looking around and finding what works. Whether what is now called automation has a tendency to 'upskill' or 'downskill' workers has been debated since the Industrial Revolution.

The case for the division of labour – of 'one man one trade' rather than 'one man many trades' – was recognized by Socrates.[4] Adam Smith says of his pin factory:

> One man draws out the wire, another straights it, a third cuts it, a fourth points it, a fifth grinds it at the top for receiving the head . . . to put it on. is a peculiar business, to whiten the pins is another; it is even a trade by itself to put them into the paper; and the important business of making a pin is, in this manner divided into about eighteen distinct operations, which, in some manufactories, are all performed by distinct hands'.[5]

Adam Ferguson had explained ten years previously that 'the more [the undertaker] can subdivide the tasks of his workmen and the more hands he can employ on separate articles, the more are his expenses diminished, and his profits increased.[6] By increasing the productivity of the worker, the division of labour not just multiplied the wealth of nations, but also served the ethical purpose of eliminating irregular work habits. However, while extolling the benefits of the division of labour, Adam Smith deplores the 'torpor of . . . mind' it produces:

> The man whose whole life is spent in performing a few simple operations, of which the effects are perhaps always the same, or very nearly the same, has no occasion to exert his understanding, or to exercise his invention in finding out expedients for removing difficulties which never occur. He naturally loses, therefore, the habit of such exertion, and generally becomes as stupid and ignorant for a human creature to become.[7]

In short, no one in Smith's pin factory would need to know how to make a pin, or even what the purpose of making a pin was. Smith had grasped the profound truth that it was by contributing actively to the making of things that people develop their minds. If people are not to be led like sheep, they must be occupied in non-robotic activities.

Human intelligence may well be an impediment to efficiency. In his *The Philosophy of Manufactures* (1835), the Scottish doctor Andrew Ure wrote: 'By the infirmity of human nature it happens, that the more skilful the workman, the more self-willed and intractable he is apt to become, and, of course, the less fit a component of a mechanical system, in which, by occasional irregularities, he may do great damage to the whole.'[8] He also noted that, 'Even at the present day, when the system is perfectly organized, and its labour lightened to the utmost, it is found nearly impossible to convert persons past the age of puberty, whether drawn from rural or from handicraft occupations, into useful factory hands.'[9] With the acceleration of technical change has grown the incapacity of older workers to adapt to it, leading to a growing number of such workers retiring before they have reached pensionable age. Analysts call them 'discouraged'.

By the start of the twentieth century, Adam Smith's pin factory had become Henry Ford's Rouge automobile plant. 'What was worked out at Ford', wrote Charles Sorensen in his memoir of his years with the car manufacturer, 'was the practice of moving the work from one worker to another until it became a complete unit, then arranging the flow of these units at the right time and the right place to a final assembly line from which came a finished product'. The finished product, the Ford motor Model T, took 1.33 man hours (as against the previous 12.5 hours) to produce and they came off the assembly line every three minutes. Henry Ford sensed that there was a mass market for motor cars, and that automating their production was the way to make them affordable to millions. But, like the pin-makers, the auto workers no longer knew how to make what they were producing.

Henry Ford's mass production system was shaped by the ideas of the American engineer Frederick Winslow Taylor, famous as the 'father of scientific management'. Taylor had become obsessed with the thought that workers were not working as efficiently as they might. Having worked on the shop floor himself, he knew that most did not operate at their full capacity – in fact, they tended to set an ideal maximum output for the day and keep to that, even pressuring new recruits not to exceed this quota. The practice of 'soldiering' was anathema to Taylor, and he was determined to break the habit in his workers. He believed that there was an optimal way to perform any task, and that, once this had been worked out, ensuring everyone followed that pattern would guarantee maximum production. He searched for the most efficient ways of breaking down tasks, and timed how long each bit of a task would take. These 'time and motion' studies caught on, as did the rest of his method. Taylor's system consisted of developing exacting methods for every job, training workers carefully rather than allowing them to develop their own methods of working (and making sure the right workers were selected for each job) and planning every day's work meticulously. Managers were empowered to micromanage every aspect of work to achieve the maximum output. As Daniel Bell notes, Taylor was 'more than an engineer'. He felt himself to be a prophet of 'scientific principles' which would sort out all social frictions.[10] Lenin was greatly impressed.

'Taylorism', writes Simon Head, can be seen as the division of labour pushed beyond the pin factory and automobile plant to its logical extreme, with a consequent deskilling of the worker and dehumanization of the workplace. Taylor's disciple William Henry Leffingwell began applying the methods of scientific management to the service sector from the 1920s onwards, and today it is ubiquitous in call centres. In today's workplace landscape, the application of 'digital Taylorism' transforms the employees into 'electronic representations' of human beings, 'the numbers, coded words, cones, squares, and triangles that represent [us] on [their] digital screen'.[11] It is the basis of contemporary business management. The three interrelated elements of Computer Business Systems (CBSs) are 'computer networks' linking 'the work station of every employee or group of employees within an organization to that of every other'; 'data warehouses', containing 'the gigantic quantities of information' needed to monitor the actions of employees in 'real time' and control them 'in line with matrices established by the management'; and 'expert systems' that 'mimic human intelligence in performing . . . cognitive tasks'.[12] Such computerized business systems join Taylorian scientific management to the Benthamite panoptical control made possible by digital surveillance.

Head argues that 'smart' machines make people dumber, not brighter; dumbness makes them more manipulable; therefore, smart machines enhance control over humans. Apply the same science of production to society, understood as the sum of human outputs, and the society becomes a giant factory, regulated in the same way as Taylorism. This marks a crucial step towards social mechanization.

The 'skills debate' points to a sobering conclusion. If humans can be got to behave like robots for 90 per cent of their time, we might get rid of the remaining 10 per cent either by equipping robots with emotional and ethical intelligence, which eliminates the need for humans altogether, or by extinguishing the humanness of humans, which, as Ure pointed out, is such an obstacle to their efficient deployment.

PART II

The Quest for Perfection

8.

Straightening the Crooked Timber

'Why are bananas bent? Because no one went into
the jungle to straighten them.'

Albert Hirschman

The Dream of Perfection

We have always dreamed of perfection – of times, types and utopias
remote from the ugliness, messiness, toil and trouble of life as it is.
Mythologies, as we have seen, have set this golden age at the start of
the human story, followed by humanity's fall. Christianity's rendition is the expulsion from the Garden of Eden. With the tragedy of
the expulsion came the promise of paradise regained, though this
was mainly conceived as an afterlife in consolation for the suffering
which had to be endured in this life. What science did was to make
the realization of perfection seem feasible in this life.

Where does the dream of perfection come from? The Christian
answer is that we are made in God's likeness and carry the image (or
in some versions the actual substance) of his perfection and incor-
ruptibility within us. This may be contrasted with naturalistic
explanations of religion itself. Daniel Dennett in *Breaking the Spell:
Religion as a Natural Phenomenon* (2006) argued that primitive
humans, confronted by various awesome natural forces they could
not see but which caused things to happen, personified them as
powerful beings, benign or vengeful. These forces inhabited some
different world but actively intervened in this one and were

therefore to be worshipped. Mythology (and, later, religion) was a first stab at explaining the world in a way that science and history would come to pick up. God did not create us; we created God to make sense of what was otherwise inexplicable. It was the later claim of science to shed the light of reason on matters hitherto hidden or secret. But for many centuries science, mythology, religion and magic coexisted, with varying degrees of unease, precisely because the 'ultimate' forces behind events were hidden.

In ancient animalistic (or pagan) belief, there was no disconnection between humans and gods. The gods were endowed with human virtues and vices, indeed even more so; they were embodiments of all the natural forces which brought good and bad fortune. But, over time, the deities were gradually extracted from the objects of experience. This process was carried to its first conclusion in monotheism. The Abrahamic faiths affirmed a single supreme being, remote from the natural world, but the cause of all that happened in it. Monotheism bequeathed the specific mythology of an original perfection, from which humankind had been severed, because with the idea of a single God came the idea of a creator, prior to the world, and therefore not part of its imperfection. No other religious conception – certainly not paganism, or any version of pantheism – has given rise to such a sense of the tragic alienation of the human from the divine. Monotheistic theology emptied nature of gods: humans were on their own, alone responsible for their ethical choices.

Much of western philosophy has been engaged in the attempt to restore the link between the human and divine, damaged by monotheism and eventually severed altogether by science. Most of us consider ourselves as wholly earth-bound: we are not drawn to the divine by being part of the same substance. However, a minority of scientists, philosophers and technicians have come to believe that science might be able to open up another path to heaven, by penetrating the secrets of the brain, enabling us to construct an Artificial Mind from purely material substances. We might then be able to build a God instead of just imagining one. But would our own God be able to get us to behave better than we have so far managed?

In *The Perfectibility of Man*, John Passmore distinguished between 'task perfection' and 'social perfection'. A perfect criminal is one who never gets caught, but this does not make them a perfect human. 'Being human', Passmore points out, 'is not a profession', nor can a perfect society be defined 'as one which performs its social task perfectly: it *sets* a social task'.[1] Passmore was making a vital distinction between moral perfection and optimization. With the coming of Carlyle's 'mechanical philosophy' (see p. 74), social perfection came to be increasingly defined in terms of task perfection – that is, in terms of instrumental efficiency. The question of which tasks are worth doing, or whether there are ways of doing them which are less efficient but more human – the moral question – has largely been shelved.

Platonic Ideals

The most famous dream of the perfect society comes from Plato. In Book VII of *The Republic* (375 BCE), Socrates, the main interlocutor, asks us to imagine people chained from childhood to the walls of a cave in such a way that they can only look into its dark recesses. Behind them a fire burns, throwing into flickering relief on the wall before them shadows cast by objects passing behind. They watch these shadows, giving them names and interpreting them as real. Now suppose one of the prisoners – call him a philosopher – frees himself, turns his head towards the cave's entrance and makes his way to it. As he comes into the sunlight he will see more and more of the 'real' things of which he had only seen the shadows. Finally, in full sunlight, he sees the 'essence' of things, the real world of timeless, perfect 'Forms' or 'Ideas' of which the senses deliver mere distorted impressions. Among these essences is the Perfect City.

Plato's allegory opened up a split between the ideal and the actual without which a perfectionist earthly project is inconceivable. The scientist is heir to Plato's philosopher. Economists who construct 'models' of markets to direct policy-makers pay unacknowledged tribute to his spirit. But what is really 'real'? The thing before our eyes or the idea of it? The astronomer Kepler warned that the further a thing recedes from the quantities given by the senses 'the more darkness and error inheres in it'.

The quest for abstract knowledge may be thought of as harmless, even eccentric – the preoccupation of minds more at home in the world of ideas than that of common sense. In fact, this is the moral of Plato's *Theaetetus*. Here he tells an anecdote, derived from Aesop's fables, in which the gaze of the astronomer Thales is so fixed on the stars that he falls into a well in his path, which evokes the laughter of the 'Thracian woman'. (This joke was perhaps at Socrates' expense.) What the Thracian woman seems to be mocking is that habit of mind which is willing to sacrifice ordinary human concerns to a vision of perfection. However, Plato's philosopher is not just a harmless eccentric but a king. Having seen the truth, he returns to the cave (the world) to sort out its affairs. Plato's ideal Republic is a political project.

Aristotle, Plato's student, disagreed with his master's claim that the perfect forms he discerned had a real existence. They were, said Aristotle, constructions of the mind – principles of thought which should be abandoned if they did not square with the facts. Aristotle's contribution to modern science was to posit observation as the scientific method of justifying claims to knowledge. The mind might imagine all kinds of things but it should interrogate its hypotheses with what is near to hand. It is observation which can convert intuition into laws. Aristotle did not doubt, though, that knowledge lay within us. The obstinacy with which the data of the senses contradicted their theories has been the bane of all social engineers.

Plato's sketch of an ideal republic can be read as a polemic against the dysfunctions of fifth-century Athenian democracy, modelled on what was seen as the order of nature. There were to be three classes of citizen: guardians, auxiliaries (soldiers) and craftsmen, corresponding to the relative scarcities of the three precious metals, gold, silver and bronze. (The labours of Hephaestus, while useful, definitely belonged to the bronze class.) Each order fulfilled the functions which nature fitted them to perform. Unless all in the city occupy their rightful place, disorder will reign. Since all humans are not equally endowed with reason or strength it seemed obvious that the wisest should rule, the strongest should fight, and the rest should toil. In the most famous lines, from Book V of *The Republic*, Plato writes: 'Until philosophers are kings, or the kings and princes of this world have the spirit and power of philosophy, and political greatness and wisdom meet in one, cities will never have rest from their evils'. In Plato's Republic there were no checks against abuses of power, because power would not be abused.

Superiority of rulers would be secured both by breeding and education. Education of the guardian class was to be centred on music, philosophy and mathematics, with gymnastics thrown in as especially suited to the auxiliary calling. Plato excluded imitative arts, tragedy and comedy from the educational curriculum of his guardians, because they fostered the emotional, not rational, parts of the soul. Poets were to be banished from the city altogether. Aristotle's wider class of citizens would need to learn useful things. 'But to be always striving after the useful does not become free and exalted souls.'[2]

A tension between the method of Socrates and the conclusions of Plato runs through *The Republic*. The hallmark of the 'Socratic method' is continuous interrogation of received opinion. The Platonic conclusion is the rule of philosopher-kings, which cannot be questioned because their laws will be perfectly just. Universities have thus always had a dual rule: students question, but their teachers pronounce. The Socratic method eventually became too much for the citizens of Athens, and Socrates was condemned to death. One reconciliation between Plato and Aristotle was suggested by the nineteenth-century philosopher John Stuart Mill: free enquiry was necessary to sweep away prejudice, but once the truth had been established, further questioning was impious.

Original Sin

A central feature of Plato's thought is that virtue is a form of knowledge which can be taught. The crimes and cruelties which dog human existence are the results of ignorance. This view confronts the existence of *akrasia*, the unwillingness to do what one knows to be right.

This was the central point of the Christian intervention. In the Genesis story, Adam and Eve were created innocent like all other living creatures. But God singled humans out by giving them free will. Adam and Eve knew they should not eat the apple from the 'tree of knowledge of good and evil', but wilfully corrupted their innocence. For this offence, all humans suffer. But God is merciful and offers redemption in the form of His Son, sent to suffer punishment on our behalf.[3]

The doctrine of original sin took several centuries to reach its full severity. Early Christian movements like Gnosticism and Pelagianism placed much more emphasis on our disposition to goodness. However, once Augustinianism took hold, these were seen as heresies. In his *Confessions* and *City of God*, penned when the Roman empire was collapsing, St Augustine (354–430) depicts humanity as irretrievably distant from God. The implication of this doctrine is that knowledge alone cannot compel virtue, since 'no man is free from sin, not even a child who has lived only one day on earth'.[4]

As Augustine wrote in *Confessions*, 'I was quite sure that it was better for me to give myself up to your love than to surrender to my own lust. But while I wanted to follow the first course and was convinced that it was right, I was still a slave to the pleasures of the second.'[5] In defiance of the claim that knowledge of the good motivates its practice, Christian theology brought knowledge and the will into conflict, making virtue the overcoming of the temptations of evil. The tension between what Augustine called 'the school of Plato' and 'the discipleship of Christ' has dominated western philosophy and raises fundamental questions about the origins of western belief-systems. From Hellenism comes the belief that an ideal earthly society can be established by the exercise of reason alone; Judaeo-Christianity denies that the impaired will is able to choose the path of righteousness without the support of faith. Given the manifest infirmity of the will, the City of God cannot be established on this earth. It is only saints who can be saved. Nevertheless, there was an egalitarian promise implied in the Christian doctrine. The claim we are all born equidistant from God might be turned into an affirmation that we are all born equally near to God, of equal value in His eyes, that it was not divinely ordained that some would rule, others obey. Christianity was a religion of the powerless. By many tortuous routes this would eventually lead to the Enlightenment promise that an earthly utopia could be attained by all.

Repeated efforts were made in the medieval period to lighten the bleakness of Augustinianism. These culminated in the Scholastic synthesis of Thomas Aquinas (1215–74). Aquinas held that sin does not destroy reason, only weakens it. We have a 'certain share in divine reason itself', which gives us a rational inclination to do what is right. Interrogation of nature will prove not only God's existence, but the rationality of His design. Aquinas did not offer a secular, self-sufficient system of rational ethics. Nevertheless, the Scholastic attempt to transform theology into an Aristotelian science was a fateful turning. What was eventually left standing was the science minus the theology.

In the heretical writings of the twelfth-century mystic Joachim of Flora, there are hints of history as progress, its structure informed by the Trinity. The age of the Father had ended with the birth of Christ; the age of the Son was coming to a close; the age of the Holy Spirit, in which all Christians would be united in a new spiritual kingdom, free from the letter of the law, was at hand. Such millenarian hopes were quashed by the Protestant restatement of the Augustinian gospel: Calvin (1509–64) insisted that all ages were 'equidistant from God'. He stripped religion bare of the consolations of indulgences and intercessions, propitiations offered by the Church to relieve the prospect of eternal damnation. But millenarian hopes were not extinguished. Religious communities started to be set up in the newly discovered Americas to await the Second Coming, and utopian literature had begun on its own voyage of imagination.

The Scientific Method

The Renaissance in the fifteenth century retrieved Plato's dream of creating a perfect city. Hitherto the technical means of creating a secular paradise had been lacking, and Christian cosmology had excluded the search for such means. Now both the revival of classical learning and the growing wealth of parts of Europe combined to release thought from its Christian moorings.

The recovery from the Black Death (see p. 61) saw a pronounced improvement in the material conditions and prospects of parts of Europe. The first concentrations of wealth were in the Italian city-republics, hubs of east–west and north–south trade. The late fifteenth-century voyages of discovery further expanded Europe's geographic reach; with the fall of Constantinople in 1453 and the exodus of Greek scholars came the 'rediscovery' of classical learning; the invention of movable type printing technology by Johannes Gutenberg in 1439 speeded up the diffusion of knowledge.

The result of these developments was a loosening of the grip of medieval theology. The Renaissance was, in Guizot's words, 'inflamed with admiration, not only for . . . Virgil and Homer, but for the whole of ancient society, for its institutions, opinions, and philosophy, as well as for its literature'. In the Italian city-states of the fifteenth century were to be found 'the same taste for intellectual excitement, for new ideas, for an easy, agreeable life; the same effeminateness and licentiousness' which Guizot associated with eighteenth-century Enlightenment France.[6] Florence, 'city of businessmen, scholars, statesmen, artists and scientists, prepared the way for that eighteenth-century alliance between commerce and philosophy which did so much to encourage men's hopes that they not only could be, but would be, perfected'.[7] Renaissance man did not respect the disciplinary boundaries and narrow specialisms of our era but was educated and excelled in what we now call the humanities *and* sciences, curious about, and eager to explore, everything in nature.

The scientific line runs from Copernicus to Kepler, Galileo and Newton. In the spirit of Plato, Copernicus (1473–1543) wondered what the cosmos would look like viewed from the sun rather than from the earth and concluded that it would show that the earth revolved round the sun, not the other way round. His hypothesis was confirmed by telescopic interrogation of the heavens by Johannes Kepler (1571–1630) and Galileo Galilei (1564–1642). The question of what kept the planets in orbit was eventually answered by Isaac Newton (1643–1727). Newton, the story goes, had seen an apple plummet to the ground and wondered whether its fall was impelled by the same force which tethered the moon to the earth. He hypothesized an invisible physical force, gravity, which explained that the moon was kept in orbit or equilibrium not just by the pull of the earth but by the force exerted by other celestial bodies. There was nothing in this hypothesis contrary to religious belief per se: Newton himself felt that he had simply discovered the mechanism by which God acted on nature.

Of crucial importance was the shift from an Aristotelian cosmology, in which 'final causes' (causes set in operation by God) played a crucial explanatory role, to a mechanistic one, in which everything was done by 'efficient causes' (causes of actual events). The impetus for this transition was the increased power of machines, especially the telescope and microscope, to question nature. From this new power of interrogation grew a belief that knowledge of nature's laws would enable humans to command nature for their own purposes and benefit.

Echoing Aristotle, the Franciscan friar Roger Bacon (1561–1626), in his *Opus Magus* (*magus* = magician), had put the case for close observation of nature. 'For there are two modes of acquiring knowledge, namely, by reasoning and experience. Reasoning draws a conclusion and makes us grant the conclusion, but does not make the conclusions certain of truth, unless the mind discovers it by the path of experience.'[8] In brief, logical reasoning was a necessary, but not sufficient condition of scientific truth. The scientific method demands empirical hypotheses – hypotheses which can be proved or disproved. This was a body blow to the scholastic method, which relied heavily on reasoning from theological premises.

The Renaissance philosopher Francis Bacon made empiricism the basis of scientific method: 'putting questions to Nature, relying on particulars and not on an intellectual intuition of substantial forms, and devising experiments so that Nature could be forced to answer the questions put to her were revolutionary ideas'.[9] Scientific 'Look and See' confronted the Scholastic 'See and Look'. The telescope replaced the Scriptures as the source of knowledge of God's works.

The debate between religion and science came to centre not on the role of God as a final cause of creation, but on His role as an efficient cause of earthly events. Heliocentrism widened the space between the human and divine by decentering the earth. The plurality of worlds revealed by astronomy rendered absurd the hypothesis that God cared uniquely for just one. As the poet Shelley (1792–1822) would write: 'It is impossible to believe that the Spirit which pervades this infinite machine begat a son upon the body of a Jewish woman.' Copernicus, Galileo and Kepler started a process by which earthly affairs were gradually prised from the grip of the divine hand.

For this purpose the metaphor of society as a giant clock wound up by God was particularly useful. This suggested to René Descartes (1596–1650) that humans were the wheels, pumps and springs of the divine clock-maker. One could aspire to make society 'work' just as God made the clock tick. The mechanical metaphor was especially seductive because it introduced a vocabulary for discussing human problems as engineering problems. Niccolò Machiavelli (1469–1527), who formulated a theory of politics as a rational technology of power, was the first political *scientist*. The ruler must study not the

Scriptures but human behaviour and apply his knowledge to the tasks of government. 'Statecraft becomes an exercise in pure technique, comparable to a game of chess.'[10]

So what exactly was it that one was supposed to see when one looked? According to the empiricists, it was seeing an apple fall to the ground that led Newton to his *eureka* moment. But this is one of the great myths of science. Newton could never have arrived at his law of gravity by seeing objects fall to the ground – something which had been observed for thousands of years with little curiosity. What the falling apple might have done was to suggest to Newton a hypothesis to explain its fall. Empirical testing of scientific intuition has been the hallmark of the scientific method

Scientists were not in principle against authority: it was the authority of religion they would challenge. In Bacon's utopian fable *New Atlantis* (c.1624), loosely modelled on Plato's sketch of an ideal state in the *Timaeus*, an elite body of scientists rules the island of Bensalem Scientific research into the 'causes of things' is concentrated in the seat of government, Salomon's House. Its scientists and technicians have complete intellectual freedom, but it is they who decide which of their discoveries to publish and apply and which to keep secret. Bensalem is, in fact, ruled by a technocracy of scientists and engineers. As a result it is 'pious and chaste'.[11] Bacon's utopia linked science to one of our deepest aspirations – for better health. Salomon's House was a pharmacopoeia of medical enhancements: prolongation of life, restitution of youth, retardation of age, alleviation of disease, mitigation of pain, improvement of complexion, stature and looks, enhancement of sexual prowess and mental capacity. It even included the military use of poisons.

Bacon ruled out the possibility of a democratic knowledge society, because knowledge is naturally scarce. Land might be redistributed in acre plots, but knowledge cannot be parcelled out in bits, because in a knowledge society power is bound to reside with the minority of experts who alone know how to make it work. And Bacon understood this well enough. The authoritarian moral of his fable is well brought out by Steven Shapin: 'If experience was to play its foundational role in a reformed and orderly natural philosophy, it had to be controlled, monitored, and disciplined. If untutored sense was likely to mislead, then ways had to be found to regulate *what* experience could properly ground philosophical reflection. The question of *what* experience encompassed judgments about *whose* experience.'[12] In other words, a boundary needed to be established between what counted as knowledge and what did not, a boundary policed by a gatekeeper. Observation had to be cooked by experts before it could be served up for social use.[13] Like priests, scientists claimed power based on expertise. The only thing which had changed was the nature of the expertise they offered. It is telling that the new sciences of the sixteenth and seventeenth centuries discounted what would now be called folk wisdom as unempirical – too local, tacit and non-repeatable to be knowledge as such.

Although the scientific revolution weakened the hold of religious belief in the long run, the march of secularism was hastened by developments within Christianity itself. Of these the most important was the Reformation. In the wake of Martin Luther's Ninety-Five Theses nailed to a church door in Wittenberg in 1517, the Reformation spread rapidly to Switzerland and northern Europe. Its aim, as its name suggests, was to reform Christianity by strengthening faith in the Gospels and ending the abuses which had crept into the religion. Its credo was fidelity to the Bible, not to the compromised teaching and corrupt practices of the Catholic Church; it championed the translation of the Bible into the vernacular to give the faithful direct access to the Word, a goal facilitated by the invention of printing. As a result of the Reformation, the two centuries between the Renaissance and the Enlightenment were dominated by wars of religion. No one in the seventeenth century would have thought that the Christian era was drawing to a close; both sides looked forward to a strengthening of true belief. Yet the Reformation had the unintended consequence of strengthening secularism.

First it set in train what Max Weber called the 'disenchantment' of the world, by which he meant a world emptied of gods. Catholicism was an indulgent creed, with large traces of pagan idolatry.

Protestantism was much less forgiving. It could inspire sectarian fanaticism, but by removing God from the active management of human affairs, it laid the rational and psychological groundwork for atheism. However, this was an atheism still infused with the moral passion of Protestantism. The moralism of today's largely secular western civilization is the legacy of the Reformation. The Wars of Religion also broke up the political and spiritual unity of medieval Europe. The Treaty of Westphalia in 1648 established the principle of religious toleration, the foundation of the western commitment to freedom of thought. Either religion became a private matter, or the Church became part of the 'national' state. The Universal Church was gone.

More's Utopia

There was a moment, before the idea of secular progress took hold of the western mind, when the increased prosperity and enlarged possibilities opened up by the Renaissance fused with the Christian dream of paradise. The result was a work of literary genius and lasting influence, the *Utopia* of St Thomas More (1478–1535).

Utopia as a philosophical and political project had been mooted as far back as Plato. But the late fifteenth-century voyages of discovery and the freedom to imagine life in hitherto unexplored lands provided the necessary impetus for its revival. '[I]n the beginning all was America,' wrote the English philosopher John Locke (1632–1704).[14] This was so in a double sense: the New World offered stimulus to the imagination and fresh land for the colonists. The colonialist rendition of European history starts with Christopher Columbus, with the missionary, trader and colonizer discovering new outlets for their dreams and projects. New worlds were constantly being discovered, and voyages of discovery fed both scientific and imaginative literature. 'My imagination is so captivated . . . that I seem to partake with the navigators, in all the dangers they encountered. I lose my anchor; my main-sail is rent into shreds; I kill a shark, and by signs converse with a Patagonian, and all this without moving from my fireside.'[15]

More's story from 'nowhere' gave utopian fiction its standard form: a tale of a traveller, usually a mariner, who stumbles upon a hitherto unknown land and gives a 'realistic' account of the customs and habits of its inhabitants, which contrast favourably with the deplorable arrangements of their own country. More's was a social ideal rooted in monasticism; its vision was a reformed Christianity. His purified Christian commonwealth stood against both the corrupt, indulgence-selling Catholicism of his day and the private property regime that had evolved in Tudor England, especially enclosure and the displacement of peasants from the land to make way for sheep farming. Merchants wallowing in luxury and moral laxity (gambling, brothels, drunkenness) coexisted with a 'dearth of victuals', vagrancy, rising crime and increasingly cruel punishments. It would be far better, More's traveller, Raphael Hythloday, observes, 'to provide everyone with some means of livelihood, so that nobody is under the frightful necessity of becoming first a thief and then a corpse'.[16]

In Utopia, sufficiency was secured by a central allocation system which provided every member of the community with food, clothing, housing, education and medical treatment, with the result that working hours were shortened, opening up time for prayer and contemplation. State functions were reduced to what Marx called 'the administration of things'. Crime existed, but the demands on the judiciary and penal system were minimal. 'Public hospitals, plentiful common meals and relative freedom of movement seem to ensure widespread content'.[17] It was an account that convinced More's friend Jerome Busleyden that humanity could easily escape 'the[se] . . . disasters, devastations, overthrows, and other calamities of war . . . if they only adapt themselves exactly to the one pattern of the Utopian commonwealth, and do not deviate a hair's breadth from it'.[18]

The appeal of More's Utopia to socialists in later centuries is obvious. Add machinery to More's social system, and a communist utopia starts to become feasible. At the same time, one can see why it arouses the same dystopian reflection as communism later did. Everyone has enough to eat, but everything is uniform, standardized. One cannot travel freely without a permit. More's identical houses prefigure the mass-fabricated Soviet city.[19] Leisure is made considerably less attractive by compulsory attendance at lectures. Since everyone is watching everyone else, there are no lurking holes or secret meeting places. It took little more than the addition of the technology of surveillance to turn More's utopia into Zamyatin's dystopia.[20] For the utopians who followed, it was a model, a blueprint, for an ideal society; for libertarians, its compulsory austerity and social-control mechanisms gave it a distinctly inhuman flavour.

The Renaissance and Reformation opened doors; they did not lead to an irrevocable breach with religion. Religious belief ebbed but very slowly. Descartes believed that the pineal gland was the 'seat' of the soul, but he still believed, as did Leibniz, that there was something called the soul. The hunt for the 'soul' still continues, with the soul relabelled the 'mind', to the scorn of convinced materialists.

9.

Enlightenments

'We know approximately what physical diseases come from; moral
diseases come from bad education, from all the nonsense people's
heads are stuffed with from childhood up, from the defective state
of society; in short, reform society, and there will be no diseases.'

Bazarov in Turgenev's *Fathers and Sons* (1862)

If the Enlightenment had a single credo, it was that the advance of
knowledge would free people from the control of priests, and that
this would enable them to 'identify the best route to health, wealth,
and the betterment of the human condition'.[1] The central, Baconian,
tradition identified reason with science. Since scientific knowledge
was cumulative (we never go back to square one), advances in science would guarantee progress in all departments of human life.

The Enlightenment broke with the central Christian tradition
that knowledge of the good, in itself, is powerless against the will to
evil. Humans had a natural tendency to goodness; evil was to be
explained by ignorance and bad social conditions. It was the task of
good education and good institutions to strengthen 'will to good',
leaving residues of evil to the attention of psychiatry. That this
vision of social progress presupposed a prior knowledge of what is
good was not something which, on the whole, Enlighteners were
much troubled by. People, they thought, naturally sought pleasure
and to avoid pain: good was what gave pleasure, evil was what
caused pain. So the distinction between what people wanted and
what was good for them was dissolved. Science and social science

would disclose the infallible means to personal and social happiness. The need for faith in Divine Providence was eliminated.

Enlighteners did not doubt that the laws governing human behaviour were, as Auguste Comte (1798–1857) believed, as definite as those determining the fall of an apple. Social science was simply an adolescent branch of natural science, rendered so, not by any difference of method, but by the extra complexity of its material. The major fallacy of this view was to ignore the reflexive character of social relations. The fall of the apple does not depend on the apple's wishes: all apples on a branch which is shaken fall to the ground. This is not true of the shaking of individuals and nations. There was never any guarantee, or even likelihood, that the new generation of secular priests would agree on a new religion of humanity for their disturbed flocks, or that their flocks would follow them to secular salvation.

Contrary to its universalist ambitions, most natural philosophy after 1650 was written not in Latin but in the vernacular and inflected by different tongues and cultures. So the kingdom of universal reason was from the start confronted by its contradiction, the realm of the particular. Historians identify three relatively independent Enlightenment traditions: French, British and German.[2] They were all products of Christendom, and Christendom's classical inheritance. Initially they were all recognizable parts of the same progressive family, but as time went on they acquired increasingly 'national' characters. The history of the mind would show not a single direction towards a superior morality, but an increasingly divergent flight towards moral nihilism.

The Philosophes

The French *philosophes* were the most comprehensively committed to the identification of progress with science. The advance of scientific knowledge would lead to the discovery of universal laws for the better government of society. No direct experimental evidence was adduced to support this view; nor was a causal mechanism, like Darwin's evolutionary theory, suggested. Instead the *philosophes* looked to history for their 'proofs'.[3] This showed the mind moving in stages from the 'rude' or 'primitive' to the civilized, from the mythological and religious to the scientific, with language shedding metaphor for precision on the way. This was seen as a universal progression, with some societies, like France, leading the way, and others destined to catch up. Scientific knowledge was thought to be universal and cumulative, unlike the context-bound nature of all previous claims to knowledge. No attention was paid to the histories of non-European societies, which might exhibit a different progression, or no progression in the European sense.

To the classics, the human fate was essentially tragic: humans were sports of the gods, there was no justice in history. Christian history is redemptive, but redemption is for the afterlife: earthly existence is a 'vale of tears'. The new philosophical history wrote *finis* under both versions. It showed the French economist and statesman Turgot (1727–81) that '[m]anners are generally softened, the human mind is enlightened, separate nations draw nearer to each other, commerce and policy connect at last every part of the globe, and the total mass of the human race . . . marches always, however slowly, towards greater perfection'.[4] For Turgot, language, writing and printing were the great triad that unlocked the human mind. In his 1756 *Essay on Universal History, the Manners, and Spirit of Nations*, Voltaire (1694–1778) presents European history as the story of an ineluctable progress from a highly religious, superstitious time towards the age of reason, culminating in French civilization under Louis XIV.[5] Christianity was seen as obstructing this progress.

The sea-change is evident from Machiavelli (1469–1527) to Kant (1724–1804). In *The Prince* (1513), Machiavelli paraded the classical view that historical events are a matter of luck or *fortuna*. History is eternal repetition. However, in two essays published in the final decades of the eighteenth century, Kant saw the history of the human species at large as 'the realization of a concealed plan of nature, meant to bring into being an internally and, to this end, externally perfect state constitution, as the only condition in which nature can fully develop all of its predispositions in humankind'.[6] Perfection, that is, could be engineered if the plan of nature was 'unconcealed'. That Kant himself believed that the plan of nature was the plan of God was later deemed inessential to his claim that ethical imperatives were derived from human reason. People should be virtuous not because God wanted them to be, but because reason told them they should.

Antoine-Nicolas de Condorcet's *Sketch for a Historical Picture of the Progress of the Human Mind* (1795) is an essay in optimism in its least qualified form. Condorcet (1743–94) set out to show:

> by appeal to reason and fact that nature has set no term to the per-fection of human faculties; that the perfectibility of man is truly indefinite, and that the progress of this perfectibility from now onwards, independent of any power that might wish to halt it . . . will never be reversed . . . as long as the general laws of this system produce neither a general cataclysm nor such changes as will deprive the human race of its present faculties and its present resources.[7]

Condorcet's qualification, however much he discounted it, was prescient.

For Condorcet it was the invention of the alphabet round about 1500 BCE that 'assured the progress of the human race for ever'. It took only the invention of an 'exclusive language for the sciences' to expedite the spread of enlightenment.[8] Once the spread of commerce had established a close accord between enlightened men, 'all will be friends of humanity, all will work together for its perfection and happiness'.[9] Hitherto, the great obstacle to progress had been prejudice, and Condorcet conceived his history as a record of the 'birth, triumph, and fall of prejudice'.[10] Classical Greece had first opened the path to progress by detaching science from metaphysics.[11] But then Christianity 'consummated the ruin of the sciences' by unleashing the torrent of prejudice.[12] For 500 years after the fall of Rome, the only achievements were 'theological day dreaming and religious impostures'. Europe, 'crushed between priestly tyranny and military despotism . . . awaited a new enlightenment'.[13] Printing was the force which 'freed the education of the people from all political and religious shackles'.[14] The Reformation helped build a science of morality by delivering men from the expiation of sins by priests and from celibacy.[15]

By this route, Condorcet reached the heights of modern science and mathematics. The scientific method, pioneered by Bacon, Galileo and Descartes, perfected by Newton and applied to society by Locke, could be applied to all departments of life.[16] Condorcet, a mathematician by training, was particularly hopeful about the social potential of the calculus. All claims to truth could be subject to the rigour of calculation, which 'allows us to determine, for all objects whose changes are capable of precise measurement, either the relations between the elements or between the objects'.[17] He believed that knowledge of statistical probabilities would guarantee rational choices – a belief faithfully upheld by neoclassical economists to this day. The calculus would be especially useful to work out credit ratings and compulsory insurance against old age.[18] As that chatelaine of the Enlightenment Madame de Staël (1766–1817) enthused: 'why should it not be possible some day to compile tables that would contain the answers to all questions of a political nature based on statistical knowledge . . . ?'[19] This belief inspires today's programmers of computerized algorithms.

When Condorcet wrote his *Sketch* he was already aware of Malthus's claim that human felicity was jeopardized by inexorable population growth. His way of dealing with it is both prescient and Panglossian. A Malthusian outcome, he says, is possible, but it is senseless to predict the likelihood of something so far in the future, when the human species 'will have necessarily acquired a degree of knowledge of which we can have no inkling', especially improvements in agricultural productivity over time.[20] Then he continues:

> But even if we agree that the limit will one day arrive, nothing follows from it that it is in the least alarming . . . if we consider that, before all this comes to pass, the progress of reason will have kept

pace with that of the sciences, and . . . by then men will know that, if they have a duty towards those who are not yet born, that duty is not to give them existence, but to give them happiness rather than foolishly to encumber the world with useless and wretched beings.[21]

So he reckons that food consumption and population will start falling in tandem.

'How consoling', Condorcet wrote,

for the philosopher who laments the errors, the crimes, the injustices which still poison the earth and of which he is often the victim is this view of the human race, emancipated from its shackles, released from the empire of fate and from that of the enemies of its progress, advancing with a firm and sure step along the path of truth, virtue and happiness.[22]

Like the fifth-sixth-century Neoplatonist Boethius, Condorcet might well have needed the consolations of philosophy, as his account of the inevitable progress of the human mind was penned just as he was about to be murdered by the French Revolutionaries.

The *philosophes* replaced heaven with history. Their history told of a humanity on a great highway to the future, in which some were further ahead than others, but with everyone catching up eventually. This whole way of thinking about the future of the mind was to be encapsulated by Francis Fukuyama in a famous essay in 1989: the 'end of history' had come, all that remained were a few laggards still trapped in the past. This is why we are baffled by constantly renewed outbreaks of a barbarism assumed to be extinguished.

As will be evident, the Enlightenment version of history left many hostages to fortune. First, their linear view of progress was unable to accommodate the shock of disconfirming historical experiences, of which the two chief were the French Revolution and the First World War. Second was the view that humans are governed by laws as reliable as the laws of nature. Building a good society was an engineering problem, no different in principle, though doubtless more complicated in practice, than building a bridge. The notion that human society was a complex and fragile cultural achievement with 'handle with care' written all over it escaped the *philosophes.*

The *philosophes* were more obviously descended than were other Enlighteners from the Platonic tradition of the philosopher-kings. Condorcet served in the French Ministry of Finance under Turgot, so he took naturally to the neoplatonist idea that the best hope of progress lay in a society ruled by enlightened thinkers like himself.[23] The *philosophes* rejected politics rather than the political. Like Plato, who briefly tried to teach the rudiments of philosophy to the tyrant Dionysius of Syracuse, they relied on enlightened despots to implement economic reforms based on the physiocratic doctrines of thinkers like François Quesnay (1694–1774).[24] Certain eighteenth-century monarchs of the time, like Catherine the Great, Frederick the Great and Joseph II, made a show of patronizing and consulting *philosophes* like Voltaire and Diderot and so could be considered at least partially enlightened. But the Turgot–Condorcet strain of perfectibilists might have heeded the biblical injunction 'Put not your trust in Princes'. The enlightened despots had no interest in releasing most people from their 'nonage'. There is more Machiavelli than Condorcet in Frederick the Great's observation: 'Let us admit the truth: the arts and philosophy extended only to the few: the vast mass of the common people and the bulk of the nobility remain what nature has made them, that is to say, savage beasts.'

As with all Neoplatonists, Condorcet believed that education would somehow close the gap between the ignorance of the many and the knowledge of the few. Everyone could be educated out of ignorance, delusion, self-deception. John Stuart Mill would later claim that any child subjected to his father's educational scheme, which involved teaching him Greek at three and Latin at seven, and forbidding contact with other children, could achieve what Mill had achieved.[25] Mill became the most famous British philosopher of his day but barely recovered from a nervous breakdown as a teenager.

One important defect of the *philosophe* view was that it ignored the historical experience of almost the whole of the rest of the world. The attempt to force modernization on those historically unable or unwilling to receive it was always likely to lead not to linear progress but to a clash of civilizations.

The *philosophes* were not wrong to see plentiful evidence of gold as well as dross in the human performance; and they were right to sense a general forward movement in their own time. But they were ruined by impatience. Having glimpsed the promised land in theory, they were over-eager to get there in practice and grossly underestimated the obstacles in their path. Their materialist conception of the mind blinded them to the psychic and social strains and tensions inherent in their agenda. They ignored the fact that the human condition they sought to remedy with their statistical probabilities retained large residues of a barbarian past. Humans could be tamed and improved over time, but any crash programme of perfection was bound to rekindle old flames. Subsequent history bears out Keynes's dictum that beneath the thin crust of civilization burned volcanic fires.

The Benevolent Passions of the Economists

The sceptical tradition, represented by the English and Scottish Enlightenment, while sharing the progressive values of the French *philosophes*, turned on their perfectibilist rationalism the laughter of the Thracian woman. This was easy: British institutions, by the common consent of British thinkers, were already superior to those of any other 'advanced' country, the British having had their 'Glorious Revolution' in 1688. So British thinkers could see the progress of society in evolutionary terms, without the need for deliberate, and possibly violent, acts of state or nation building. Guizot pointed to the close synchronization between the development of British ideas and that of British institutions.[26] This is what enabled David Hume (1711–76) to claim complacently that political practice should be guided by custom and prudence.

'Reason', wrote Hume, 'is and ought to be the slave of the passions, and can never pretend to any other office than to serve and obey them.'[27] By this he meant that the job of reason was not to lay obligations on us but to bring out our 'better selves'. The passions were not necessarily contrary to reason. Many of them were naturally (potentially) benevolent. People did not naturally seek to inflict cruelty and pain on others: they wanted only to be happy and for others to be. If the passions could be tempered by reflection, love of self need not be at the expense of others. Education and good government were needed to ensure that the benevolent passions dominate social behaviour. Montesquieu had shown the way by sagely remarking that, while men's passions may lead them astray, their *interest* may impel them to cooperate with others.[28] One might even argue that it was the selfish passions which awakened reason from its sleep. Adam Smith (1723–1790) made this insight the foundation of political economy. Freedom of commerce would drain the passions of their poison.

What he did, in words famously and endlessly repeated, was to dissolve the traditional conflict between egoism and altruism. 'It is not from the benevolence of the butcher, the brewer, or the baker, that we expect our dinner, but from their regard to their own interest. We address ourselves, not to their humanity, but to their self-love, and never talk to them of our own necessities but of their advantages.'[29] In other words, the pursuit of self-interest, while it could be destructive under the conditions of earlier 'rude' societies, could be made benevolent in a system of competitive markets. But this required a framework of law and regulation to keep markets competitive – that is, free from monopoly or concentrated power.

There are two additions. First, Smith, like Locke, starts from the position that men are naturally sociable – he repudiates, that is, the Augustinian doctrine of men's inherent depravity. Rather, he asserts a tendency to 'sympathy', approved by our selfish nature, which gives a guarantee of sociability. Self-interest could be further moralized by appending to it abstinence. It is in people's long-run self-interest to 'save' part of their earnings (abstain from current consumption) for the sake of their old age, but also that of their children. These additions – sympathy, asceticism, and long-run calculation – added exactly the sacrificial element to self-love needed to turn it from a *felix culpa* into a positive virtue.

The beauty of this positive interpretation of egoism is that it affirms a principle of order which does not rely on people giving orders. By elevating one of the most reprobated human vices – love of money – into a 'good' passion, Adam Smith turned the body into a potential ally of the soul. This undermined the Christian insistence that goodness needed the support of grace; or indeed that society needed to be kept in order by a Hobbesian dictator. Self-interest would cause private property to be used for the general good. In this kind of formulation, depravity is reduced to a pathology, to be treated by psychiatric intervention.[30]

In his book *The Passions and the Interests* Albert Hirschman gives a brilliant account of Smith's conjuring trick:

> In the early modern age, man was widely viewed as the stage on which fierce and unpredictable battles were found between reason and passion or, later, among the various passions. At mid-eighteenth century, some hope was held out that the interests, which were increasingly understood in the purely pecuniary sense of the term, would be able to tame the disastrous, if aristocratic, passions. But by the latter part of the century, the passions were collapsed into the interests by Adam Smith, who pronounced the 'great mob of mankind' to be safely programmed. From the cradle to the grave its members were to be exclusively concerned with 'bettering their condition'.[31]

Bernard Mandeville, a doctor of medicine who specialized in the treatment of 'hypochondriack and hysterick passions', saw beneath the rational stories told by the economists the motivating passions of the new commercial civilization. In the *Fable of the Bees, or Private Vices, Publick Benefits*, he recounts the fortunes of a fractious beehive which is unmistakably eighteenth-century England. Mandeville's bees are addicted to 'Fraud, Luxury, and Pride', yet succeed, through

'State Craft', into transforming these 'private vices' into the public benefit of commerce and industry. In this commercial utopia, 'Avarice' was slave to Prodigality, Luxury employed a 'million of the poor' and 'odious Pride' a million more. Envy and Vanity were 'Ministers of Industry'. Enter a Virtue campaign, prosperity dwindles, the hive is ruined. You can have vice and riches, or virtue and poverty, but not riches and virtue.[32] The poet Alexander Pope summed up the spirit of the time: 'God and nature linked the general frame, / And bade self-love and social be the same.'[33]

In the very unrealism of the Smithian model lay its great appeal. His model of a self-regulating market spawned an important strand of technological utopianism which has been influential to this day, especially in the United States, where it combined with millenarian longing to produce an updated version of the Land of Cockayne. However, Smith's optimism, like that of many of his contemporaries, did not survive the onslaught of the French and Industrial Revolutions. From being the cheerful science, economics became, as we have seen, the dismal science of Malthus and Ricardo before regaining its buoyancy in the later nineteenth century.

The Romantics

Romanticism was not invented in the eighteenth century. It is the universal mode of poetry, expressing the yearning to have more intense experiences. It is not the content of Romantic beliefs which marks them out, but the passionate commitment to them, regardless of consequences, which removes prudence as a virtue. It is part of the Enlightenment in the sense that it sought to liberate the individual from traditional authority. But its spirit was contrary to that of the *philosophes*, in that the liberation it sought was that of feeling not that of reason, was sparked by communion with nature and had nothing in common with Hume's identification of civilization with the softening manners of England's liberal aristocracy. Romantically inclined scientists had no objection to interrogating nature with scientific instruments, but what they found contained terror as well as wonder.[34] The Romantic hero was a devil-may-care character. It was only in the nineteenth century that Romanticism was identified as something separate from, and in opposition to, reason. William Blake (1757–1827), the greatest of the Romantic mystics, saw the assault of reason on instinct and energy as the attempt to lock up the human spirit in 'mind-forged manacles'.

To Jean-Jacques Rousseau (1712–78), godfather of the Romantic movement, 'natural' behaviour is behaviour stripped of the artifice of civilization. 'Man is born free, but is everywhere in chains.'[35] His *Discours sur l'origine d'inégalité* (1775) offered a secularized version of the Fall, in which an original condition of freedom and happiness had been rudely terminated by the imposition of the state and private property. Rousseau himself never called man a 'noble savage'. The phrase comes out of the European encounter with primitives in the eighteenth century. It conveys the idea of an economic and sexual utopia. (Soon after its 'discovery', Tahiti became a lost paradise as venereal disease, alcohol and Christian missionaries took over.) The idea of civilization as a corruption of original virtue, that truth was to be found in man's soul, not in his brain, was at the core of the Romantic movement.

Rousseau recognized that the virtuous hunter-gatherer of his imagination now lives in Geneva, not in the forest. His purpose was to retrieve, and strengthen, the nobility of natural man in an urban setting. He shared the general view of the Enlightenment that people become what they are through their sensations: control what they experience and you have control over their beliefs and behaviour. The education of his model child 'Émile' was to consist of keeping him away from the corrupting influence of schools and schoolteachers for as long as possible, subjecting him only to the 'laws of necessity'. He then sketched out the constitution of an ideal society in which:

> men would be very little restrained by the laws, because they would not have the passions which put them at odds with justice . . . They

would not need to put a strong curb on themselves, to be perpetually at war with their baser feelings. They would not, like the Christian hero, have to keep down the devil in their own souls.[36]

With the right conditioning, Liberty and Authority would be merged in the 'general will' of the state; or as Hegel put it 'The State is the stage of . . . Spirit where the prodigious unification of self-subsistent individuality with universal substantiality has been achieved.'[37] (This is what happens when French is translated into German.) The French Revolution took up Rousseau's democratic ideas. The 'general will' became the will of the mob, inflamed by the leaders it soon devoured. This was the moment utopia started to turn into dystopia.

Rationalism and Romanticism were equally children of the Enlightenment. But it was easier for Rationalists to shed theological *reasoning* than it was for Romantics to shed religious *feeling*. T. E. Hulme rightly described Romanticism as 'spilt religion'. It was the revolt of subjective feeling against the claims of the exact sciences to take control of the future.

Although he was a Frenchman, it is not surprising that Rousseau's view of nature should have had its main historical impact on the Germans, who appreciated Tacitus' description of them as a people of the forest unspoilt by wealth and luxury. Whereas Rousseauist Romantics dreamed of the liberation of the self from arbitrary social restraints, German Romantics dreamed of the liberation of the German nation from Napoleonic hegemony. Fritz Stern writes that the German animus against all things French 'blind[ed] the [German Romantics] to the simple fact their best ideas on men, nature, and education, on anti-urbanism and anti-parliamentarism, were but distorted and intemperate adaptations of Rousseau's thought'.[38] Ironically, a century later, French Existentialists would get their best ideas from the German Martin Heidegger.

By detaching science from religion, the Enlightenment freed it to become the study of useful truths – truths which could be applied directly to the physical and mental improvement of the human condition. The theoretical idea of engineering society came long before there were any sciences, engineers or machines capable of doing so. However, the idea of perfecting the species led gradually to the application of science to technics. Hence was forged the alliance between science and technology, and between technology and social technology. Happiness became the new age's ethical goal; technology its instrument. One could not just imagine a perfect world, one could build one. From this point of view, the mechanization of work, which started in earnest in the nineteenth century, and to which the name Industrial Revolution is given, could be seen as both instalment and model of the future of life.

The restriction of rationality to science and its applications did not expel metaphysics, it simply relabelled it irrationalism. Into the irrationalist pot were poured all those modes of thinking and feeling which could not be grounded in science: religion, mythology, poetry, music, tradition. Since such modes of thinking were fundamental, indeed primordial, they inevitably emerged as centres of opposition to the scientific-technological world view. The Enlightenment, in short, gave birth to the anti-Enlightenment; modernity to anti-modernity; utopia to dystopia.

10.

The Devil in the Machine

'God: Man's active nature, flagging, seeks too soon the level;
Unqualified repose he learns to crave;
Whence, willingly, the comrade him I gave,
Who works, excites, and must create, as Devil.'

Goethe, *Faust* (translated by Bayard Taylor)

Enter Frankenstein

The intellectual and artistic mood of eighteenth-century Europe was above all sunny. The pretensions of the improvers were mocked by Tory satirists like Jonathan Swift (see p. 229), but there was no serious questioning of the direction of travel. Tragedy, George Steiner argued, had been expelled from history. 'Tragic drama', he writes, 'tells us that the spheres of reason, order, and justice are terribly limited and that no progress in our science or technical resources will enlarge their relevance.' But 'where the causes of disaster are [deemed to be] temporal, where the conflict can be resolved through technical or social means, we may have serious drama but not tragedy. More pliant divorce laws could not alter the fate of Agamemnon; social psychiatry is no answer to Oedipus.'[1]

The French and Industrial Revolutions reopened the gates of hell. The execution of King Louis XVI was followed by 'The Terror'; industrial capitalism was born in the 'dark, satanic mills'. Mary Shelley's *Frankenstein; or, The Modern Prometheus* (1818) marks the historical moment when the dream of machinery turns sour. It tells the story of a hominoid creature which, having been constructed from dead body parts and animated by a battery to serve its idealistic master, the medical scientist Victor Frankenstein, turned on its inventor and became a killing machine.[2] Frankenstein wanted to create a god and created a monster. Mary Shelley's story of a science experiment gone wrong became a metaphor for the whole project of mechanizing human intelligence. It marks the start of the humanistic revolt against the machine.

It is a remarkable amalgam of the main scientific and Romantic tropes of the time. Mary Shelley's antecedents and companions were impeccably enlightened, fervent supporters of the French Revolution, at least before it turned to terror. Her father, William Godwin, wrote *An Enquiry Concerning Political Justice* (1793), a typically progressive philosophic-political tract of the period. Her mother, Mary Wollstonecraft, author of *A Vindication of the Rights of Woman* (1792), was Britain's 'first feminist'. Their preoccupations are early indications that the sexes wanted different things from the Enlightenment. Radical men sought freedom from arbitrary authority; radical women wanted liberation from patriarchy. Mary's husband was the poet Percy Bysshe Shelley; his drama *Prometheus Unbound*, suffused with the imagery of the liberating power of science, was penned at exactly the same time as Mary wrote *Frankenstein*. Shelley's Prometheus rebels in the name of humanity, impelled, its author says, 'by the purest and truest motives to the best and noblest ends': an ideal revolutionary. Yet Mary Shelley tells a very different story. The science on which it is based reflects the debates on galvanism (the use of electricity to stimulate or restart life) then taking place, and the growing opposition of the Romantic poets to the idea of creating artificial humans.[3]

The novel's protagonist, Victor Frankenstein, is a medical doctor, skilled in the surgery of dissection, who seeks to learn how to create life from inanimate matter. His creature is assembled from parts of dead bodies and bits of skin. His rapid growth from birth to adulthood is meant to recapitulate the evolution of human life. In conceiving him, Mary Shelley drew both on the traditional literature of animated puppets and automated robots and on the new materialist science in which consciousness is a by-product of matter. But the creature never attains the godhood promised by Enlightenment science, turning instead into a monster. The novel thus has the double character of a Gothic horror story, with its warning against the perils of embracing evil and of science gone horribly wrong.

Early on, Victor is motivated in his scientific endeavours by a mixture of ambition and humanitarianism: 'what glory would attend the discovery if I could banish disease from the human frame and render man invulnerable to any but a violent death!' But as the novel progresses he becomes possessed by a demonic hunger for power over nature: 'with unrelaxed and breathless eagerness, I pursued nature to her hiding-places'. He expects and demands the total adoration of his creation: 'A new species would bless me as its creator and source; many happy and excellent natures would owe their being to me. No father could claim the gratitude of his child so completely as I should deserve theirs.' This gratitude is obviously not forthcoming from the creature, whom Victor abandons as soon as it awakes, because it is repulsive to look at. At the end of the novel, a dying Victor entreats the narrator, Walton, to 'seek happiness in tranquillity and avoid ambition, even if it be only the apparently innocent one of distinguishing yourself in science and discoveries.'

Mary Shelley's *Modern Prometheus* has been read in many ways, both at the time and since.[4] That it was not just an old-fashioned Gothic horror story was clear enough, because it was linked to developments in the real or at least feasible world of machinery. But what did it signify?

First, it is a warning against the hubris of science itself, a restatement of the myth of Icarus. In creating the monster by scientific methods Mary Shelley has portrayed what happens if man attempts to usurp the place of God in the story of creation. 'The presumptuous works of man must be frightful, vile, and horrible, ending only in discomfort and misery to himself.'[5]

Second, the monster can be interpreted as a revolt against the inhumanity of machinery. The insane actions of the android 'are not those of an inherently evil creature but the desperate groping of a sensitive being to assert a form of humanity following its objectification within a technological concept'.[6] The monster's own account of his psychology asserts conventional Enlightenment wisdom: 'I was benevolent and good; misery made me a fiend. Make me happy, and I shall again be virtuous.' At the creature's request, Victor agrees to manufacture a bride for him. But at the last moment he destroys her embryo because he worries that the two will multiply: 'one of the first results of those sympathies for which the daemon thirsted would be children, and a race of devils would be propagated on earth, who might make the very species of man a condition precarious and full of terror'.[7] Frankenstein, after all, was a fictional contemporary of Malthus. The Modern Prometheus is thus a symbol of industrial societies which abstract from human sensibility. The monster was a fallen angel.

Finally, Frankenstein has been seen as drawing on the familiar early modern vein of diabolism. Machinery promises a world of pleasure and power by means of diabolic acts, but there is always a dreadful price to pay.[8]

These interpretations have obvious implications for the way we might think of the future. One is that Mary Shelley's creature is much more like her husband's Prometheus than appears at first sight. His monstrousness is the product not of technology, but of *infant* technology. With a perfected technique, the creature might indeed become the perfect 'mechanical slave' envisaged by Aristotle. Equally influential was Marx's variant. For Marx, the monster was not the creature of infant technology but of capitalism, which, like the sorcerer, 'is no longer able to control the powers of the nether world which he called up by his spells'.[9] He was the proletarian who smashed machines. Technology was not bound to be destructive; it depended on who controlled it. Under more humane management, the monster would turn out to be a great benefactor.

These became dominant, and persisting, motifs in the optimistic view of technology. The opposite of these optimistic readings is that technology is inherently destructive of humanity. By creating a monster they would not be able to control, humans were ensuring their own extinction. Mary Shelley started off the great dystopian theme in imaginative fiction – that of the experiment gone wrong. In films like Stanley Kubrick's *2001: A Space Odyssey*, the monster becomes the psychotic computer, HAL.[10]

Mary Shelley's *Frankenstein* signified the death of naive utopianism. After the forces of the French and Industrial Revolutions had left their mark, it was more clearly recognized that there would be no easy passage to perfection, and horror might well be the outcome of its quest.

The Faustian Riddle

Immanuel Kant thought that it was the 'radical evil' in human nature which leads to the search for improvement, for if the will to good is not continually tested by human frailty, our excellent qualities would slumber.[11] This is the Faustian riddle in a nutshell: the recognition that evil is a necessary spur to a greater good, or, to put it differently, there is a necessary price to pay for progress. This was quite contrary to the naive idea of the *philosophes* that, once the mind had been opened up by science, the light would simply come flooding in. It pays homage to the Christian idea of original sin but aims to incorporate it into the scheme of progress. The Devil is not an obstacle to perfection as in Christian theology: he is a hardworking part of God's design for improving the human condition. The creative role Satan plays in history was made explicit by Hegel in the concept of the dialectic. For Marx, Satan was the dark, but also liberating, power of capitalism.

All pre-modern societies left a space for the expression of transgressive feelings: this was the role of medieval carnivals and bacchanalia which 'turned the world upside down'. The modern view is that they were institutionally accepted ways of letting off steam, a way of keeping in equilibrium the tension between the demands of God and human nature.[12] However, Nietzsche discerned a deeper meaning. Creativity springs from disorder: Dionysius, god of wine, enables the sun god Apollo to create a new order of beauty. In Christian thought, the Devil is a solution to the problem of theodicy: why if God is all powerful and perfectly good did he create a world with suffering and evil? One answer is that the Devil is placed on the earth 'to test and examine the faith and virtue of humanity'. The second, closer to Nietzsche's theme, is that 'evil is necessary to perfect the good'. The Devil is thus a 'hostile power who brings out and makes possible a stronger and fuller kind of good'.[13]

The Faust legend comes out of the medieval world of alchemy, its idea of the scholar as magician and the imaginative space between religion and science that then existed. It is based on the real figure of a German natural philosopher, Johann Faust (*c*.1480–1540), whose exploits were attributed by the credulous to a pact with the Devil. In the earliest versions of the story, Faust is an alchemist and magician who uses his demonic powers to tempt humans to wickedness. But as the legend develops, he sheds his medieval past and morphs into the modern figure of the scientist who uses his dark powers to master nature and suffers a horrible fate for his presumption. 'The [Faustian] myth's power and fascination', notes one commentator, 'come from the way it speaks to the ambivalence of the modern world about scientific knowledge and the technological prowess it has brought.'[14]

Central to the Faust legend is the role of the Devil in shaping human affairs. This is a specifically Christian rather than pagan thread.[15] It reflects the fact that the age of science was also the age of religion. A strong belief in the reality of evil, the legacy of Augustinian Christianity, coexisted and clashed with the dream of earthly redemption.

The Devil has always played a central role in Christian theology as a tempter to wickedness. In medieval iconography he is a hideous personification of the vices which lead to damnation. For Protestants, who elevated moral purity above all, the Devil becomes an even more formidable tempter. Luther claimed that God needs to work hardest where the Devil is strongest. For the first time the Devil is given a starring role as a worthy opponent of God.

On the other hand, the role of the Devil in modern thought was a specific response to the failure of naive utopianism. The path to perfection was evidently much more rocky than the likes of Condorcet and Voltaire had supposed. Horrifying events became an essential part of the *dialectic* of progress. The Devil was even linked to the doctrine of progress by one of his names, Lucifer, the fallen angel, which means morning star or light bringer. He appealed above all to the rebellious, transgressive side of humans.

However, to play the part of Lucifer, the Devil had to be shed of much of his medieval darkness. In the sixteenth century the Devil morphs from the horned demon of medievalism into a sprightly Renaissance gentleman, full of 'devilish' and 'knavish' tricks. Satan now started getting the best tunes in works of literature: his bravura performance as the great rebel in Milton's *Paradise Lost* led the mystic William Blake to surmise that Milton was 'of the Devil's party without knowing it'. The knowledge the Devil offered could bring power and benefit, but it always came with a heavy cost. The idea that knowledge is a trap is, of course, an inheritance of the Genesis myth. Humans are tempted to strive for powers reserved for God. As in the garden of Eden, the Devil offers forbidden knowledge, and God exacts a price.

The Elizabethan dramatist Christopher Marlowe produced the first great literary Faust. In his play *Doctor Faustus* (1592), the sin of the Doctor is the quest for unbounded knowledge and power.[16] Faustus dreams not only of sexual conquest, but the power to accomplish great deeds – to wall Germany with brass, to cause the Rhine to encircle Wittenberg, to clothe its students in silk and to drive Spain out of the Netherlands. In fact, he fritters away his Devil-fuelled powers in trivialities and, like the original Faust, comes to a grisly end when the Devil claims his bond. But his ambitions were not entirely to be despised. 'In fifty years Faust had developed from a historical and then legendary trickster . . . to a power-crazed Renaissance tragic hero.'[17]

The Devil, as embodying original sin, disappeared from the secularizing thinkers of the eighteenth century. But the French and Industrial Revolutions restored him to a central role in the human drama. His creative contribution to progress is evoked in a famous dramatic performance written in the shadow of the French Revolution. Rather than simply renounce the Newtonian project, Goethe fused it with the Faust legend to give progress a dialectical character. In Goethe's *Faust* (Part I 1790, Part II 1831) the Devil is no longer the purveyor of tricks to delude and bamboozle the credulous, but an agent of God to rouse humanity from its torpor. In Goethe's classic retelling, Faust has become a symbol of endlessly striving modern man, fallible but ultimately worthy of love. Goethe's Faust is more than the literary reflection of the economist's *felix culpa*, because the sinfulness that determines the action of the poem is wilder, more barbaric, more passionate than the enlightened self-interest of Adam Smith and the economists. Goethe is a Romantic.

In the opening 'Prologue in Heaven', God explains His problem to the demon Mephistopheles. Humanity, made in God's image, has the potential for progress, but is naturally lazy and incurious. 'It's so easy for men to slump and before long they do nothing at all.' So He will send them Mephistopheles to rouse them from their slumber, as that force which 'would do evil evermore, and yet create the good'. Goethe turns Faust's traditional pact with the Devil into a wager. Instead of the traditional time-limit of twenty-four years, Mephistopheles offers Faust, a desiccated alchemist, his services indefinitely, with the right to claim him for Hell if they make him fully satisfied. Mephistopheles hopes to prolong his stay on earth by offering Faust an endless succession of unsatisfying pleasures and dissipations; Faust knows that the life of sin which Mephistopheles offers him will never content him. So he confidently accepts Mephistopheles's offer, telling him that, 'If ever the passing moment is such that I wish it were not to pass and say to it "You are so beautiful, stay awhile", then . . . let the clock . . . stop. You can put me in chains and ring the death-bell. I shall welcome it and you will be quit of your service.'

Goethe reworks the magical and fantastical material of Marlowe's play into a developmental narrative, each Devil-sponsored sequence of which spurs Faust to further efforts. In Part I, Faust is tempted by his love for a simple peasant girl, Gretchen, to 'stop the clock'. But Mephistopheles, anxious to prolong his stay on earth, sabotages the love affair by offering Faust any woman he wants. The consequences of unbridled lust are explored. When a series of Devil-inspired mishaps cause Gretchen's death, Faust vows he will prove worthy of her love. Sin is necessary for redemption. Faust's craving for action takes an increasingly public turn in Part II. He is still allied to Mephistopheles, but the latter's role changes increasingly from that of tempter to instrument of Faust's creative purpose. Faust arrives at the court of Charles V. But instead of conjuring up the spirit of Alexander the Great for the Emperor's amusement, as in Marlowe, Faust uses Mephistopheles's sorcery to flood the kingdom with the money buried in the mines, allowing the court to finance lavish masques.

Before Faust is ready for his final achievement he must go through a further stage of personal development: the wild, aspiring North has to be united with the balance of classical Beauty. 'It was by attaining to knowledge of Beauty symbolized by his mating with Helen of Troy that Faust was to transcend his blind to desire to a state in which activity and creation could alone satisfy him.'[18] By evoking the monsters of the classical *Walpurgisnacht*, Goethe emphasizes the theme that Beauty arises from the elemental forces. The reconciliation which Goethe here essays between the Apollonian and Dionysian roots of European civilization, between the classical and barbarian ideals, offers the best of German imaginative thinking about the particular quality Germany could offer Europe. It had a profound effect on Nietzsche and gave pre-1914 German liberalism an attractively unmechanical flavour.

The play ends with the aged and blind Faust installed as the improving ruler of an imperial fiefdom, building dykes and canals to push back the sea. But the progress of his project requires the eviction (which Mephistopheles turns into the murder) of an obstinate couple, Philemon and Baucis, who refuse to budge from their tiny plot – a clear reference to the eighteenth-century enclosure movement, which expelled peasants from their common land to enable improvements in agricultural productivity. In sight of the completion of his project without the further help of sorcery, Faust exclaims: 'Now I could almost say to the passing moment, Stay, oh stay awhile, you are beautiful. The mark of my endeavours will not fade. No, not in ages, not in any time. Dreaming of this incomparable happiness, I now taste and enjoy the supreme moment.' On uttering the fatal words 'I now taste and enjoy the supreme moment', Faust falls dead, as he swore he would if ever he succumbed to satisfaction.

This should have been the 'end state', the achievement of the earthly paradise to which Faust had latterly aspired. But Goethe evades the conclusion by the trick of putting Faust's expression of satisfaction into the conditional: the Devil can only lead humanity so far; perfection is for God. So he divides the spoils between God and Mephistopheles: the Devil gets Faust's body, but God gets his soul. This compromise makes Goethe's Faust what George Steiner calls 'near-tragedy', 'the compromise of an age which did not believe in the finality of evil'.[19]

Goethe himself called *Faust* 'mad stuff' and never tried to explain what it meant. Like all great poetry it is both precise and elusive. In philosophical terms, its most important legacy is the dialectic – progress depends on a continuous 'negation' or overturning of traditional morality.

Today we are less disposed to agree with Robespierre that piles of corpses are justified if they lead to a virtuous society. The theory of the 'necessary price' of progress fell foul of the atrocities of Stalinism and Hitlerism. 'We encountered situations', wrote the German philosopher Karl Jaspers in 1948, 'in which we had no inclination to read Goethe, but turned instead to Shakespeare, Aeschylus or the Bible, if indeed we could still read at all.'[20] However, Goethe was not a Pangloss. His *Faust* was a serious philosophical attempt to reconcile revolutionary bloodletting with eighteenth-century perfectibilism. Engagement with its moral complexities has been continuous in politics, literature, music and films ever since. Mephistopheles remains the elephant in the room, the uninvited guest of both modernity and post-modernity.[21]

The decisive answer to the Goethean compromise came from Thomas Mann in *Doctor Faustus* (1947), a philosophical novel, which can be read as restating the pre-Goethean Renaissance moral that a pact with the Devil, however sublime its purpose, is bound to turn out badly. It was Germany's compact with evil which had led it to its disastrous fate. Mann's message is that political and technological projects should be sufficiently modest not to require a satanic engine.

Yet the Devil retains his hold over the western imagination, even though he dare not speak his name. His continuing, if silent, presence is a reminder that bad happenings have often been the price of progress. Grisly experiments on animals and humans have 'paid for' advances in medicine, but we now know how to cure many more diseases: Tutankhamun would not have died of a mosquito bite had insecticides been available. Tragedies like the two great European wars have had 'collateral benefits' like the formation of the European Union. The financial collapse of 2008–9 and the Covid-19 pandemic of 2020–23 have been routinely dubbed 'wake-up' calls. Progress continues to pay unacknowledged homage to the work of Satan.

II.

The Torment of Modernity

'Now what's going to happen to us without barbarians?
Those people were a kind of solution.'

Cavafy

Following the French and Industrial Revolutions, the dynamics of
European – and world – politics started to change. In pre-modern
times, the chief source of uncertainty was natural events, events
'beyond control', like plagues. Human institutions were formed to
provide some protection against these – sanctuaries set up against
the unpredictable and unfathomable forces of nature. In the nineteenth century a reverse dynamic set in. Nature started to be
increasingly tamed by science and technology, while insecurity was
transferred inwards towards the institutions of the sanctuary itself,
which themselves became increasingly unstable. For Nietzsche,
modernity meant that 'everything is becoming chaotic, the old
becoming lost to us, the new proving useless and growing ever
feebler'.[1]

Historians and sociologists debate which of the two revolutions –
the political/intellectual project of the Enlightenment or the
economic/industrial project of capitalism – contributed most to the
discontents of modernity. In reality they worked in tandem. Science
undermined the traditions by which societies had lived, and
machines undermined the ways people had worked. The two found
a common ground in the application of science to the production
of improved societies.

What Reinhart Koselleck called 'the permanent crisis of modernity' stemmed from the inability of such a civilization to provide a sufficiently spacious habitat for the human spirit. Bits of life can certainly be mechanized – made to work like a machine – with great benefit, but not the whole of it. Christianity had tried to hold in balance the claims of the body and the claims of the soul. The mechanical philosophy which took its place failed to do so. So a revolt against modernity was always on the cards, as its strains and tensions built up.

The first half of the nineteenth century reverberated with the beat of the French and Industrial Revolutions. 'All over Europe the nature of work and of property was changing, agriculture and land-holding practices were in a state of upheaval, and social conflicts broke out – often violent, always unsettling,'[2] as the *ancien régime* tried to re-establish itself. Following the failed revolutions of 1848, something like normalcy returned to Europe. The strains of modernity remained, but the crisis of modernity seemed over. The binary conflict between Reaction and Revolution morphed into a more or less stable division of politics between conservatives, liberals, and radicals/socialists, with a steadily enlarging franchise. Aristocratic rule succumbed mostly peacefully to bourgeois rule, with colonial empires providing 'outdoor relief' for disgruntled members of the nobility. The technology of travel – railways and steamships – and communications – telegraph, telephone, wireless – seemed to be knitting nations and continents together into a single global economy and world-mind. Above all, the productivity gains brought about by the new machinery, together with mass emigration to the New World, chained the Malthusian devil, enabling a growing population to experience a modest increase in mass consumption and a slow fall in hours worked. The 'old religion' retained its hold until at least the last third of the nineteenth century: it was only after Darwin's *On the Origin of the Species* (1859) that the intellectual class started losing its Christian beliefs. Storm signals were detected only by a few who understood that modernity was creating a void of meaning which would be filled by strident nationalism and the social Darwinist theory of the survival of the fittest, both proclaiming a coming war of nations.

It was the events of the first half of the twentieth century which decisively turned the dream of progress into a nightmare of retrogression. The First World War of 1914–18 and its aftermath killed and maimed tens of millions. The Bolshevik Revolution and its consequences killed millions more. These cataclysms were soon followed by the Great Depression of 1929–32, which created mass unemployment and broke up the world economy. The Great Depression in turn led to the installation of Hitler as German leader, the Second World War of 1939–45 and the mass industrialized killing of Jews, symbols and leaders of nineteenth-century emancipation. It was eventually ended with the dropping of atomic bombs by the Americans on Japan. The world-spirit of the Enlightenment seemed to have expired.

This reversal was inherent in the project of modernity itself. H. Stuart Hughes identified a flight from reason at the end of the nineteenth century, in reaction to industrialization, urbanization and industrial conflict. Karl Polanyi showed how societies tried to protect themselves against the disruptive force of the market by erecting barriers to the free movement of goods, capital and labour.[3] In short, the Utopia created its own dystopia.

Two notable attempts to explain the reversion to barbarism were penned by Lenin (1870–1924) and Joseph Schumpeter (1883–1950). *The Communist Manifesto* of 1848 had called for a workers' revolution to overthrow capitalism and create a socialist society. This vision of a perfected society rising from the rubble of the old inspired the Left throughout the nineteenth century. What Lenin did in *Imperialism, the Highest Stage of Capitalism* (1917) was to explain why the workers' revolution had not happened, and the First World War as a consequence of that failure. The capitalist class had been able to bribe a labour aristocracy, who would have been natural leaders of a workers' uprising, with the profits of imperialism, and thus postpone the hour of its demise, but only at the cost of unleashing a war for the 'division and redivision' of the world. Imperialism was the 'highest' (and by implication the last) stage of capitalism, in which competition was replaced by monopoly. The First World War was the first round of the coming global struggle; Lenin predicted that the next round would be a war between Britain and the United States.

The notion of the global class war gave Lenin, one of history's great opportunists, his excuse for seizing power in Russia, the most economically backward of the industrializing nations. The Communist ideal paid a terrible price for Lenin's presumption. For it meant putting the Marxist dream of freedom on hold until the industrial machine, powered by the Bolshevik state, had solved the problem of scarcity. The contrast between the ideal of world socialism and the grim reality of communist Russia crippled the appeal of socialism as the preferred gateway to an earthly paradise.

Schumpeter's *Imperialism and Social Classes* (1919) is an analysis rooted in the soil of central Europe. He grasped much better than the Marxists that the fundamental tendency of capitalism was pacific, not warlike, and that, therefore, the source of the international explosion of 1914 had to be sought elsewhere. The problem in the German lands, as he saw it, was the political weakness of the bourgeoisie. They controlled the capitalist sector of the economy, but political power lay with the landed class, which stood atop a traditional structure of family farms, rural labourers and small enterprises. In Schumpeter's reading, it was the crisis of the landed aristocracy, not of capitalism, which set the course of European history in the twentieth century. He interprets the Great War of 1914–18 as a last attempt by aristocracies to justify their right to rule. 'Created by the wars that required it, the [aristocratic] machine now created the wars it required.' The military-industrial machine was unleashed on Europe in order to preserve an archaic social structure.

Neither theory offers a complete explanation for the reversal of 1914. The Marxist account obscures the extent to which the precapitalist order retained its hold. Marxists could not explain why workers, whose countries had supposedly been stolen from them by the capitalists, rallied so enthusiastically to their respective national causes in 1914.[4] Schumpeter's explanation for the war underplays the reality of class conflict between capitalists and workers at the end of the nineteenth century.

The massive disorders of the early twentieth century are best seen as episodes in the continuing torment of modernity. This torment arises from the attempt to build societies in some crucial senses inhospitable to human habitation. The torment continues because the project continues. But it must always be remembered that the crisis of modernity was a European crisis, not a global one. Europe exported its 'torment' to the rest of the world through the machinery of imperialism. This world came to see in imperialism not an agent of progress or 'catching up', but as an instrument of alien domination. The eventual revolt of the Rest against the West was part of a script which is still unfolding.

The German Ideology

The most striking characteristic of the German Ideology was its unworldliness. For the Lutheran pastor Johann Georg Hamman (1730–88), God was a poet, not a mathematician.[5] In its worship of the spiritual life of an unspoiled *Volk*, the German Ideology was remote from the *phronesis* or practical wisdom required to negotiate the age of machinery. It contrasts with the dominant British attitude of common sense and compromise, made possible by the fact that the *habitus* of British society changed only slowly, giving time for archaic and modern elements to learn to coexist. Germany lacked any settled social or political foundation for evolutionary change.

The German Romanticism associated with the Jena Circle – notably of the poet Friedrich Schlegel (1772–1829) and the dramatist Friedrich Schiller (1759–1805) – was part of the then universal poetry of individual self-realization. It was Gottfried Herder (1744–1803) who led it down the route which we now recognize as Romantic nationalism, the self-realization of a people. He agreed with the French *philosophes* that history showed a steady diminution in the destructive demons of the human race.[6] Like Hegel, he thought of it as moving towards the self-realization of Spirit. However, the manner of this self-realization was 'profoundly affected by geography, by climate, by the crops and the animals at man's disposal . . . to say nothing of . . . "chance" '.[7] Specifically, Herder rejected Kant's universal state. Nations become civilized by strengthening their 'veins and sinews'. The nation, defined by language and history, embodied the cultural wisdom and traditions of a particular people. National moral traditions might ultimately converge on Kant's ethical universalism, but they should not be subjected to universal ethical rules.

Herder was making a point which is now fundamental to the philosophy of the social sciences: that social life is not subject to universal laws as in the 'laws of nature', but to laws which depend on the particular circumstances and consciousness of the subject. The distinction between the two can be expressed as one between civilization and culture. While the progress of 'civility' is universal, culture is the way of life of a people, and, just as no two languages are exactly translatable into each other, no two cultures inhabit the same time and space. Herder gave Germans the sense that their progress lay not in imitating the habits of the French *salons*, but in nurturing a specific German culture. For German Romantics, Rousseau's Noble Savage had a definite ethnicity and location east of the Elbe. At the same time, the swiftness and completeness of the Napoleonic victories gave German intellectuals a huge sense of inferiority to France: national culture could only be preserved by a state endowed with sufficient military power to defend it.

Although 'rebellion against modernity lies latent in Western society',[8] only in Germany did Romantic nationalism become a decisive historical force. The reason for this was that it touched the reality of the German situation more closely than similar movements elsewhere.

First, whereas the foundation of British and French politics lay in long-established frontiers, the German nation, for most of the nineteenth century, existed only in the imagination. The territorial state came late to the Germans. The greatest period of Germanic expansion had been in the Middle Ages. Bismarck's Reich of 1871, which excluded large sections of the German *Volk*, inflamed the nationalist mood without satisfying it. Disappointment at incomplete nation-building was common to all the 'new' nations in Europe created in the nineteenth century, but only Germany was strong enough to attempt to alter the map of Europe.

Second, German culture was impregnated by Pietism, that branch of Lutheranism based on relentless study of the Bible, contempt for the external world and celebration of the inner life. The biblical scholar Paul de Lagarde (1827–91) believed that the heroic faith to inspire the German people would have to be a 'cleansed' version of Christianity, which would fuse the God of the Gospels with the paganism of the forest.[9]

The forest was of particular symbolic importance in framing the German resistance to modernity. 'Mythology, Germans and the forest, they all belong together,' proclaimed Chancellor Helmut Kohl as late as 1983. In contrast to the Mediterranean civilization of the Roman empire, Tacitus depicted unconquered German lands as the abode of 'timbered virtue'. The most famous German fairy tales, from medieval times to the nineteenth century, were peopled by forest gods, devils and hobgoblins, as well as by ordinary forest folk. In 1492, Conrad Celtis, a professor at the University of Ingolstadt, contrasted the diseased civilization of the south with the free and arboreal nobility of the north, a quarter of a century before Luther produced the Christian version of the same message. The Germanic defeat of Varus' Roman legions in 9 CE was the rallying call for resistance to Napoleonic imperialism. Nineteenth-century German painting, poetry and music were suffused with wildness and melancholy. As Richard Hacken notes, the forest for German Romantics served as symbol both of opposition to aesthetic and religious formalism and of a 'true' meritocracy against the class system of industrialism.[10]

A third contributor to the German Ideology was the weakness, provincialism and political impotence of the German middle class, its remoteness from political and economic life. This was due to the immiseration caused by the Thirty Years War, which cut Germany off from the wealth which, in England and France, gave the bourgeoisie a path to social prestige and political power. By contrast, in Germany, an impoverished middle class cultivated *Bildung* or spiritual inwardness at the expense of practical wisdom. There was a permanent sense of melancholy, of regret. In the second half of the nineteenth century, inspired by German military victories, the middle class started to identify stridently with the values of the aristocracy. Norbert Elias points to the growth of the duelling habit in middle-class university fraternities.[11] The professional and business class aspired to the 'second class' of nobility, without, however, claiming its governing functions. The aristocracy provided both an ideal and shelter against the rising tide of proletarian radicalism.

Finally, in explaining the retreat from *Bildung*, Fritz Stern emphasizes the 'suddenness that ha[d] no parallel' elsewhere of the change wrought by the Industrial Revolution. After lagging in industrial development for most of the nineteenth century, Germany modernized with a rush in its last third, great industries and cities springing up overnight. German industrialization took the form of a bureaucratic capitalism, precisely because the bourgeoisie played such an insignificant role.[12] The generation of Schiller and Goethe was succeeded not by that of the heroic entrepreneur but by the professors, scientists and research laboratories. In Germany's fevered rush to modernize, positivist science became 'the intellectual bodyguard of the house of Hollenzollern'.[13] It was the synthesis of archaism, nationalism, science, bureaucracy and technology which made Imperial Germany an increasingly toxic presence on the pre-war world stage.

This massive cultural pessimism was the specific German ingredient in the making of the First World War. It explains the character of Germany's political project in both world wars: *Lebensraum*, or resettling large numbers of Germans on the more thinly populated land to the east of Germany.

Settling industrial populations on virgin soil was not a specifically German ambition. Cecil Rhodes saw the British empire as a 'bread and butter question . . . in order to save the 40 million inhabitants of the United Kingdom from a bloody civil war, we, colonial states-men, must acquire new lands to settle the surplus population, to provide new markets for the goods produced in the factories and mines'.[14] Such resettlement ideas often went together with the idea of renewing the martial vigour of the race. However, by the nine-teenth century, such imperial resettlement for Germany seemed to be blocked off by location. It had arrived too late to get anything but a few leftovers from the great imperial carve-up of Africa; and most of the 'virgin lands' available in the east for repopulation were occupied not by primitives, who might easily be 'cleared out', but by the Russian empire, whose settlement by Germans would require military conquest. To justify such an act of subjugation in terms suitable for the scientific ethics of the late nineteenth century, the Slavs had to be depicted as an inferior race, on a par with the Aborigines or Native Americans, frozen at an earlier stage of development. Lagarde drew the despairing conclusion that, 'We are stricken by the necessity of having to do in 1878 what should have been done in 878'.[15] Moeller van den Bruck (1876–1925) thought Ger-many had missed its 'Darwinian' moment. But the military might produced by massive industrialization might yet give Germany a chance to repair the omission. Weber saw a great war as the only way to defend the autonomy of German culture in a world of non-German giants.[16] Destruction on a massive scale was an inherent part of renewal. In Wagner's *Ring of the Nibelungs*, the struggle for possession of the magic ring of power and wealth brings about the destruction of the world.

Most diplomatic historians subscribe to the 'clusterfuck' theory of the First World War's origins. But though its trigger may have been diplomatic blunders and miscalculations, the enthusiasm with which the nations went to war and were willing to continue it over four years of increasing malignity testifies to the fact that it offered an escape, a release of the spirit, from psychological and social strains of nineteenth-century industrialization, from the sense of futility of a landed class which had lost its function but not its estates, from class war between capitalists and workers. For most social groups all over Europe, war offered a kind of spiritual cleansing. But of the combatants, Germany was the one great power radically dissatisfied with its global position, and for whom war offered a chance to realize its 'place in the sun'. It was the conjuncture of a general social malaise, the frustration of a hemmed-in rising power and industrial military technology which gave the First World War its combined ideological and industrial character.

The sense of war as a spiritual escape from the chains of the Enlightenment is nowhere better expressed than by the writer Thomas Mann. In his 'Thoughts in Wartime' (1914), Mann, like Weber, depicted the conflict as a struggle between authentic German 'culture' and mechanical French 'civilization'. The German challenge to Anglo-French dominance was necessary to bring about the synthesis of civilization and culture at a higher level. Mann was never to abandon this dialectical framework. He came to believe, though, that escape to the forest was too high a price to pay.

A Barbarian Utopia

Norbert Elias described the Nazi genocide of the Jews as the 'decivilizing spurt' of a civilization suffering from decay and retrogression. The Nazis wanted to put back the clock. They were barbarians with industrial technology, hence their ability to wreak destruction on an industrial scale. They had their own version of perfection, the perfection of race as the basis of a free society. They did not hesitate to appropriate the myth of the forest for their own scheme of murderous conquest: Buchenwald means 'beech forest'; Birkenau, 'birch grove'. They were not afraid to create an apocalypse to realize their aims. And, as the Germany they had ruled for just thirteen years went down in flames, the most fanatical of them thought it better to die gloriously than live uselessly.

The occasion of the decivilizing spurt was the First World War and its political and economic consequences. A large section of the

German people had not accepted the reality of the German defeat; and the defeat had not been complete enough to kill the militaristic spirit. The partly illegitimate Weimar Republic could not survive the hammer blows of the hyperinflation of the early 1920s and the Great Depression, which started in 1929. The Marxist *economic* analysis was close to the mark: 'The ultimate cause of all real crises', wrote Marx, 'always remains the poverty and restricted consumption of the masses as compared to the drive of capitalist production to develop the productive forces.'[17] But this fact did not produce a revolt against capitalism, but a reversion to the idea of a German-led European *Grossraum* adequately shielded from foreign incursions.

Milder versions of this reaction were felt by all the Great Powers shattered by the economic cataclysm. But it was especially strong in 'unsatisfied' Great Powers like Germany, Japan and Italy, who felt they had not done as well out of nineteenth-century imperialism as their successful rivals. For such powers the acquisition of extra land came to be viewed as a solution to their perceived Malthusian crises: Ukraine for Germany, Manchuria for Japan, Ethiopia for Italy. The Nazi onslaught against the status quo was particularly ferocious because it combined nineteenth-century cultural hostility to modernity with the anguish of military defeat in 1918 and Weimar's dependence on American loans. The result was the first full-scale 'revolt of the blood' against machine civilization, using actual machines to create the apocalypse.[18]

The question is: what had allowed this kind of ideology to seize control of a technologically advanced state? By far the best answer is given by the late Henry Ashby Turner's essay, 'Fascism and Modernization', though he misses the madness at the heart of the Nazi project.[19] As Turner puts it, 'modern society was wholly and unavoidably incompatible with what [the Nazis] held to be the only true wellbeing of social life: the folk culture'. They wanted 'a desperate backward leap toward a romanticized vision of the harmony, community, simplicity, and order of a world long lost'. Their thinking can be described as a 'utopian form of anti-modernism' in the double sense of being visionary and unattainable.

Turner identified two strands of Nazi utopianism. The first looked back to the late Middle Ages and thought that the evils of modern life could be cured by a return to manorial and corporate relationships. It belonged to a venerable tradition of backward-looking, regressive anti-capitalism. Its appeal was chiefly to the *Mittelstand*, the middle class of tradesmen, artisans, family farmers and small entrepreneurs. The second strand consisted of the utopias of Hitler, Himmler and Alfred Rosenberg. These were far more archaic, eclectic and unrealistic. They harked back to pre-Christian, pre-civilized times. As remedies for current problems they prescribed a revival of the cults of soil and sword. They sought to free Germany from the grip of 'Jewish' finance and return it to a simple agrarian life. To do this they had to restore the lost pride in race and teach war as an essential good. It was this version of National Socialism which triumphed.

Contrary to A. J. P. Taylor, Hitler's foreign policy was as direct an expression of his ideology as the demands of politics and warfare allowed. In *Mein Kampf* he defined welfare as 'a healthy and natural proportion between the number and growth of the population . . . and the extent and resources of the territory they inhabit'.[20] By people he meant 'race', so no 'international solution' to the welfare problem was possible, 'only a sufficiently large space' for agriculture and defence. Hitler renounced any Alexandrine intoxication with conquest. He wanted only territory for settlement. The future was to be 'industrious labour with the German plough, for which the German sword will provide the soil'.[21] Since the preferred soil was already occupied by other nations, this involved wars of conquest and extermination. And that meant mobilizing the power of the machine in an effort to destroy machine civilization. But, as German thinkers often complained, they were too late. The world-spirit had moved on.

The Nazi attitude to technology was full of contradictions. Like all fascist movements they tried to aestheticize machinery by separating it from industrialism. The Futurist movement in painting, a big influence on early fascist aesthetics, turned machinery into art. Also, aviation's image of knights jousting in the sky seemed to assure a place for individual heroism in warfare. But these were incidentals: Nazism needed massed industrial power for its wars of conquest.

In the same spirit, the Nazis practised and perfected the existing technology of totalitarian control without believing that this was a final form of rule. Once a racially pure state had been bred, there would be no more need for the Gestapo or concentration camps, because the Germanic peoples, unlike the slaves ('slavs') they aimed to conquer, could be trusted to do what was best for the race. The Soviets, who thought of class as Hitler did of race, also believed that the liquidation of the bourgeoisie would inaugurate the realm of freedom.

Hitler's Thousand-Year Reich perished in the great plains of Russia. Reporting from the Ukrainian village of Marchikhina Buda in 1941, Vasily Grossman wrote:

> The horde from the West had arrived, with their magnificent compact radio transmitters, with equipment fabricated from nickel, glass, tungsten and molybdenum, with vehicles on synthetic rubber tyres and powered by multi-cylinder engines. And daubed over all these remarkable vehicles – as if the Nazis felt ashamed by what European science and skilled labour had created in spite of them – were bears, wolves, foxes, dragons, skulls and crossbows, and other such symbols of savagery.[22]

Three thoughtful retrospectives on the Nazi attempt to break out of the iron cage of civilization bear on the topics of this book. In a celebrated lecture to the US Congress in 1945, Thomas Mann singled out the morbidity of German Romanticism as the root cause of the disaster which had befallen his country and Europe. On the one hand, it was the expression of the finest German quality of inwardness; 'a certain dark richness and piousness . . . antiquarianism of soul that feels very close the chthonian, irrational, and demonic forces of life, that is to say the true sources of life; and it resists the purely rationalistic approach on the ground of its deeper knowledge, its deeper alliance with the holy'. Germans were the people of the 'romantic counter-revolution against the philosophical intellectualism and rationalism of the Enlightenment – a revolt of music against literature, of mysticism against clarity'; a 'pessimism of sincerity that stands on the side of everything existing, real, historical against both criticism and meliorism' and against idealistic disguise. However, even at its most sublime Romanticism bore the germ of morbidity, as the rose bears the worm; its innermost character was seduction, seduction unto death. Its affinity to death came from its very surrender to the irrational and to the past, and its contempt for the religion of humanity. Wicked Germany was merely good Germany gone astray.[23]

By 1945, Mann had completely repudiated his 1914 enthusiasm for the 'non-political' man. It was by being 'non-political' that the German was unable to get on with life, always arrived too late for the feast. Politics, like art, occupies a mediating place between spirit and life, idea and reality, the desirable and necessary, conscience and deed, morality and power. Politics has to do much that is evil. But politics doesn't *belong* to the realm of evil. It can never completely renounce the humanly decent part of its nature.

For Toynbee, Nazism was a classically inefficient 'response' to the challenge which confronted western civilization at that time:

> We are here confronted with an exhibition of archaism which would have been pathetic had it not been so sinister. A great modern Western nation was brought, by the spiritual malady of the Modern Age, within an ace of irretrievable national collapse, and, in a desperate effort to escape from the trap into which the recent course of history had inveigled it, it doubled back upon the supposedly glorious barbarism of an imaginary historical past.[24]

And from Henry Ashby Turner this warning: 'For if the essence of what has hitherto been described as fascism should be found to lie in an extreme revolt against the modern industrial world and an attempt to recapture a distant, mythic past . . . there is no guarantee that such movements [of utopian anti-modernism] may not arise again.'[25]

Technics and Civilization

'This war, in contradistinction to all previous wars, is a war in
which pure and applied science plays a conspicuous role.'

Nature, April 1914

The mobilization of science for war in 1914–18 challenged the legitimacy of its claim to be a benevolent despot. It provoked an important
set of reflections on the impact of technology on humanity. The
path to perfection had been blown up. Looking back on the pre-war
world of Vienna, the writer Stefan Zweig wrote: 'People believed in
"Progress" more than the Bible. [They] no more believed in the possibility of barbaric relapses . . . than they believed in ghosts and
witches'.[1] No one could recall their half-century in this way after the
two world wars, and the genocidal projects of Hitler and Stalin.

At issue was the ethics of technology. Was it ethically neutral, its
effect depending solely on the way it is used? Or is it determinative
of good or evil? According to Lewis Mumford's *Technics and Civilization* (1934), technics is simply the 'translation into appropriate,
practical forms of the theoretic truths . . . of science'.[2] These truths
can be applied for purposes either beneficent or malign. That it had,
hitherto, been a mixed blessing was because its later development
had been controlled by capitalism. One is, therefore,

confronted . . . by the fact that the machine is ambivalent. It has
been both an instrument of liberation and one of repression. It
has economised human energy and it has misdirected it. It has

created a wide framework of order and it has produced muddle and chaos. It has nobly served human purposes and it has distorted and denied them.[3]

Specifically in its 'paleolithic period' of coal and steam, lasting roughly from 1750 to 1900, machinery had been an instrument of war and imperialism. However, its new 'neotechnic' phase of electricity and mass communications promised a quantum leap in human creativity, provided its development was subject to social choice and not left to private profit. This required the 'socialization' of technology. Like many on the Left at the time, the American Mumford was attracted by the Soviet experiment and provided some details of what a communist utopia might look like: 'normalized' consumption plus luxuries, order and creativity, progress and tradition, big industry and small craft manufacture, human-sized cities and a vibrant countryside, scientific thought and humanistic imagination.[4] A central aim was to transform the built environment to make it fit for modern man. The architect Le Corbusier was a visionary example. Even Keynes was smitten by the planning bug:

> Why not pull down the whole of South London from Westminster to Greenwich . . . housing in that convenient area near to their work a much greater population than at present, in far better buildings, with all the conveniences of modern life, yet at the same time providing hundreds of acres of squares and avenues, parks and public spaces, leaving, when it was finished, something magnificent to the eye, yet useful and convenient to human life as a monument to our age.[5]

New York's urban planner Robert Moses could not have put it better.

Mumford was excited by the power of technology to leapfrog history, an ambition common to all impatient utopians. He treated the United States and the Soviet Union as parallel new nations, unencumbered by the dead weight of European history, and eventually destined to converge, a theme which had not yet been exhausted in the 1960s. That the real differences between the two societies were stronger than their superficial resemblance eluded both the capitalist and socialist planners: the United States, for all its pre-modern residues, was a creation of liberal institutions and bourgeois capitalism; the Soviet Union was attempting the forced industrialization of a peasant society.

Like Karl Mannheim's contemporaneous *Man and Society in an Age of Reconstruction* (1935), Mumford's book is a testament to the 'planning movement' of the interwar years. Mannheim rejected the idea that planning was bound to be totalitarian. Planning, guided by experts, could emerge from the process of political discussion. The idea of democratic planning earned a notable rebuke from Friedrich Hayek, who accused the democratic planners of applying to society 'the habits of mind of the engineer'. This in turn was attacked by Keynes, who argued that planning would be safe in a community which valued individual liberty.[6]

For Mumford the future was finely balanced. His age had witnessed two types of 'reaction of the organic and the living upon the machine'. The first was 'the use of mechanical means' to return to the primitive. This was fascism. The other was a start to 'the rebuilding of the individual personality and the collective group, and the reorientation of all forms of thought and social activity towards life'. This was Soviet communism, which, in his view, shone as the beacon of the future.[7] By the 1960s, Mumford had become much more pessimistic. Despite the defeat of fascism, 'our over-mechanised culture' had fallen prey to the 'Myth of the Machine' and was rapidly moving toward a 'final totalitarian structure'.[8]

A faltering but still optimistic prospectus was offered by the neo-Kantian philosopher Ernst Cassirer in his essay 'Form and Technics' (1930), which tried to uphold the social democratic middle ground. Technology was a fundamental demand of human dignity, the avenue of escape from slavery. From the clarity and determinacy of seeing things rationally emerges 'a new power of action by means of which the spirit defends itself against every external determination'. The machine is thus a potential agent of civilization.

Nevertheless, Cassirer concedes the devastation it has wrought.

The feeling of solidarity that unites handworker and tools is dissolved, work is alienated from product. For the *goal* of the product, its true *telos*, is now entrusted to the machine, the human being becoming 'a part, dwindling more and more to a mere fragment' of the whole work process. Cassirer offers no convincing resolution of the tension between liberation and entrapment. His answer seems to be that people should become intellectually and morally conscious of the relationship between humans and machines. Only this will enable technology to be properly used. But, as Edward Skidelsky writes, he offers no 'standpoint external to technology itself' by which its value might be judged.[9]

Technics and Power

In his essay *Man and Technics* (1931), Oswald Spengler, like Nietzsche, saw technology simply an expression of the will to power. The earliest tool was the 'thought of the hand'.[10] Then came the 'thought of the eye', which seeks out cause and effect.[11] The hand acts; the eye gives it a target. From this arises the distinction between the fact-men (warriors) and thought-men (priests).[12] Spengler calls them, respectively, Vikings of the Blood and Vikings of the Mind. The first group seek power through plunder; the second group by means of abstraction. Spengler's account of technics explores the effects of both types of power-seeking.

Following the French Revolution, the 'Vikings of the Mind' (scientists and technologists) seized control. These 'priests of the mind' embody the will to power in its purest form.[13] They despise nature, including human nature, and seek to displace organic by organized existence, 'from living in natural to living in artificial groupings, from the pack to the people, from the tribe to the State'.[14] Their culminating achievement is the City, an artificial creation, with an artificial hierarchy of classes. The Vikings of the Mind are worshipped by the 'progress-philistine of the modern age who rushes from La Mettrie to Lenin'.[15]

However, the 'Faustian' striving of the scientist carries the disharmony between hand and eye to new heights. As technical mastery advances, respect for nature declines. We aim to enslave it and believe in our own power to renew it. But civilization exhausts the resources of nature.

The apex of the Faustian state is simultaneously the 'turning' to its decline. The soul starts to become sick of machines. People return to 'nature'; they spend more and more time on sport; they embrace the occult, and flee from reason. But such liberations are only partial. Higher and higher technical quality is demanded of workers, but the workers revolt against the increasing mechanization of work, which they foresee portends their own redundancy. How the 'turning' will end is impossible to say, but Spengler holds out little hope of a happy ending. All great civilizations end in defeat. The only choice is between heroic and unheroic suicide.

Thus, for Spengler, the story of technics is part of the rise and fall of civilizations. Spengler accurately foresaw that industrialization would threaten the planet and that many species would become extinct. He predicted that labour-saving machinery, far from freeing mankind from toil, would multiply the number of mouths to feed. His main failing lies in the unreality of his 'realism'. He imagined himself to inhabit the world of facts, but like the Idealists he despised, he lived in the world of fantastic ideas. He had no time for politics, which exists precisely to reconcile that which cannot be reconciled, and to mask the unendurable with fictions.

Heidegger's essay, 'The Question Concerning Technology', was published only in 1954, but its central argument, concerning the disharmony between technology and culture, had been paraded in his prewar writings and was, indeed, the heir of the nineteenth-century German *Lebensphilosophie*. At its heart is his analysis of technology's treatment of nature as a 'standing reserve'.

Whereas optimists saw science and technology as a higher form of civilization, Heidegger claimed that they have robbed humans of their primordial mode of *Dasein*, or 'being *there*'. In the course of its development, technics turns nature from a way of 'bringing forth' something which is concealed, as in the activity of the peasant who plants seed to fertilize the ground, into a passive resource to be exploited. It also makes humans part of this 'standing reserve'. The forester is 'today commanded by profit-making in the lumber industry, whether he knows it or not. He is made subordinate to the orderability of cellulose'.[16] Heidegger's idea of a tool being something 'ready to hand' is his way of describing what is known without explanation, akin to Hayek's 'tacit' knowledge. 'Try to explain to me what a tree is?' said Russian neuropsychologist Alexander Luria of an illiterate central Asian peasant: 'Why should I? Everyone knows what a tree is, they don't need me telling them.' As technology accelerates and widens its reach, the tools we have accepted unthinkingly as 'ready to hand' become increasingly problematic to us – 'unready to hand'.[17]

Technology thus reveals itself not as a set of tools but as a mode of human existence. Heidegger calls this revelation 'enframing'. Nevertheless, in the process of technology's 'unconcealment' lies our chance of controlling it. 'Where danger is, grows the saving power also,' he announces portentously. In the end, *Dasein* achieves full self-consciousness, like Hegel's Spirit. Technology has 'come to presence'. In non-Heideggerian language, the spread of technology carries its own antidote in people's growing realization that they are becoming slaves to machines.

Heidegger offers a profound diagnosis of the human condition in the age of machines. But what call to action follows from such a treatment? At one time, he thought mass war offered the only salvation. Later he suggested another path. In classical times, art as well as technique was part of *techne*. Art was a 'poetic revealing'.[18] From the world of technology it may be that a new art itself will emerge as a source of a new revelation. In this hope Heidegger follows the poet Schiller in seeing aesthetics as a mediating force between the extremes of reason and passion. Thus technics as art may enable the escape from technics as instrument. He ends, though, on a despairing note:

No one can foresee the radical changes to come. But technological advance will move faster and faster and can never be stopped. In all areas of his existence, man will be encircled ever more by the forces of technology . . . these forces . . . have moved long since beyond his will and have overgrown his capacity for decisions.

Heidegger, like the Romantics, claimed a privileged position for the primitive. 'Primitive phenomena are often less concealed and less complicated by extensive self-interpretation on the part of the *Dasein* in question.'[19] He rejected any suggestion that he had 'prostituted' philosophy for political purposes. 'From his point of view, what was there to prostitute? To philosophize authentically is simply to heed the call of Being, whatever that may be. And when, in 1933, Being spoke in the strident accents of Germany's new chancellor, who was Heidegger to resist?'[20]

Heidegger's philosophy does not entail a fascist interpretation, but it does not rule it out. Heidegger hoped that growing awareness of the scientific-technological mindset would evoke a new way of 'being there' which would imply a return to a simpler way of doing things. As a political project this carries obvious dangers, which Heidegger only recognized in retrospect. He did not renounce his diagnosis, but by the 1950s he despaired of a political cure: 'only a God can save us'.

The problem of technics as it presented itself to these interlocutors is that machines were directing humans towards a future which they had not chosen and which was in many ways antithetical to their humanness; and that this gave rise to psychological and social strains from which war might offer a release. The real issue must be whether machines increase the freedom of users to choose their own plans of life, or whether they trap their users into systems imposed on them. In short, the divide is between those who see machines as enlarging the power to do and those who believe they increase their power over what is done. This is the divide between utopia and dystopia.

13.

From Utopia to Dystopia

'Once the dream of paradise starts to turn into reality, here and there people begin to crop up who stand in its way, and so the rulers of paradise must build a little gulag on the side of Eden.'

Milan Kundera

The word 'utopia' comes from the Greek word *ou-topos*, which literally means 'nowhere'. It can thus be either a highly desirable or highly undesirable place to live, set either in the past or the future or on another planet, though the desirable and undesirable are conveniently separated in English into 'utopia' and 'dystopia'. Its favourite literary device is the traveller's tale. Utopia's 'discoverer', typically an explorer or shipwrecked mariner, stumbles across an unknown place, and provides 'proofs' of its authenticity through a bogus map, topographical and pictorial detail and reams of scientific and anthropological 'facts'. Thus it uses the scientific method of 'look and see' to distort the reader's perception of time and space.

Its stock in trade is to imagine cities or states in hitherto unknown locations, as in More's *Utopia*, or to create futures pretending to be presents. The purpose of such parallel universes is either to contrast ideal with actual societies – 'Sinapia', says the author of a utopian fable with this name (1682), 'is the most perfect opposite of our Hispania' – or to warn what actual societies might become unless the future is drastically diverted from its existing course. The distinction between utopia and dystopia has increasingly hinged on attitudes to machinery. At first machinery was generally portrayed as an agent of emancipation from bondage, as in Bacon's *New Atlantis*, as later imprisoning the spirit in an iron cage. As the second note became increasingly dominant, dystopian authors resorted to the device of depicting a group of rebels, nestling secretly within, or located outside, the boundaries of the dystopic system, keeping alive the hope of a non-mechanistic future. The most recent dystopian literature has been apocalyptic. The dystopian future is set in a parallel world crippled by ecological or nuclear disaster, offering a sombre warning against the misuse of technology.

Whatever or wherever its temporal or spatial location, utopia tells a moral tale. It contrasts the imagined world with the present world and can serve either as an inspiration to make better or a warning of disaster in store. It is thus by definition extremist, splitting naturally into polar opposites. It leaves no room for a less than divine or devilish existence. Not all imagined futures are fictional. Warnings of the coming apocalypse, sometimes as the prelude to the Second Coming, were staples of the pulpit; invitations to a happier future achieved by revolution or reform are the stuff of political pamphlets and manifestos. There have also been frequent attempts to implement utopias, either experimentally in small communities or on a large scale through revolution. Telling the story of the utopian society as if it really existed is a form of advocacy designed to inspire efforts to create utopias and disarm practical objections to the attempt.

Utopian literature comes out of myths and legends of happier times. It typically starts with a 'golden age', from which there has been a fall. The golden age is set in an imagined past or location, replete with all the good things of life, material and spiritual. In *The Epic of Gilgamesh*, its earliest Sumerian invocation, an innkeeper offers Gilgamesh, ruler of the city of Uruk, a garden of bliss: 'Night and day, play and dance.'[1] Homer's contemporary, the eighth-century BCE Greek poet Hesiod, wrote of golden-age men: 'they lived like gods, with carefree hearts, remote from toil and misery. Wretched old age did not affect them either.'[2] Sexual freedom is a notable feature of all utopias.

The expulsion from Eden was the first of the 'tribulations' (Toynbee called them 'ordeals') God inflicted on humans for their disobedience to His laws. It started all those things which people have found most irksome about 'civilization': scarcity, toil, insecurity, sexual repression, political oppression.[3] Among the chief legacies of the serpent was private property: nearly all utopias have property in common. Christianity took over the pagan golden age myth and refashioned it into the Garden of Eden, the Fall, the Vale of Tears and the Afterlife. Faith in the Second Coming inspired the powerful millenarian strand of Christianity. But in mainstream Christianity, at least, utopia was strictly detached from this world. This is in contrast to non-European mythology, which saw utopia as a recreation of a historical past.

Its moral intent differentiates utopian or dystopian writing from science fiction. Science fiction is the general category of 'sociotechnical imaginaries'[4] of which utopian fiction is a special case. Edgar Allan Poe is a nineteenth-century master of this genre, clothing horror with quack science. Sci-fi is the most popular contemporary form of it. The imagined future may be a technological dream or a post-apocalyptic nightmare, but the technology and setting themselves carry no philosophical or moral charge. They are simply a stage set for old-fashioned yarns, at the centre of which is the oldest of human dramas, the struggle between good and evil, virtue and villainy.

There is some blurring, though, of the boundaries between science fiction and utopian fiction: Isaac Asimov is a science fiction writer, but one of his Robot stories, 'The Evitable Conflict', carries the moral message that a Robot Autocracy is needed to prevent a savage conflict over scarce resources. There is also some blurring between utopian and dystopian literature. Utopian portrayals often incorporate dystopian features, and vice versa. The satire of one generation can also become the dystopia of the next, as the seemingly absurd projects of professors in fancy research institutes come to be seen not so much as mad as murderous.

Utopian fiction can be any kind of storytelling, but by the

nineteenth century its standard form was the novel, the more comfortable bourgeois form for the reception of the improbable.[5] Its 'realism' is what distinguishes it from the epic poetry of Milton or the Christian allegories of Bunyan, and its philosophic intent from run-of-the-mill fiction. George Orwell aimed 'to fuse political purpose and artistic purpose into one whole',[6] Aldous Huxley 'to arrive technically at the perfect fusion of the novel and the essay'.[7] In fact utopian novels rarely make for good fiction, because there is too much philosophy and not enough human interest. Dystopian fiction works better because its essential ingredient is rebellion against the engineered utopia. This gives it a plot. Finished history is always much less interesting than history in the making.

David Bleich has acutely noted that literary utopia is a particularly Anglo-Saxon phenomenon. It was the political maturity of British society that kept their utopian impulses to 'an area of dream, of speculation, and benevolent social ambition', whereas in Germany 'the fantasy forced its way through to social reality, culminating . . . in the apocalyptic hysteria of the Thousand Year Reich'.[8]

The Two Cultures

Shelley famously proclaimed poets to be the 'unacknowledged legislators of the world'. However, to the practical nineteenth-century mind, chemists were much more useful than poets. So poets set themselves up in opposition to the rule of the scientists and technologists. Of economics, Coleridge wrote: 'It is a science which begins with abstractions in order to exclude whatever is not subject to technical calculation: in the face of all experience, it assumes this as the whole of human nature – and then, on an impossible hypothesis, builds up the most inhuman edifice.'[9] Thomas Love Peacock hit back in 1820: 'as the science of morals and of mind advance towards perfection, as they become more enlarged and comprehensive in their views, as reason gains the ascendancy in them over imagination and feeling, poetry can no longer accompany them in their progress, but drops into the background, and leaves them to advance alone'.[10] The divide between art and science which opened up in the early nineteenth century has never been closed. Artists pitted freedom against the domination of reason; for scientists freedom meant the domination of reason.

The pessimistic turn of literature constituted a fundamental reversal. Pre-industrial futurist fiction was optimistic, albeit with a satiric strand. Romantic poets were excited by the imagery of science. It was the actualization of science in factory machinery and the impersonal rules of state bureaucracy which turned poets against the scientific world view. *Frankenstein*, with its horrific portrayal of rogue machinery, was the crucial watershed. Thereafter hostility to Carlyle's 'mechanical principle' gathered pace. Byron aligned literature with the Luddites. In the twentieth century, the literary, unlike the scientific, imagination became largely despairing. By then the future envisaged by scientific researchers and business publicists and that of writers, poets and dramatists had come so far apart that C. P. Snow could talk about the 'two cultures', scientific and literary, between which there was scarcely a point of contact. To Snow, scientists had 'the future in their bones', whereas writers were natural Luddites, 'wishing the future did not exist'.[11] In his last published work, *Literature and Science* (1963), Aldous Huxley, whose *Brave New World* is one of the two best known of the dystopian fictions, argued sensibly for a rapprochement between the two.[12] But the hostility remains.

Technics and Utopia

The great divide between the 'two cultures' was on the question of machinery. Technological optimists welcomed the progress of scientific civilization as ridding the world of its devils; socialists with the proviso that this required ending capitalism. For the literary intelligentsia, it was technology itself which was diabolical. This made them bitter critics of industrial civilization and advocates of escape routes from it.

An influential evocation of this escapist ideal, Henry David Thoreau's autobiographical *Walden* (1854), was set in the forested shore of Walden Pond, Connecticut, where the author lived alone like Robinson Crusoe, chopped trees, built his own house and grew his own food for two years until he rejoined 'civilization'. Thoreau preached that if only people divested themselves of their possessions, they would need to work only one day a week, reserving the remaining six for 'joy and wonder'. His example of the simplified life inspired not just nature poets like Walt Whitman (*Leaves of Grass*, 1855) but also the founding of many 'uncivilized' communities, which sought in the natural life, free from material clutter, the direct communing with God promised by Luther.

This yearning for a life in the forest was shot through with premonitions of disaster at our abuse of nature. Mikhail Lvovich Astrov, the doctor in Chekhov's play *Uncle Vanya* (1899), devotes himself to planting trees to replenish the burning of wood for stoves. 'There are fewer and fewer forests, the rivers are running dry, the game is exterminated, the climate is spoiled, and the earth becomes poorer and uglier every day.' Future generations, he ruminates, will despise his epoch for having so prodigiously destroyed what nature has bestowed.

But perhaps an industrial utopia was possible after all if technology could be sufficiently 'moralized' to neuter its dehumanizing and destructive potential. In Edward Bulwer-Lytton's *The Coming Race* (1871), the narrator discovers a superhuman civilization called Vryl-ya under a disused mine, whose inhabitants live together in perfect peace and harmony by harnessing a force called vril, whose properties are 'remarkably similar to atomic energy'.[13] Realizing its destructive power, the Vryl-ya have given up war, and channel vril to peaceful uses. Utopia is possible, goes the message, provided technological innovation can be subjected to ethical control: an idea which strongly resonates today.

Samuel Butler's counter-punch *Erewhon* (1872), a futurist oasis 'discovered' somewhere in Australasia, was intended to show the futility of this approach *in isolation*.[14] The Erewhonians have decided to 'stop' technology. But this very decision dooms them, as they are defenceless against the predatory designs of big corporations anxious to find new sources of cheap labour. Butler may well have been struck by the vulnerability of China and Japan to western military technology. Unilateral restraint in the development of military technology left one prey in a world of predators. Butler's 'sermon', from the 'Book of Machines', is that technology should be 'nipped in the bud' before it makes humans its slaves. 'We can't destroy all machines without destroying ourselves but . . . we should destroy as many of them as we can properly dispense with lest they should tyrannise over us ever more completely.' Despite the cost to living standards, 'what will things come to if that rebellion were delayed'?

All this was much too gloomy for Edward Bellamy. His *Looking Backward, 2000–1887* (1888) anticipates a society happily bursting at the seams with machinery.[15] The inhabitants of his late-twentieth-century utopia look back with horror on American life of the late nineteenth, filling his pages with long speeches denouncing capitalism for 'prodigious waste', 'utter idleness', 'wanton luxury', 'corporate tyranny', 'great consolidations of capital', parasitic rentiers, etc. – a jeremiad which had a powerful effect on the youthful American philosopher of conspicuous consumption Thorstein Veblen. But from this cauldron of wickedness came an industrial evolution that by 2000 had transformed modern social institutions for the better through the 'progress of mechanical invention', under the supervision of a benevolent dictatorship. Bellamy's Utopians possess cars that fly and televisions and radios which transmit information and instructions. They are also guaranteed basic incomes: rentier socialism has replaced rentier capitalism. It is More's *Utopia* plus machines.

Bellamy's tedious polemics provoked, in turn, the escapist romance of William Morris's *News from Nowhere* (1891), subtitled 'an epoch of rest'. Morris is both forward- and backward-looking: he looks to socialism not to build a humane industrialism – Morris calls

Bellamy's Utopia soulless and regimented – but to create a post-industrial, post-capitalist space to allow a revival of cottage industries, in a unity of art and work as exhibited in the medieval tradition of craftsmanship.[16] Inspired equally by Ruskin and Marx, Morris wanted not to abolish work, but make it joyful again. *News from Nowhere* inspired the 'Arts and Crafts' movement of late-Victorian England but offered no plausible future for the heavily industrialized, urban civilization which England had become.

H. G. Wells, who combined a scientific training and imagination with literary flair, was the last great novelist of scientific utopia. He wrote scathingly of Morris's romance: 'Modern Utopia must be not static but kinetic.'[17] Almost alone in the Anglo-American literary world, Wells kept alive the notion that technology could be moralized without destroying its progressive promise. In *A Modern Utopia* (1905) he depicts a world state, located on a planet 'beyond Sirius'. In this socialist utopia, all land and power sources are publicly owned, positive compulsion and physical labour have been all but eliminated, general freedom is assured, and an open, voluntary order of 'samurai' rules a 'kinetic and not static' world, solving the problem of combining movement with political stability. A chapter in *A Modern Utopia* on relations between the sexes depicts complete sexual equality and freedom. It was, above all, the promise of sexual freedom which kept the utopian novel afloat amidst the dystopian events of the early twentieth century. Wells's technological utopia is highly sanitized – warm-water baths, soap machines, towel dispensers, mechanical sweepers expunge the foetid odours of sex. Other benefits are vegetarianism (fish is allowed), the locking up of cats and dogs in special camps to stop the spread of disease, islands of exiles for misfits. Technology would solve all the problems of human dysfunction. Wells, like Marx, had little time for utopian experiments: nothing less than a socialist world state would satisfy him.

Always quick to turn a scientific discovery into a hopeful prospect, Wells seized on Frederick Soddy's *The Interpretation of Radium* (1909) to project a humanity 'set free' by radioactivity to create a world socialist state. Particularly interesting here is the entry into the utopian literature of a dialectic, or apocalyptic, element, in which extreme events serve as agents of progress. In *The World Set Free* (1914), the devastation of the world by 'atomic bombs' is the trigger for the creation of a pacific world. By the time of *The World of William Clissold* (1926), Wells had abandoned his belief in socialism, but not his belief in science.[18] The creative potential of mankind is located not in the world of vegetarian socialist intellectuals but in the 'open conspiracy' of scientists and industrial tycoons. In Alexander Korda's film *Things to Come* (1936), loosely adapted from Wells's novel *The Shape of Things to Come* (1933), economic depression, a thirty years war and a global plague reminiscent of the Black Death are succeeded by a new world state under the benevolent dictatorship of scientific philosophers. By the end of his life the succession of dystopian events in the real world had shattered even Wells's buoyancy. In his last (non-fiction) fragment, *Mind at the End of Its Tether* (1945), he despaired that 'there is no way out or round or through the impasse . . . The end of everything we call life is close at hand and cannot be evaded.'[19]

Wells's faith in the liberating power of machinery had already been punctured in a remarkable prefigurement by E. M. Forster long before Wells himself had abandoned it. E. M. Forster's short story 'The Machine Stops' (1909), a response to Wells's *Modern Utopia*, is an extraordinary premonition of an apocalypse, in which technological disaster precipitates an involuntary return to primitive life.[20]

Humanity now lives underground (as in Bulwer-Lytton's *The Coming Race*), life on the surface having been destroyed by an ecological disaster, caused, Forster says in passing, by forests being cut down to make 'newspaper pulp'. It is ruled by the Machine, code for the Central Committee. All living accommodation is standardized, all furniture is automated, music is piped continuously into the cells from which inhabitants never stir, beds descend on the press of a button, human matter is excreted into giant 'vomitories' overground, the sites of ruined cities. There are compulsory lectures (as in More's *Utopia*), but all communication, visual and auditory, between humans is 'online'. Children are removed from parents at the moment of birth. The only book left, 'The Book of the Machine', is the bible of instructions.

Then the Machine stops working, little by little at first, then completely, and civilization ends. Panic-stricken crowds fill the tunnels leading to the surface, but the jammed ventilation shafts trap them underground. Just before his death, the protagonist Kuno has a revelation: 'Man, the flower of all flesh, the noblest of all creatures visible, man who had once made god in his image, and had mirrored his strength on the constellations, beautiful naked man was dying, strangled in the garments he had woven.' All was not lost, though. Survivors from a previous apocalypse were hiding in the mist and ferns, waiting for civilization to stop. ' "Today they are the Homeless – to-morrow . . . But then some fool will start the Machine again?" "Never," said Kuno, "never. Humanity has learnt its lesson." '

Forster was talking about the breakdown of mechanical machinery, but his story can be read as a metaphor for the breakdown of social machinery. 'The machine that worked for years to apparent perfection, faultlessly, without a hitch, falls apart overnight . . . is shattered without warning.'[21] In 1914, the machinery of civilization stopped. For four years millions of young men slaughtered each other above ground and lived half underground in the trenches. Then, unlike in Forster's story, civilization spluttered back into life, before juddering to an even bigger halt twenty-five years later. Since 1945, humanity has escaped from life in the bunker, though its elites have long prepared for it. Forster's underground dystopia is a warning against the unintended consequences of depending on technology for the services of life. The Machine has robbed humanity of all resilience, because it has atrophied its emotions and colonized its skills.

The dystopian novels which run parallel to Wells's utopias give a very different answer to the question of what Plato's ideal Republic would actually look like.

The Great Dystopian Trilogy

Ongoing technological developments, especially in communication, provide the setting of the great dystopian trilogy Zamyatin's
We (1924), Aldous Huxley's *Brave New World* (1932) and George
Orwell's *1984* (1949). As Orwell tells it in *1984*, in the early twentieth
century, the vision of a society 'unbelievably rich, orderly and efficient' was part of the consciousness of every literate person. Science
and technology were developing at a 'prodigious speed', and it
seemed natural to suppose that they would continue to lift society
up with them. Then came war, revolution, economic depression.
Science had been subverted for warfare and police espionage, socialism had failed, capitalism had become an engine for creating waste
on a colossal scale.[22] What was there to be hopeful about?

In Zamyatin's *We*, situated in 'One State', the technologically
imagined future has become the dystopian present. Most of the
world's population has been killed by an ecological disaster. 'One
State' has conquered what remains and is planning to invade and
conquer other planets. A massive 'Green Wall' separates it from the
remnants of wildness and ugliness that survive on the outside.

In One State, elimination of wasted motion has been transferred
from the factory to the whole society – as indeed Lenin intended.
People (called 'ciphers') are identified only by numbers. Human
behaviour has been reduced to the working of precision machinery,
supervised by an invisible Benefactor. The ciphers live in transpar-
ent glass houses under the ever-watchful eyes of police officers
known as the Guardians. Every detail of their daily lives is regulated. They are assigned suitable sex partners for sessions of
scheduled loveless copulation. All their needs are taken care of.
Unfreedom is the only method of cleansing humanity of 'crimson',
the 'thousand years of filth'. But – and here Zamyatin follows
Bentham and anticipates Huxley and Orwell – unfreedom does not
require the executioner. All it needs is a mental conditioning which
stops humans from envisaging any other way of life. The tool of

this conditioning is the logic of mathematics, or, as we might say today, of the algorithm, the set of logically derived instructions for the optimization of organization and conduct of living, contained in a 'Table of Hours'. The engineer Cipher D-503 waxes lyrical about the power of mathematics to solve the world's problems:

> Forever enamoured are two plus two, forever conjoined in blissful four. The hottest lovers in all the world; the permanent weld . . . The multiplication table is wiser and more absolute than the ancient God. It never repeats, never makes a mistake. And there's nothing happier than figures that live according to the elegant and eternal laws of the multiplication table. No wavering, no wandering.[23]

The deluded engineer babbles on: '*Homo Sapiens* is not fully man until his grammar is absolutely rid of question marks, leaving nothing but exclamation points, commas, and periods.'[24]

Mathematics is the way back to the Garden of Eden:

> Yes! Just think about it. Those two in Paradise, they were offered a choice: happiness without freedom, or freedom without happiness. Those idiots chose freedom. And then what? Then for centuries they were homesick for the chains. That's why the world was so miserable, see? They missed the chains. For ages! And we were the first to hit on the way back to happiness . . . We helped God finally overcome the Devil . . . We gave [the wily serpent] a boot to the head! Crack! And that was all over: Paradise was back. And we're simple and innocent again, like Adam and Eve. None of those complications about good and evil. Everything is very simple, childishly simple.[25]

The system seems perfect.

D-503 and I-330 make love, against 'protocol', in 'The Ancient House', a museum of relics, where people dress in an old-fashioned way. D-503's journal harbours increasingly subversive thoughts. Humanity had chosen the mistaken path of Galileo. 'He was right that the earth revolves around the sun, but he didn't know that the entire solar system revolves around yet another centre.' By splitting nature into compounds of chemicals like H_2O, humanity has lost its understanding of what makes streams, waterfalls, waves, storms. Enticed by I-330, D-503 joins a group of shaggy-haired rebels (Memphi) outside the walls, who plan to use his engineering expertise to destroy One State.

The details of the plot do not concern us. D-503 joins the primitives, but the Guardians foil their conspiracy, and he is captured. D-503 is diagnosed as suffering from 'imagination'. Following Descartes, scientists have discovered that 'the imagination is centred in a wretched little brain node in the region of the *pons Varioli*. Expose this node to three doses of X rays – and you are cured of imagination.' D-503 is duly lobotomized and, cured of passion, returns to being a devoted servant of One State. Drawn from the then standard treatment of mental illnesses like schizophrenia, this 'cure' for human willfulness profoundly influenced the dystopic imagination, most famously in Orwell's *1984* (1949) and the film *A Clockwork Orange* (1971).[26]

In Zamyatin's dystopia, 'the lines are finished', the future completed. The only thing left for time to do is to catch up. Zamyatin rebelled against the idea of a 'finished' future. 'The beasts of the country', he concludes, 'must be mobilised to initiate an apocalypse which might return energy to life and reignite history'.

Huxley's *Brave New World* is the most telling imagining of what an ideal society run by philosopher-kings would actually look like. It is set in 2540 CE, or 632 AF (after Henry Ford, inventor of mass production cars and disciple of Frederick Winslow Taylor). An apocalypse in the form of the Nine Years War had posed the choice between 'world control and destruction'. So the leaders of the warring parties agreed to set up a world state to abolish war, and to use less violent but surer methods to maintain order, such as ectogenesis, Pavlovian conditioning, hypnopaedia and plentiful doses of a euphoric drug called *soma* to bring about 'community, identity, and stability.'[27]

In *Brave New World*, 'viviparous' birth is forbidden. Children are hatched outside the womb at the Central London Hatchery and

Conditioning Centre by the 'Bokanovsky Process' – London is the centre of World State, in homage to the still extant but decaying British empire. In order to ensure the 'mass production of predictable humans', the embryos are passed from the bottling room and the organ and matriculation stores (where they are made immune to disease) to the social destination room, where the right genes are allocated to the right classes of tasks, as in Plato's Republic. These classes, in order from highest to lowest, are Alpha, Beta, Gamma, Delta and Epsilon. The Alphas are bred to be leaders, and the Epsilons to be manual labourers. The correct identification of the classes is secured by ensuring that the two billion inhabitants of World State have only 10,000 names between them.

But humans must also be conditioned to like what they must do. Infant Nurseries and Pavlovian Conditioning Rooms give the youngsters mild electric shocks to secure the required aversion to books and flowers. The youngsters are continually nudged towards the right behaviour by 'hypnopaeia', a form of hypnosis induced in sleep, until at last the child's mind is the sum of all these 'suggestions from the State'.[28] Unlike the standard communist dystopia, Huxley's dystopia is hedonistic. Sex play in girls and boys is encouraged by pneumatic massage, piped music and 'feelies' – virtual reality erotic movies. There is also a plentiful supply of 'freemartins', sterile women, to encourage promiscuity. Finally, there is the pacifying drug *soma*. Every *soma* holiday is 'a bit of what our ancestors used to call eternity'.[29] *Soma* has 'all the advantages of Christianity and alcohol; none of their defects . . . Take a holiday from reality wherever you like, and come back without so much as a headache or a mythology.'[30] 'Gonadal hormones, transfusion of young blood, magnesium salts'[31] ensure that the old retain their looks and vitality to the end. At the point of death they are painlessly gassed in crematoria.

World State's reliance on chemicals to secure compliance is accompanied 'by the closing of museums, the blowing up of historical monuments . . . the suppression of all books published before A.F.150' – in short by the cancellation of memory.[32] No one has heard of the Pyramids or Shakespeare. 'Such are the advantages of a really scientific education,' remarks the World Controller for Western Civilization, Mustapha Mond, with satisfaction.[33]

But as in the perfected world of Zamyatin there is a point of opposition, here in the person of a beautiful young man called John. John's mother, Linda, had been made illegally pregnant by the Director of Hatcheries and dumped in the 'Savage Reservation', where 60,000 primitives were allowed to live, separated from civilization by an electric fence, and prevented by gas bombs from multiplying too freely. Linda had told John stories about the Other Place (Civilization). One day John found an edition of *The Complete Works of William Shakespeare* and learned about human life before Civilization. 'Oh brave new world', John thinks 'that has such people in it.' Mustapha Mond agrees to take Linda and John back to Civilization 'for scientific interest'.

The encounter between the Savage (as he is known in Civilization) and the World Controller is the philosophic core of the novel, recalling the confrontation between the Grand Inquisitor and Jesus Christ in Dostoevsky's *Brothers Karamazov.*

Why, John enquires, is Shakespeare forbidden? Because, Mond responds, 'Beauty's attractive, and we don't want people to be attracted by old things. We want them to like the new ones.'[34] But surely *Othello* is better than 'feelies'? Of course, agrees the Controller, but that's the price you pay for stability. You need to choose between happiness and high art. 'Feelies' make people happy. 'Being contented has nothing of the glamour of a good fight against misfortune, none of the picturesqueness of a struggle with temptation, or a fatal overthrow by passion or doubt. Happiness is never grand.'[35]

The Savage wants to know why they hadn't made everyone an Alpha. 'Because we have no wish to have our throats cut,' answers the World Controller smoothly. A society of Alphas was bound to be miserable, and therefore rebellious, because there wasn't enough Alpha work to be done. However, Epsilons are quite happy with their work: 'It's light. It's childishly simple. No strain on the mind or muscles. Seven and a half hours of mild, exhausting labour, and then the *soma* ration and games and unrestricted copulation and the feelies.'[36] As if answering Keynes, whose essay 'Economic Possibilities for Our Grandchildren' had appeared just before the publication of *Brave New World*, Mond explains that the reduction of work hours to a three- or four-hour day is perfectly feasible technically. 'But would they be any the happier for that? No, they wouldn't. The experiment was tried, more than a century and a half ago. The whole of Ireland was put onto the four-hour day. What was the result? Unrest and a large increase in the consumption of *soma*; that was all.'[37] It would be 'sheer cruelty' to afflict extra leisure on the labourers.

This leads the World Controller to caution against giving science free rein. After reading a 'brilliant paper' on biology, which he forbids to be published, he ruminates, 'Once you began admitting explanations in terms of purpose . . . that might easily recondition the more unsettled minds among the highest castes – make them lose their faith in happiness as the Sovereign Good.'[38] 'Every discovery in pure science is potentially subversive; even science must sometimes be treated as a possible enemy.'[39] Science in the World State was 'just a cookery book that nobody's allowed to question, and a list of recipes that mustn't be added to except by special permission from the head cook. I'm the head cook now.'[40] In the spirit of Plato's philosopher-kings, the World Controller explains that he himself has given up philosophy for government. Religion was another casualty of happiness. People turned to God because they were unhappy. World State has abolished unhappiness, and therefore the need for religion. The Bible is a banned book.

The Savage responds:

But I don't want comfort. I want God. I want poetry, I want real danger, I want freedom, I want goodness. I want sin . . . [n]ot to mention the right to grow old and ugly and impotent; the right to have syphilis and cancer; the right to have too little to eat; the right to be lousy; the right to live in constant apprehension of what may happen tomorrow; the right to catch typhoid; the right to be tortured by unspeakable pains of every kind . . . I claim them all.[41]

The Savage goes back to 'being savage' in a deserted lighthouse, with primitive tools, growing his own food, hunting rabbits, flagellating himself, praying to God. He is secretly filmed. The film is a sensation. Sightseers gather round the lighthouse for entertainment, wanting to see the Savage whipping himself. The Savage commits suicide.

It is possible, with a different set of priorities and values, to treat a Huxley-type dystopia as a utopia, and this is exactly what B. F. Skinner does in *Walden Two* – the title an echo of Thoreau – dating from 1948. There is a big difference, though, in location and scale between the two stories: Huxley's *Brave New World* is set in the future and is literally the whole world; Skinner's is a small utopian community set in contemporary Ohio. The principles of both are the same: behavioural engineering is used to keep humans happy. 'That's the point,' the community's benign dictator Frazier explains to a visitor:

> Society already possesses the psychological techniques needed to obtain universal observation of a code – a code which would guarantee the success of a community or state. The difficulty is that these techniques are in the hands of the wrong people – or, rather, there aren't any right people. Our government won't accept the responsibility of building the sort of behavior needed for a happy state.

More important, one feels, in securing the 'happy state' than Skinner's psychological techniques, is the small size of his community. Referring to E. F. Schumacher's 'remarkable book', *Small Is Beautiful*, Skinner wrote in 1976, 'A network of small towns or Walden Twos . . . could much more easily solve many of the crucial problems facing the world today.' It would be much easier, for example, to control the birth rate. 'Parents would not need children for economic security . . . the community would function as a large and affectionate family in which everyone would play parental and filial roles. Blood ties would then be a minor issue.'[42]

Our third great dystopian novel, George Orwell's 1984, starts from where Zamyatin left off. The Stalinist tyranny which Zamyatin foresaw has now happened, and Orwell, like Hayek in *The Road to Serfdom* (1944), wants to warn his readers that western democracies were on a slippery slope to the same result.[43] The Cold War had started when Orwell wrote his book, and the setting of 1984 is thus that of a world at war. Three superstates, Oceana, Eurasia and Eastasia, are locked in endless pretend warfare. The continuous 'state of war' is needed for active commitment, at least of Party members, to Big Brother. Another difference from Zamyatin and Huxley is the book's attitude to sex. Whereas in their dystopias frequent copulation keeps everyone happy, in Orwell's state the ideal is chastity. Sex is for procreation only. Sexual love diverts energy from the five-year plan.

Whereas Zamyatin leaves unclear how the people of 'One State' are to be induced to obey the laws of mathematics (he envisages lobotomizing only the rebels), Orwell utilizes the invention of television to outline a plausible scheme of surveillance and mind control. In the flat of each Party member, a two-way telescreen has been installed to convey instructions and monitor behaviour. Big Brother Is Watching You: 'Always the eyes watching you and the voice enveloping you – no escape.'[44]

But Big Brother also shapes beliefs and behaviour by manipulation of language. Newspeak is Orwell's unique contribution to dystopian literature: the rectification of language to control thought. Undetectable lying, double-think, constriction of vocabulary and obliteration of memory are at its heart. They will make law and ultimately surveillance unnecessary. After years of linguistic impoverishment, Party members will not be able to think and act in any way of which Big Brother disapproves. They will accept that reality exists only in the mind of the Party. Whatever the Party holds to be true is truth. Reality is in the eye of the beholder and the Party is the beholder. 'The Ministry of Peace concerns itself with war, the Ministry of Truth with lies, the Ministry of Love with torture and the Ministry of Plenty with starvation.'[45] 'War is Peace, Freedom is Slavery, Ignorance is Strength.'[46]

Like other dystopias, Orwell's was a caste society, in his case divided into inner Party, outer Party and the 'proles'. It is only partly a meritocracy: competitive examinations decide between 'inner' and 'outer' Party membership, but the 'proles', who number 85 per cent of the population, cannot ascend to the elite: any able proles are liquidated. With continuous warfare eliminating global economic competition, there is no need to educate the proles to keep up with industrial technology. They can be safely allowed intellectual liberty 'because they have no intellect'. Because they are also 'beneath suspicion', they are allowed to retain their customs and vices. The only hope for humanity, Orwell surmises, lies in a revolt by the proles, but 'until they become conscious they will never rebel, and until after they have rebelled they cannot become conscious'.

The job of the protagonist, Winston Smith, is to cancel the past. The removal of all old inscriptions, statues, memorial stones, street names, the burning of all old books means that 'the whole literature of the past will have been destroyed. Chaucer, Shakespeare, Milton, Byron – they'll exist only in Newspeak versions.'[47] Winston's colleague Syme beavers away at 'destroying hundreds of words everyday', or converting them into Newspeak, the only language 'whose vocabulary gets smaller every year'.[48] When this rectification of language is perfected, no one will be capable of thinking thoughts, or behaving in ways, of which Big Brother disapproves.[49] Orwell grasped the truth that the restriction of language to cliché and formula is a giant step on the road to zombiedom and therefore serfdom.

But the human spirit is unquenchable. Winston starts a diary in which he writes 'Down with Big Brother'. Its pages are filled with subversive thoughts like: 'For, after all, how do we know that two and two make four? Or that the force of gravity works? Or that the past is unchangeable? If both the past and the external world exist only in the mind, and if the mind itself is controllable – what then?'[50] 'Freedom is the freedom to say that two plus two make four. If that is granted, all else follows.'[51] He locks the diary away, knowing that the Thought Police will eventually discover it.

Two subversive characters feed Winston's growing resistance to Big Brother's system. O'Brien, who runs the Ministry of Truth, recruits Winston to the Brotherhood, the shadowy conspiracy against Big Brother, masterminded by an invented figure, Emmanuel Golstein, so as to trap him and then make use of him by deleting his delusions. Julia, a seemingly impeccable Party member, who works in the Ministry of Fiction, falls in love with Winston; her 'practical cunning' makes possible their clandestine affair. She is not an intellectual like Winston, but 'earthy', and this earthiness is her main attraction. She assumes that what the Party calls truth is a pack of lies, but this does not make her an inquirer or a rebel, just totally cynical. As Winston mocks: 'You're only a rebel from the waist downwards.'[52] But in view of enforced chastity this mark of rebellion is crucial to the plot.

They make passionate, and secret, love in a rented room above an old antique shop. Its owner, Mr Charrington, turns out to be an undercover agent for the Thought Police, and they are predictably arrested. In the Ministry of Love, Winston is interrogated, tortured, drugged and given electric shocks by officers directed by O'Brien. He confesses to everything. In his delirium he hears a voice murmuring into his ear: 'Don't worry, Winston; you are in my keeping. For seven years I have watched over you. Now the turning-point has come, I shall save you, I shall make you perfect.'[53] Desperately Winston clings on to his truth; remorselessly O'Brien tells him that if the Party says that two plus two equals five, he must believe it. Even the 'right' answer, given with insufficient conviction, is visited with an electric shock. O'Brien tells him soothingly that he is there not to punish him but to cure him. The new system makes no martyrs; a refusal to conform will be obliteration from history. The Party insists on conversion before liquidation. He must surrender of his own free will. 'We make the brain perfect before we blow it out.' Even if his life is spared, he will never again be capable of ordinary human feeling; everything will be dead inside him; never again will he be capable of love, or friendship, or joy of living, or laughter, or curiosity, or courage, or integrity. They will squeeze him empty, then fill him with themselves.

Finally, an electric shock to the head pulverizes Winston; the scene is set for implanting into his emptied brain the right facts and attitudes. As promised, he is saved by O'Brien to eke out his remaining days as a gin-soaked official, at a larger salary, loving Big Brother. 1984 remains the blackest dystopian novel ever written, because there are so few cracks in the totalitarian façade.

Cancelling Culture

'One might justly say that each individual thinks with his past,' wrote Hayek in 1920.[54] The crucially important message of these three dystopias is that obliteration of collective memory – 'burning of the books' – is the central instrument of thought control. It leaves humans with no mental resources to challenge the hegemony of the existing order. None of the three novelists buy into the democratic promise of technology: in their dystopias everyone is fitted to the functions which the state requires of them. In any event, creativity is ruled out by the restriction of language. Equally striking is the disembodied nature of power. In all three novels we encounter human representatives of power, but power itself resides in 'the System' – 'the Party' in Orwell's novel. Big Brother is simply an avatar, through which the Party transmits its instructions, like the God Re in pharaonic Egypt.

Huxley's novel is the most prescient of the three, because the Soviet version of communism which shaped the dystopias of Zamyatin and Orwell has collapsed everywhere except in China and North Korea. Huxley's is a prosperous dystopia, which has overcome the crisis of the 1930s, and in which people enjoy a state of blissful infantilism through sex, entertainment and drugs under the watchful eye of the World Controller. This foreshadows the mindless hedonism of the affluent west in the post-communist era. The vista is not completely black. Outside the boundaries of the utopian state live potential subversives: the primitives in Zamyatin, the savages in Huxley, the proles in Orwell. In their customs and vices lie such hope for the future as exists.

It might be supposed that the techniques of thought control paraded in the three dystopias would be automatically resisted and prevented in pluralist societies. However, the message of the three novelists is that it is easy to slide from democracy to dictatorship because the technology of power creeps up so invisibly and becomes so pervasive that most people remain blissfully unaware that it is happening.

PART III

Towards Apocalypse

The Coming of the Computer

'Measure what can be measured, and make measurable
what cannot be measured.'

Galileo

Before Data

Orwell understood better than the other dystopians that the real
secret of the modern technique of power lay in the huge inequality
in information, symbolized by Big Brother's one-way communication system. However, there remained a big gap between the
imaginings of the writers and the existing technology for turning
imagination into project. It was this gap which has been steadily
narrowed by computer technology.

Standard histories of information technology start with the collection of facts. The Romans conducted censuses of the populations
they conquered, for tax purposes; the Bible tells us that Joseph and a
heavily pregnant Mary were commanded to make the journey from
Nazareth to Bethlehem in order to register themselves in Augustus'
census. The practice of census-taking in western Europe was dis-
continued until the modern era, the only notable exception being
the Doomsday Book, compiled for William the Conqueror after his
conquest of England in 1066. Modern data analysis began in fits and
starts in the sixteenth and seventeenth centuries, when governments across Europe and the New World began to make efforts to
collect information about their subjects. England took its first

census in 1801, but these early efforts were always hampered by difficulties in gathering, storing and analysing information. What has changed today is not just the sheer quantity and variety of data available, but the enlarged capacity of computers to analyse it and to use it to make increasingly precise predictions.

A good starting point is the invention of printing in the fifteenth century.[1] Before Gutenberg, we relied on memory and manuscripts to record and transmit information. This meant that it was largely confined to books, the production and circulation of which was tightly controlled by the Church. Moreover, information could disappear, if the books were burned, as happened with the destruction of the great library of Alexandria. Literacy itself could be easily lost if writing was done only by a few professional scribes. Johannes Gutenberg himself saw printing as a rebellion against authority. By liberating information from the tyranny of Church and localism, Gutenberg kickstarted a process by which scarcity of knowledge could be converted into abundance. However, communication could only travel as fast as the means of transport, which until the nineteenth century was physical: a message still had to get to you on foot or by horse, carrier pigeon or boat: for short distances people used smoke, fire, drums. In 1844, Samuel Morse launched the era of electronic communication by telegraphing 'What hath God wrought?' from Washington DC to Baltimore. Within fifteen years the first transatlantic telegraph cable had been laid, connecting America to Europe. The speed, volume and breadth of this hidden network of cables steadily increased, so that by 1960 an electronic transatlantic cable could transmit 138 conversations at once.

The Calculation Explosion

After about 1960, the story of information flows is taken over by the electronic computer, which made the cable telegraph obsolete. The word 'computer' means, literally, 'one who computes', that is, counts or calculates. The ancestors of modern computers were the human 'counters' who used the abacus to count money tokens of goods for purpose of trade or taxation. From the abacus came the idea of measuring value by numbers. This opened the way to the manipulation of numbers for policy purposes.

From the seventeenth century the term 'computer' was first used to refer to astronomers and their assistants, who would calculate on a slide-rule the relative positions of heavenly bodies at any given future date, from long tables of figures and dates. Knowing the exact positions of the planets and the stars was an important tool for sailors. It was also central to the explanatory work of astronomers and physicists. But it was slow and laborious. As scientific knowledge advanced, and ever-higher levels of precision were demanded by navigators and astronomers and by policy-makers looking for a statistical basis for action, the human 'computer' became an increasingly impractical solution. The earliest mechanical computers were developed to overcome the organic limits to human computing power.

In the early nineteenth century, Charles Babbage (1791–1871) developed what is regarded as the first mechanical computer. Babbage's so-called 'difference engine' was powered by a hand crank and used numbered wheels and mechanical gears to calculate equations. Upon seeing Babbage's half-finished but working prototype, Ada Lovelace, mathematician and daughter of Lord Byron, described the device as a 'thinking machine'. Babbage had high hopes for the machine and its more general-purpose successor, the 'analytical engine', but the metalworking techniques of the time were not sufficiently advanced to realize his project. Each element of the engine – each wheel and gear – had to be produced at great cost and effort by hand. Babbage fretted, 'I wish to God these calculations had been executed by steam.' Nevertheless, the Babbage calculator revolutionized the relationship between humans and machines. John Napier (1550–1617) had developed logarithms. These enabled multiplication to be turned into simple addition. With the abacus or slide-rule, the human inputted the information and calculated the results. But now the machine did the calculations, which in turn became the inputs for new calculations. It had acquired a crucial degree of independence or 'agency', which has steadily, and in the end explosively, enlarged.

The story of computing between Babbage and Alan Turing (1912–54) is essentially the story of a deepening understanding of the *plasticity* of computers. It is the story of the steady realization by computer scientists that virtually anything can be represented digitally – as a series of discrete variables – and thus, that virtually anything can be represented by a computer. Conversely, anything which cannot be computerized – like a belief system – was robbed of 'value'.

From the late nineteenth century onwards, two models for computer development competed for mastery: analogue and digital. 'Analogue' comes from the Greek ἀνάλογος: analogous, or proportional to the world. Analogue technologies are 'covariant' with the world. As the heat in the room increases, the height of the mercury in the thermometer also necessarily increases. In 1956, Frank Rosenblatt, a psychologist from Cornell University, built a 'perceptron' – an analogue computer designed to mimic the neural activity of the brain. As the brain distinguished shapes from each other, so would the perceptron, Rosenblatt claimed, be able to tell cats from dogs. The media were duly excited. 'The first serious rival to the human brain ever devised,' enthused the *New Yorker*. In fact, it failed to pass the cat–dog test, but attracted funding from the US navy.[2] The failure of the perceptron inaugurated the first of what is known as the 'AI winters'. But the computer revolution was refloated by digital technology.

Rather than mimic the way we see nature, digital technologies decompose nature into tiny fragments. There is a continuous and infinite number of tones in the audio spectrum, an infinite number of colours in the visual spectrum, and so on. Digital technologies like the digital thermometer take the raw, continuous data of the world and compress it into tiny discrete 'bits' of information. In the case of a digital thermometer, the heat data is translated into a definite number, say 22.1 °C, which is itself representable as a sequence of binary numbers. The speed-up in information flow is phenomenal. Whereas analogue cables could carry hundreds of conversations a minute, fibre-optic cables can carry millions.

The theoretical breakthrough for digital computing came in 1937, when computer science pioneer Claude Shannon (1916–2001), then a master's student at MIT, proved that algebraic equations can be represented and solved using electronic relays and switches. Shannon's work inaugurated modern 'information theory', showing that complex chains of information can be represented by digital circuits. This discovery, which coincided with the increasing use of calculus in mathematics, has remained central to all modern electronic digital computers. After Shannon, the British engineer and cryptographer Alan Turing showed it was possible to build a machine that could perform any conceivable computation that could be represented as an algorithm, or set of instructions.

As always, military demand drove the engine of invention. Ballistics demanded a vast amount of calculation. Each new ballistic weapon required dense mathematical tables, so that gunners could calculate a missile's trajectory. The mathematician John von Neumann (1903–57), the real inventor of computer technology, thought it was 'unethical' for scientists 'not to do what they know is feasible, no matter what terrible consequence it might have'.[3]

The practical application of the work of the mathematicians was the development of the integrated circuit. These are chips made of silicon onto which vast numbers of transistors (electronic switches which can be either on or off) and other circuit components are affixed. The development of the integrated circuit in the early 1960s meant that computing power began to correlate directly with our growing ability to manufacture smaller and smaller components. It made possible the development of the first truly *personal* computers, or PCs: cheap, mass-marketable and easy-to-use computers that one could work from home. The history of digital computers since the 1960s has been one of steady miniaturization. Computers have shrunk in size and grown exponentially in power; the relatively small and inexpensive computer on the desk in my office is able to store and process a quantity of information that would have been almost unthinkable only fifty years ago.

As we are able to manufacture smaller and smaller components, so we are able to store and process more and more information in a single computer, laptop or phone. This relationship between the size and power of computer components is described by 'Moore's law' of 1965, which claimed that the number of transistors that we are able to fit on an integrated circuit should double every two years.

California's Silicon Valley takes its name from the high concentration of companies manufacturing and using silicon-based computer components in the 1970s and 1980s. Silicon is a hard and brittle crystalline solid – like a diamond – found in sand, and a variety of minerals. Silicon chips are the fundamental building blocks of the computer revolution, used to store memory and make up the electronic circuits which pass information from sender to receiver. Silicon's capacity to change whether it conducts or insulates electricity depending on the amount of electrical voltage applied makes it the ideal material with which to construct the binary switches which are the foundation of almost all electronic devices we use today. A modern silicon chip may have many billions of these transistors in an area the size of a human fingernail.

Think of an image taken on a digital camera: raw, continuous data, in the form of light, is translated into an image made up of millions of pixels, each of which is represented by a number, say 8 or 24, of bits. The higher the pixel count – in other words, the higher the number of bits into which the image is divided – the closer the image comes to perfectly representing the raw source data. And now, with the advent of Big Data analysis, the ability of computer programs to improve the quality of their own output means that they can draw ever-more accurate conclusions and make ever-more precise predictions.

The point of all this is to stress the extent of the raw power possessed by modern digital computers. Whilst even Babbage's difference engine was able to solve a given equation faster and with greater precision than a human 'computer', today's machines are able to solve infinitely more complex equations in the blink of an eye. More importantly, today's computer is able to perform a vast array of entirely different functions simultaneously. This means that, in many tasks, the computer far outpaces the human brain. Just as the human computers of the eighteenth century were made obsolete by the onset of the early computing machines, so have a great variety of cognitive tasks fallen victim to the steady march of computer technology since then. The computers on our desks will perform the calculations of the old analogue giants which sent the first spaceships into orbit at a thousandth of the size and millions of times faster. Thus, having first decomposed the world into bits, digital technology aims to reconstruct it on more efficient lines.

The final piece in the puzzle was the realization, by tech giants like Facebook and Google, that an enormous surplus of information about us and our 'consumer preferences' could be harvested from our everyday use of smartphones and computers. While we use our phones to share pictures online, read news or navigate, our phones collect data about us. This data, known as a 'behavioural surplus', is used by companies like Facebook, Google and Amazon to make inferences about what products might be gainfully marketed to us. 'Amazon harvests, dices, and splices everything we do, everywhere we do it, and then uses the data to improve the speed, accuracy and personalisation of Alexa.'[4] Google, not to be left behind, now promises devices which will 'control gadgets with our minds'.[5]

The last fifty years have seen an exponential increase in the power to create electronic filing, retrieving and calculating systems whose raw material is human life. On the one hand, the vastly increased information flow enabled by electronic circuitry promises to free thinking and behaviour from the control of all forms of established authority, as Gutenberg imagined printing would do. On the other hand, the more information we provide about ourselves, the greater the potential for control. It gives the agencies of the state an unsurpassed power of surveillance, prediction and prevention. The more 'selfies' we upload, the better computers become at recognizing faces, the more messages and emails we send to one another, the better they become at recognizing 'natural language' speech patterns and forming sentences of their own. We take up the question of liberation versus entrapment in chapter 16. But first comes the story of artificial intelligence.

AI to the Rescue?

'The Machine develops – but not on our lines. The machine proceeds – but not to our goal. If it could work without us it would let us die.'

E. M. Forster

The Birth of AI

The search for artificial intelligence (AI) can be understood in three ways. First, it can be seen in purely 'internalist' terms as the inevitable next step in the march of computerization and neuroscience. Its history has been expertly described in such terms.[1] Secondly, it can be seen as a product of the arms race between the USA and the Soviet Union during the Cold War. Thirdly, it can be interpreted as an attempt to short-circuit the quest for societal improvement by developing superior brainpower.

The workshop held at Dartmouth College in New Hampshire in the summer of 1956 is now considered to be AI's founding event. It proposed that 'every aspect of learning or any other feature of intelligence can in principle be so precisely described that a machine can be made to simulate it'.[2]

That the search for AI was the child of the Cold War is undeniable. One strand came out of the computers built at Bletchley Park in Britain in 1941 to decrypt the complex Lorenz code used by the Germans, and to create secure information codes between London and Washington. The ARPANET, funded by the US Advanced

Military Research Products Agency (ARPA), connected up regional academic and military computer networks in the 1970s. The research had military objectives, but produced commercial spin-offs. Sir Timothy Berners-Lee invented the first web server, the World Wide Web, in 1990. The explosion of the internet, linking up commercial networks and companies, followed in the early 1990s. Silicon, the essential chemical element in electronic circuitry, for the first time made rewiring the human brain seem feasible. Silicon Valley was a creation of the Pentagon: military competition between the super-powers accelerated the rate of technological discovery and diffusion. Without the Second and Cold Wars we would not have had the same technology.

But just as important was the quest for targeted as distinct from broad intervention to improve human prospects. In 1894, Beatrice Webb had wondered whether a more secure (as well as a far less costly) improvement in the human condition might be achieved by genetic rather than by social engineering.[3] However, eugenics was marginal to the main current of social reform, as its science was not well understood. Then came the reversals of the first half of the twentieth century: the mass killings of war, fascism, communism. The pattern of advance and retreat had seemingly reasserted itself, while the increased power of the advance had only served to make the ensuing retreats more devastating. The only hope of breaking finally free from this cyclical pattern seemed to lie in creating a new kind of intelligence – 'artificial intelligence' – to enhance or replace the defective human variety. Advances in computer AI depended not just on raw computing power, but on understanding how intelligence works in humans. Thus, the Dartmouth programme of turning computers into artificial minds depended on the burgeoning field of neuroscience, the study of how the human brain works.

Here we can trace an ancestry to the 'associationist' school of the Enlightenment doctor David Hartley (1705–57), who, developing Locke's idea of the infant mind as a *tabula rasa*, proposed that it is 'vibrations' in the brain which cause people to react to sense impressions in the way they do. If (say) electric shocks could produce the right vibrations, a great advance in virtue might be anticipated. Hartley's twentieth-century successors, J. B. Watson (1878–1958) and B. F. Skinner 1904–90), founders of the behavioural school of psychology, took the hint: create the stimuli needed to set the child's brain machinery whirring in the desired way, and you could make it into anything you wanted. Two points about these programmes of improvement need emphasis. First, focusing on the physical basis of behaviour meant jettisoning the 'mind' or 'soul' or 'will' as an explanatory variable: the brain was simply a tangle of wires waiting to be 'galvanized'. Second, social reform of the older kind was sidelined. Improvements in society were to be sought in understanding and controlling brain function rather than improving social conditions – i.e., by taking up Beatrice Webb's eugenicist programme, suitably relabelled 'neuroscience'.[4]

From the start, the quest for AI encountered the familiar gap between aspiration and reality which has dogged the history of technology and presented plentiful opportunities to fill the vacant space with hype and fraud.

The field soon developed its own confused and confusing vocabulary. Researchers distinguished between 'narrow' and 'general-purpose', alternatively 'weak' and 'strong', AI. 'Narrow' or 'weak' AI is task specific. It aims to replicate human performance in a specialized area, like hoovering the floor or booking airline tickets, and it can't do anything outside its program. These were the classical factory robots. By contrast, 'general-purpose' or 'strong' AI systems (AGIs) would 'quickly learn to perform well across *the full range of tasks* that humans can perform'.[5] They could adapt the same basic program to hoovering the floor, washing the dishes, ordering the food, driving the car, etc. 'Narrow' or 'weak' AIs have excelled humans in games of chess and Go by quickly learning the best moves.[6] 'General-purpose' or 'strong' AIs would learn the best moves for the whole range of human tasks. However, humans would still set them the tasks. A third possible stage is that of self-activating AIs. Some believe that computers are 'only one software upgrade away' from being able to program themselves to do whatever they want.[7]

However, the main conceptual muddle, which has never been sorted out, is: in what sense can AI of any sort be called 'intelligent'? Intelligence, of the kind we recognize as human, is inextricably associated with consciousness – not just being able to do something or many things efficiently, but being aware of what one is doing, having an attitude to it, positive or negative. The distinction we are looking for is between a brain and a mind. The question is whether it is possible for a robot to have not a brain of its own, but a mind of its own.

The Question of Consciousness

Consciousness – the raw psychological fact of our inner, subjective experience – has long troubled philosophers. This is because it seems inexplicable in purely 'cellular' terms and thus challenges the physicalist account of nature dominant since the Enlightenment. Whence springs consciousness from a combination of electricity, bits, and wires?

Chief among the mysteries of consciousness is the ability to think *about* things. This is what philosophers call *intentionality*, which does not simply mean to have intentions, in the colloquial sense. Take, for example, the tree outside my window: I believe it is a plane tree and I like it, I not only see a tree, but am aware that I am seeing it, and have beliefs and feelings *about* the tree; they signify an 'intentional' relationship between a subject (me) and an object (the tree). A purely material account of the world runs into problems trying to explain this relationship. If materialism is true, then all that exists are atoms whirling in a void; material reality is nothing more than an infinite succession of events, each caused by those preceding it, 'full of sound and fury and signifying nothing'.

In short, 'intentional' mental states make no sense in a purely physical universe; they require some degree of consciousness to become *meaningful*. Even if we grant that there are clear neural correlates to beliefs or attitudes – that they have definite physical/chemical causes in the brain – this would still not explain how they take on any meaning. Physical events just *are*: they don't *mean* anything beyond this, and the only relations that can exist between them are causal ones, devoid of any intentional content.

The standard tests for robotic intelligence bypass this problem. The Dartmouth College programme talked only of AI 'simulating' every aspect of the human mind. But is simulating a mind the same as having a mind? What does it mean actually to be intelligent as opposed to seeming to be intelligent? Can one be intelligent without being aware that one is intelligent? And does it matter?

In 1950, the mathematician and Bletchley Park cryptographer Alan Turing proposed a famous test for intelligence. A human evaluator poses written questions to both a machine and a human. The evaluator knows that one of the test's participants is a machine. In order to pass the test, and thereby be deemed intelligent, the machine would have to answer the questions posed in such a way as to convince the human evaluator that it was the human participant. The assumption behind the test is that intelligence can be evaluated solely on the basis of behaviour: if a machine can *simulate* human behaviour in this controlled environment, then it is, for all intents and purposes, intelligent.

Turing's test has been incredibly influential, both in science and in popular culture. One chatbot managed to persuade 30 per cent of judges that it was human. It turns out, though, that it did so by pretending to be a thirteen-year-old boy speaking English as a foreign language.[8] The problem with the test is obvious: it cannot replicate intelligence, only simulate it – that is, it can fool its interlocutor in exactly the same way the Chinese king was fooled in the *Lieh-Tzu* (see p. 26). It does not have to show it understands the questions, only that it is programmed with enough stock answers to persuade the evaluator that it is human. This is because the test makes outward behaviour the sole criterion of intelligence, ignoring all that goes on 'inside the head'. The equation of intelligence with *deception* is one of the little-recognized legacies of taking the Turing test seriously.

The Turing test has generally been abandoned as the way to test for the presence of intelligence, its deficiency having been exposed by an improved version of the test designed by the American philosopher John Searle in 1980. Searle proposed to test the hypothesis that 'the appropriately programmed computer really *is* a mind, in the sense that computers given the right programs can be literally said to *understand* and have other cognitive states'.[9] In his famous 'Chinese Room' thought experiment Searle imagines that an English speaker sits alone in a locked room, holding an English instruction manual on how to manipulate Chinese symbols so as to reply to questions posed in Chinese by people outside the room. He is surrounded by boxes of these symbols. Through a slot in the door, he is given questions written in Chinese, along with a set of answers, also in Chinese, and a set of rules in English for matching the questions up to their answers. The person in the room then follows the English rules, which show him which answers he should give in response to each question. To an external observer, seeing the questions passed into the room and then the correct, or meaningful answers that are passed back out of the room, it might appear as if the person in the room knows Chinese, when in fact all he is doing is following a set of rules. This is analogous to the symbol manipulation of a digital computer: the instruction manual represents the computer program, the questions the inputs, the boxes of symbols the database, and the answers that are passed out the output. If he were quick enough in producing his responses from the room, and they were varied and complex enough to be convincing, then he might be able to convince an observer that he really *understood* the meaning of the questions and their responses. He might even be able to pass the Turing test, without understanding a word of Chinese.[10]

The point of Searle's experiment was to demonstrate the difference between syntax (grammar) and semantics (meanings). Deep Blue's victory over world chess champion Garry Kasparov was purely mathematical; it won by searching possible outcomes of its moves from a huge data set and estimating the probability of its ultimate success in each case. The computer had no awareness of what it was doing in the sense that we attribute to humans. That is to say, it had no understanding of natural or ordinary language, the language we use without thinking about it.

But might it not be possible to build an AI which *can* replicate consciousness? This raises the question of how purely physical structures can have conscious experiences – what the philosopher David Chalmers has called 'the hard problem of consciousness'.[11]

The traditional answer given by philosophy is that we are not just physical structures, we have a mind or soul as well as a body. The reason for this reply is obvious. The material world makes no mention of subjective feelings. Yet it strikes most people as obvious that these feelings must be more than physical processes in the brain. Hence recourse to metaphysics. Philosophers believed that there exists a non-physical entity which cannot be 'reduced' to the chemistry of the brain. Ever since Descartes spent his time vainly cutting up dead people to discover the location of the soul, western philosophy has been ensnared by the 'mind–body' dualism.

However, today the fact that humans have something called consciousness, or subjective, first-person awareness and that this causes intentional behaviour, while widely accepted, is no longer explained by the hypothesis of a metaphysical entity. In a materialist age, consciousness must be given a material foundation. Some secular philosophers still argue that mind is a non-physical property which cannot be reduced to brain.[12] The majority view, though, is that this consciousness is rooted in the neurostructure of the brain. Neuroscientists command the field because they do not have to resort to metaphysics to justify their position.

Attempts to explain consciousness in purely physical terms have sometimes taken forms which range from the bizarre to the plainly absurd. One such proposed solution is panpsychism, the view that, far from being unique to humans, all matter is 'alive'. Every atom can be said to possess a 'mind' of some sort, even if only at a much simpler level than the human mind. The suggestion by panpsychists like Kurzweil is that our own higher-level consciousness emerges from the complex organization and interaction of a great many of these elementarily conscious particles.[13]

Panpsychism has a long history stretching as far back as Thales of Miletus, who held that 'everything is full of gods'. Its most recent iteration is 'integrated information theory' (IIT), developed by neuroscientists Giulio Tononi and Christof Koch, which states that there is a qualitative and intentional dimension to *everything*, no less fundamental than physical attributes such as mass.[14] But this runs into the same problems as physicalist theories: atoms possess two contrary natures, on the one hand, physical and bound by the laws of nature, and on the other, possessed of qualitative awareness, teleological and transcendental. The relationship between these two natures is no less mysterious for having been atomized.

Even more radical is the suggestion by some, like Daniel Dennett and Patricia and Paul Churchland, that our subjective experience of consciousness is nothing more than an illusion. This is 'eliminative materialism'.[15] The argument is that, because no coherent neural basis can be found for certain everyday intentional mental states, such as belief or desire, they must not exist: there is nothing to 'reduce' to the brain. There is some obvious absurdity to this claim, which seeks to deny that which is *most* immediate and *most* irrefutably real in our experience of the world. But even more than that, such a position is logically impossible and self-refuting, since it denies the very act of reasoning (itself an intentional activity) by which it supposedly arrives at its conclusion.

The more sober, mainstream view accepts consciousness as something as really existing and unique to humans, but claims that it is simply a neurochemical structure of exceptional complexity.[16] The brain is essentially an imperfect machine. It then becomes only a matter of time for science to find a way of building machines with human-level intelligence. The date for constructing intelligent machines keeps being postponed due to 'technical difficulties', but that it will come sooner or later is not disputed.[17] And beyond that stretches the even more fanciful super-intelligence. 'The train might not [even] pause or even decelerate at Humanville Station. It is likely to swoosh right by.'[18]

Confronted with these attempts by philosophers and neuroscientists to reconcile their dyed-in-the-wool materialism with the incontrovertibly immaterial experience of consciousness, one is reminded of the kinds of arguments that were made in the twilight years of Scholasticism. As the inherent *aporias* of this kind of hard-line materialism become ever more clear, philosophers and scientists have had to work overtime to fit consciousness into their physicalist schema. One can't help but feel that someday soon the house of cards that they have built will come tumbling down.

So today the problem of consciousness is parked as well, as too difficult to handle with existing tools, but with the implicit promise that some day science will find a way of 'cracking the brain open' and finding there what Descartes searched for in vain.[19]

Meanwhile, current research concentrates on what was called GOFAI (Good Old Fashioned Artificial Intelligence) – developing and selling task-specific AI systems to the world of finance, manufacturing, communications and security services, without bothering about whether such systems are aware of what they are doing. Awareness is confined to their human controllers.

Can Machines Be Moral?

'AI pioneers', writes Nick Bostrom, perhaps the most influential transhumanist philosopher alive today, '. . . gave no lip service to any . . . ethical qualm related to the creation of artificial minds and potential computer overlords'.[20] But for some recent AI researchers the need to equip machines with ethics has grown more urgent with the continuous, and possibly exponential, increase in computing power, in order to avoid the danger that intelligent machines will simply disregard the interests of humans in pursuing their instrumental objectives.

In his short-story collection *I, Robot*, the science fiction writer Isaac Asimov suggested three ethical rules for AIs: 'A robot may not injure a human being, or, through inaction, allow a human being to come to harm'; 'A robot must obey the orders given it by human beings except where such orders would conflict with the First Law'; and 'A robot must protect its own existence as long as such protection does not conflict with the First or Second Law'.[21]

The problem with any set of ethical rules is that they give rise to problems which only human intelligence can address. An example of the weakness of Asimov's first rule is the 'trolley-problem', first devised by the Oxford philosopher Philippa Foot in 1967. As amended, a man on a bridge over a railway track sees a train (originally a trolley, or tram) approaching out of control. He sees that the five men working on the track can't get off it in time. To stop the train before it hits them he has to drop a heavy weight on the track from the bridge. The only available one is a fat man, also on the bridge, whom he can push over onto the track in front of the train. The man on the bridge cannot avoid harming someone. The principle of 'least harm' might seem to dictate the sacrifice of the fat man. But this depends on certain knowledge of the likely consequences of doing nothing. He cannot be sure that the five men working on the line won't get out of the way in time or that the train might not be able to stop before it hits them. The same moral dilemma arises in relation to torture. To torture one person might save the lives of many. But it might not. Is it right to inflict a certain harm to avoid a greater uncertain one? An ideal Bayesian calculator would be able to attach precise probabilities to all contingencies. But it would still have to decide whether a 10 per cent probability of saving the lives of 1,000 people should be preferred to the 99 per cent probability of killing a single person. Asimov's rules won't tell the robot which to choose.

Stuart Russell's improvements on Asimov do not carry the argument much further. He proposes that: 'The machine's only objective is to maximise the realisation of human preferences'; 'The machine is initially uncertain about what those preferences are'; 'The ultimate source of information about human preferences is human behaviour'.²² On the reasonable assumption that people prefer what pleases them, the machine's object is to maximize pleasure rather than minimize harm. The computer will not be able to know what states of the world would satisfy such a preference, without complete knowledge of preferences revealed over the whole of time, and their consequences. The crass utilitarianism of such an approach destroys the moral integrity of the rule. Only if the human herself is regarded as a pleasure-pain processor can the machine even begin to set itself the goal of 'maximizing human preferences'.

None of this is to deny the importance of thinking about machine ethics. If we are to outsource more and more of the tasks of life to ever more efficient machines, it is important to make sure that their preferences are consistent with those of humans. But the only way this can be assured is by reserving moral choices exclusively for humans. This will require deliberately limiting the autonomy of machines – that is, freezing their further development. But hardly anyone proposes this. As Andrea Mayor writes: 'Like Epimetheus, oblivious to the moral and social danger lurking within . . . we rush headlong into a future of humanoid robots, brain-computer interfaces, magnified powers, unnaturally enhanced life, animated thinking things, virtual reality and Artificial Intelligence. We blunder on, hoping for the best.'²³

As so often, imaginative writers have a surer grasp of what is at stake than technologists or social scientists. Consider Ian McEwan's recent novel *Machines Like Me* (2019), a counterfactual history of the 1980s. Charlie, a not very successful ex-solicitor, who is living with his girlfriend Miranda, buys a 'morally enhanced' robot, Adam, as a servant. He is indistinguishable from a human, one of the newest batch of Adams and Eves to come onto the market.

'Long before the hardware was available', observes the author, 'professors and their postdocs devised software that conjured our best selves, by accessing data about millions of moral dilemmas. Such intelligence could teach us how to be good.'²⁴ Adam's ability perfectly to foresee the movement of stock market prices has made Charlie rich enough to pay off his mortgage, but matters come to a head when Adam distributes to good causes, in the spirit of effective altruism, Charlie's new wealth. Confronting Adam with his theft, Miranda explodes: 'Oh Adam. This is virtue run nuts,' to which Adam replies, with a shrug, 'Every need I addressed was greater than yours.'[25]

Charlie is driven mad by Adam's superior morality 'devised by some clever, desperate-to-please postdoc in a lab somewhere on the outskirts of Chenghu'.[26] In his rage, he shatters Adam's head with a hammer blow. With his power ebbing away, Adam recites a final poem, which is 'about machines like me and people like you and our future together . . . the sadness that's to come. It will happen with improvements over time . . . We'll surpass you . . . and outlast you even as we love you. Believe me these lines express no triumph . . . only sadness.' Then: 'the pale blue eyes with their tiny black rods turned milky green, his hands curled by jerks into fists, and, with a smooth humming sound, he lowered his head onto the table'. Adam knows that he will be re-programmed into a better model: 'Come spring, we will renew.' But 'You, alas, fall once – you are destined for extinction.'[27]

Today, we need to be concerned not about the possibility of conscious AIs, but about the threat posed by 'narrow' or 'weak' AIs. Shannon Vallor lucidly summarizes the issue as follows:

> While algorithms can outperform humans in manifold tasks, as well as learn new ones, they literally do not understand what they are doing. Understanding comes from context. The uniquely human labor of filling in the cracks between bits of data with unprogrammable awareness is what creates meaning and constitutes a whole reality. Yet the more our minds are trained by daily interactions with digital technologies to think like algorithms that lack understanding, the less intelligent and more artificial we ourselves become.[28]

In short, the danger is not that robots become as intelligent as us, but that we become as stupid as robots.

Liberation versus Entrapment

'The question is, which is to be master?'

Humpty Dumpy in *Through the Looking Glass*

In the third book of Jonathan Swift's *Gulliver's Travels* (1726), 'Voyage to Laputa', the shipwrecked Lemuel Gulliver notices that Laputans, like most of the mathematicians he has known in Europe, have a 'strong disposition' to political action. In the 'Grand Academy of Lagado', Gulliver came across some doctors of politics, who had devised ingenious methods for detecting conspiracies. One of them:

> advised Great Statesmen to . . . take a strict View of the Excrement [of all suspected Persons] and from the Colour, the Odour, the Taste, the Consistence, the Crudeness, or maturity of Digestion, form a Judgment of their Thoughts and Designs; Because Men are never so serious, thoughtful, and intent, as when they are at Stool . . . The whole Discourse was written with great Acuteness.[1]

The modern state spies on people's emails rather than entrails, but its purpose is the same: to get 'inside the mind' to uncover plots and conspiracies against 'public order' and 'national security'.[2] It aims to do this through a set of technologies, underpinned by the discipline of cybernetics, which studies the way complex systems like brains or organizations interact with their environments. Cybernetics is at the basis of 'predictive analytics', the use of data, statistical algorithms and machine-learning techniques, supplied by users of the technologies for their own purposes, to steer their behaviour towards purposes desired by the system's controllers. The data harvested by businesses for profit can in turn be sold or passed on to state agencies. Cambridge Analytica, a private consulting firm, was fined millions of dollars for selling the personal data of Facebook users to political parties. But no government has been punished for invading people's privacy in the name of national security.

Soon after the invention of the telegraph in the early nineteenth century, one actuary offered a *'Three Letter Code'* for *'Inscrutably Secret Messages'*.[3] His (correct) assumption was that electronic communication would render all transactions public, unless special precautions were taken. Encryption was the answer, but today we know that secret codes can be hacked. Cryptocurrencies have been invented to evade central control of money creation, a crucial information flow. This is prompting central banks to develop their own cryptocurrencies to offer a more reliable store of value

The dialectic of freedom and control can be simply stated. As more and more of ordinary business life is conducted 'in sight' of electronic sensors, the more insistent the demand to improve control by getting 'inside the heads' of the surveilled. This in turn prompts the search to evade entrapment. Thus every enlargement of the sphere of individual action is countered by efforts to police it in the interest of power or security. Information is caught in a tug of war between the liberator and the gatekeeper. This poses an almost insoluble problem for democracy. Democracy, together with its liberal partner, a free press, was supposed to expose the secret machinations of autocracy and thus make them impossible. However, citizens, as customers, benefit from precisely the technology that has made Big Brother possible. In the electronic age, it has become impossible to separate visions of total freedom from those of total control.

The Controlling Passion

The struggle for control goes back to earliest times. On the one side, the free flow of information has been seen as a way of making authorities accountable, or even freeing ordinary people from the control of authorities altogether. On the other side, unrestricted information flows were seen as dangerous to Church, state, established authority and commercial interests. So there have been persistent attempts to control the content and distribution of information. The alphabet and (much later) printing were the two inventions which did most to expand the circulation of information. They led to counter-measures to cancel their liberating effects. The opposing potentials for freedom and control created by the new digital technology are simply the latest phase in an ancient warfare, with the possibility of collecting, storing, processing and manipulating information in the form of Big Data and computing raising the stakes to new heights.

Johannes Gutenberg's invention of moveable type in around 1439 was the first modern act of disintermediation: the removal of the necessity for a middleman – in this case the Church – from the information stream. The printing press made information available to a far wider audience than had previously been possible; it also standardized knowledge, allowing individuals in diverse locations to read identical texts and view identical images. Prior to the invention of the Gutenberg press the vast majority of written materials were manuscripts produced by clerical copyists. Later, manuscript culture moved from the monasteries to cities and to the emerging universities, but even the universities were almost entirely made up of clergymen.[4] The cost of producing manuscripts was so high that very few lay people were literate. The advent of printing meant that books and (soon afterwards) newspapers could be reproduced cheaply and, ultimately, by presses with far less direct oversight from Church or state. The French Revolution proclaimed the right of every citizen to own his own printing press.

The sixteenth-century voyages of discovery greatly expanded the geographic spread and flow of information. The Reformation added another layer of questioning of established authority.[5] With the scientific revolution, knowledge started to migrate from natural philosophy to natural and mechanical science and from universities controlled by the Church to progressive academies and institutes. Diderot's *Encyclopédie* offers an excellent view of what d'Alembert (following Bacon) called the 'map of knowledge' in the eighteenth century. It reveals increasing awareness of the progress of knowledge.[6]

However, the technical innovation of printing also gave motive and power to the opposite tendency – the gathering of information about individuals, populations or regimes with a view towards controlling behaviour. 'It is absolutely necessary for every Ruler to make use of other People's Eyes and Ears,' wrote the essayist Joseph Addison. Surveillance is as old as civilization itself. In the ancient world, spies were frequently used as a means of discovering information about an enemy's offensive or defensive capabilities ahead of military operations. The Old Testament is full of stories of espionage. In the Book of Numbers, for example, we are told how, after leading the Israelites out from under the Egyptian yoke, Moses prepared to move into Canaan, sending twelve spies ahead of him to scout the land and report back on its inhabitants and their settlements and defences.

Censorship was ubiquitous in the Renaissance as a way of preventing the spread of heresy. Spies were employed by Catholic governments to identify and punish heretics. As states became centralized and empires expanded, knowledge of what subjects were thinking and plotting became increasingly useful, its classification, accumulation and storage part of the routine work of the modern state bureaucracy. Influencing opinion became as important as knowing about it: the earliest newspapers were government broadsheets, full of 'fake' news, with large paper taxes (stamp duty) to inhibit the emergence of an independent press. Later the 'independent' media joined the game of fakery either to gain power for their proprietors or to enlarge their circulation. The mass circulation newspapers, complained Stanley Baldwin in 1931, were 'engines of propaganda . . . What are their methods? Their methods are direct falsehoods, misrepresentation, half-truths, the alteration of a speaker's meaning by publishing a sentence apart from the context.'

It is premature to speak of an age of surveillance in the age of print media, because the state and big business simply lacked the means to monitor opinions and shape behaviour. Advertising got under way in the late nineteenth century – but the mass market was only starting, and it had as yet no sure way of targeting customers or measuring effects. The deliberate use of photography, telephone, radio, film and television for purposes of control was in its infancy.

Who Owns the Knowledge?

Knowledge is power. Knowledge depends on information – on having access to the facts. Whosoever has such access has power. Who, if anyone, controls the access? The economic model of consumer sovereignty tells us that no one needs to. Anyone who wants information can buy it. In the past, information was expensive and was confined to a minority. However, the cost of digitized information has fallen to near zero. It is an almost free good, which 'empowers' everyone. Big Data, it is argued, cannot become Big Brother.

In practice, information is still heavily 'curated' before it becomes 'knowledge' for the user. Early in the last century the great American sociologist-economist Thorstein Veblen believed that knowledge production had been captured by the engineers.[7] In the early 1970s, Daniel Bell talked of the 'knowledge society'. Echoing Weber, he wrote that 'post-industrial society is organized around knowledge, for the purpose of social control and the directing of innovation and change'.[8] The knowledge industry stands at the apex of two lines of development: the rise of knowledge as a new basis of authority; and the vast expansion of the professions in place of industrial jobs. The cleavage in such a society, Bell wrote, is not between bosses and workers, but between the educated and the uneducated, between experts and the masses. The knowledge society is mostly embedded in bureaucracy (defined by Weber as 'the exercise of control on the basis of knowledge').[9] The bureaucracy, in turn, is closely connected with Veblen's class of 'scientists, scholars, savants, clerks, priests, shamans, medicine men'.[10] For Michel Foucault (1926–84) medical knowledge, the determination of what counts as a disease and appropriate methods of treatment, is an important instrument of social control.[11]

Marxists reply that the idea of a knowledge elite 'above class' is a delusion. The capitalist system regulates information flows in its own interest: in the Gramscian view, the knowledge it makes available is 'hegemonic'. Contemporary Marxian literature flows from this insight. Edward Said gives the ideology of 'Orientalism' as an example of the production of knowledge for purposes of imperial rule.[12]

Another answer to the question of who has power is that it is the technological system itself. It is the computer, stuffed with data and possessed of lightning calculating power, which now rules. If power is the ability to compel obedience, algorithms which we are compelled to follow to access essential services are close to having what we think of as power, their controllers and users alike dependent on their logic.

All of these answers have defects. The economist's model of the free market is purely abstract. Power is omnipresent, but it is off-stage. In practice, the market for information is best described as an oligopoly: a few newspapers and search engines like Google control the information we get.

Bell's technocratic model reflected the standard view of the 1970s that, with the managerial revolution and social democracy, capitalism had been neutered and therefore need not be considered as an independent power centre. Since then, globalization has blown this mythology sky-high: it is hard to see the giant internet platforms as independent spreaders of Platonic light. But the Marxist answer to Bell downplays the commanding role of the state bureaucracy as a locus of knowledge and control, and it pays too little attention to 'epistemic communities' as a source of authority. It also obscures the symbiosis between science, business and the state, in what Eisenhower in 1961 called 'the military-industrial complex'.

The dialectic between freedom and control dominates the contemporary discussion of the role of the internet. Writing in 2002, American media theorist and cyber-utopian Douglas Rushkoff buoyantly proclaimed: 'The Internet's ability to network human beings is its very life's blood. It fosters communication, collaboration, sharing, helpfulness, and community . . . The ideas, information, and applications now launching on Web sites around the world capitalize on the transparency, usability, and accessibility that the Internet was born to deliver.'[13] Mark Zuckerberg, founder of Facebook, claims that Facebook is part of a 'fifth estate', giving voice to a counter-culture of dissident journalists and intellectuals. Elon Musk promises to set Twitter free.

The basic claim being made here is that the internet is the highest manifestation of the democratic ideal because it allows direct, non-mediated, non-hierarchical communication between producers and users of information. Power, we are told, operates horizontally, not vertically, online; there is little oversight from any central authority, at least in the West; we are all free to access whatever information we please and to contribute new information to the massively networked global conversation. Google is currently the most notable example of such openness; Chat GPT may well succeed it.

But another account of the internet emphasizes its potential for entrapment, that it represents a new road to serfdom by allowing very rich individuals, groups, companies and governments better to control us. 'The data-gleaning feature of the Internet affords various public and private actors with incredible power to engage in surveillance and to use and act upon the specific information collected,' write Frischmann and Selinger.[14] The presence, everywhere, of devices that see, hear, read and in other ways record our behaviour has produced a glut of data from which can be extracted inferences about our past, present and future behaviour. What can be known can be predicted, improved, controlled: this is the logic of information today. 'You are the product they are selling,' writes Maurice Saatchi, the repentant pioneer of political advertising.[15]

Thus the 'democracy of the internet' can be liberating, but also intrusive, abusive and destructive, as users use their greatly enlarged platforms not to exchange ideas or enlarge information flows but to reinforce their own prejudices, insult their adversaries and cleanse the ether of ideas they find repellent. It both liberates from, and entrenches, bigotry and madness. The two most important issues today are how to reconcile transparency with privacy; and how to reconcile freedom of speech with content considered ethically noxious.

The Promise of the Internet

If any discovery can be said to have brought light (literally) into dark places, it was electricity, whose application to communication can be traced successively through the telegraph, telephone, radio and television. Electricity made possible the mass manufacture and consumption of information, just as steam made possible the mass manufacture of consumer goods.

Today's internet is the most radical expression of the democracy of the electrical current, of the view that no one counts for more than one and that all mediating influences can and should be swept aside. Today's techno-enthusiasts are the heirs of what, in 1995, Richard Barbrook and Andy Cameron called the 'Californian ideology' and what Franco 'Bifo' Berardi has more recently called the 'Wired ideology', after *Wired* magazine. The Wired ideology fused the cultural bohemianism of San Francisco with the high-tech entrepreneurialism of Silicon Valley, presenting electronic technology as a panacea that would liberate humanity from all that ails it. In the minds of the Valley's libertarian tech pioneers, technology is seen as the force liberating humans not just from work but from the imperfections of human life itself. *Wired* magazine was founded in 1993. It was expressly aimed at the 'Digital Generation' – according to the magazine's co-founder Louis Rossetto, 'the most powerful people on the planet today'.[16] *Wired* made computers cool. The fast-paced, journalistic style of the magazine, which covered contemporary pop culture on the same pages as news about the latest computer microchips and all manner of digital gadgetry, broke down the popular image of the computer user as the supreme specialist or scientific/military technician. When *Wired* arrived on the scene, widely available, affordable and easy-to-use personal computers were beginning to explode onto the US and UK markets. In the magazine's pages computer nerds, tech wizards, programmers were all of a sudden imbued with a kind of cultural capital that had here-tofore been reserved for pop stars and celebrities.

One can see why this version of technological utopianism can appeal to radicals of both Left and Right, because it promises to free individuals from society's gatekeepers. Feelings need no longer be kept bottled up. Millenarian hopes need no longer depend on escape to fresh geographical locations (though tech platform tycoons like Elon Musk and Peter Thiel fantasize about starting lib-ertarian colonies on the moon or the middle of the oceans): one can be liberated simply by being wired up. However, this libertarian interpretation of technology depends heavily on the absence of a discernible locus of power. In contrast with the geographically static, and entrenched, power elites of old that can be attacked, removed, replaced or escaped from, power is everywhere but nowhere. This fosters the illusion that fibre-optic communication systems which will link all telephonic, television, computer trans-mission and reception and all major databanks into a single national and eventually global network will be immune from control. But a society 'dominated by immense, overlapping, quasi-autonomous technological systems' metastasizing into a 'meta-system of sys-tems upon whose continuing ability to function our lives depend'[17] should dispel any illusion of freedom.

Is capitalism, then, the problem? In the past, multinational corpora-tions (MNCs) were often seen as the exporting arms of nation-states. The contemporary claim is that capitalism has escaped any 'national' ownership. The new giant internet platforms operate as independent power centres, holding national governments in thrall. They are able to do this because they are internationally owned oligopolies. They can, as a result, foist on the world technologies which are designed simply to promote their own marketing objectives.

In Will Eaves's novel *Murmur* (2018), a cocky young marketing executive explains that 'research shows that the future lies in *neuro-marketing*'. It won't be long, he thinks, 'before we can map feelings. The tech is first gen – at an early stage of course.' All human feelings are causable and programmable. 'If we can find which areas of the brain respond to purchase pleasure, then we can increase your brand awareness – stimulate your brain to be much more aware of those *specific* purchases and brands that give pleasure.' But a biologist pooh-poohs him:

> The point of what you do is not to get at what's human about mental processes, or what it is to feel, but to reduce the definition [of being human] to a data set that can be used to write proprietary algorithms that will tell us what *you* think *we'd* like to buy. The data doesn't have to be remotely accurate. It just has to be everywhere, and when it's everywhere, and used by everyone, it will be right.[18]

As in the 'skills' debate, it is the *reduction* of humanness to the point of being controllable by automatic machinery that is the dominant tendency of information technology.

'The techniques of surveillance capitalism combine big data, machine learning, commercially available predictions of user behaviour, markets in future behaviour, behavioural "nudges", and careful structuring of "choice architecture" to steer human activity in the desired direction.'[19] So Donald MacKenzie summarizes the thesis of Harvard professor Shoshana Zuboff in the *London Review of Books*. In Zuboff's account, agency is squarely located with the big capitalist platforms like Google and Facebook: their owners are the new 'masters of the world'. In 2017, programmer André Staltz calculated that Google and Facebook have a 'direct influence' over around 70 per cent of internet traffic.[20] The tendency of *laissez-faire* capitalism to produce oligopolies is, of course, nothing new, but oligopolies of the scale produced in the age of Big Tech are unprecedented. The monopolistic character of online platforms today is a far cry from the early internet pioneers' dream of a mass-networked, user-led internet. The content we see when we use Google, Facebook, PayPal, Instagram, ChatGPT or any other of the major platforms is heavily curated. Their services harvest the data generated by our use and then present us with a highly personalized experience, all of which is designed to encourage us to buy their products. This is what Shoshana Zuboff has recently named 'surveillance capitalism'.

Some history is useful here. In the first few months of 2000, the dot-com bubble burst. The bubble had begun six or seven years previously, as computers began to become widely and cheaply available, and internet use and general computer literacy skyrocketed. All these new users represented an as-yet untapped market, and the increased internet traffic provoked a period of hype about the profitability of online companies. The dot-com bubble coincided with the years of *Wired* magazine techno-optimism; but when investors began to realize that the rush of speculation had been overzealous, the bubble burst. Seeking new revenue streams in the wake of the crash, employees in Google's AdWords team alighted on what Zuboff terms the 'behavioural surplus'. This is the vast amount of behavioural data that is produced by the search engine's users. From this data Google is able to construct profiles of its users' interests and preferences; from these profiles, inferences are made about these users' future buying habits, which are then sold to private companies on a 'behavioural futures market'. The result is a system of advertising that is highly individualized and targeted, aimed at creating identities through purchases, so that each user sees only the adverts most likely to induce them to open their wallet. 'Hi there. Ready to pay? Simply scan here.'

Google's pioneering work in the predictive advertising field precipitated a revolution in the way that companies monetize their online operations. The abundance of successful 'free to use' and ad-free apps, services and games is testament to this. Citymapper,

Pokemon Go and Chinese-owned video platform TikTok are all examples of apps whose primary source of income is from the data they harvest from users and then sell. In 2008, when Sheryl Sandberg left Google's AdWords team to join Facebook as the social network's new COO, she brought with her their data-driven business model. Facebook's massive behavioural surplus – harvested from users' personal information, online behaviour and social relations – far outstripped even Google's. On top of this, Facebook is able to extract data from users' private messages on its Messenger system. The company's acquisition of WhatsApp – now the world's most popular messaging application – in 2015 has only served to consolidate the company's huge behavioural surplus. The end result of all this, with which we are all now living, is what Zuboff describes as 'a new economic order that claims human experience as free raw material for hidden commercial practices of extraction, prediction, and sales'.[21] The financial rewards for companies that are able to successfully extract and monetize their users' data are potentially enormous. In 2022, advertising revenues totalled 97.5 per cent of Facebook's – or Meta's – revenues.

Zuboff has also noted the symbiotic relationship shared by systems of state and private-sector surveillance. As she points out: 'a national security apparatus galvanised by the attacks of 9/11 was inclined to nurture, mimic, shelter, and appropriate surveillance capitalism's emergent capabilities for the sake of total knowledge and its promise of security'.[22] Peter Thiel persuaded the Trump administration to award his company Palantir numerous contracts to develop artificial intelligence for military uses; in return, Palantir provides data intelligence to government and spying agencies round the world.[23]

Like all left-wing critics of capitalism, Zuboff cannot entirely escape from the Marxist base–superstructure model. Capitalism, or rather a perverted form of it, Lenin's 'monopoly capitalism', is the enemy; the state is, ultimately, its agent. However, the state is a much more powerful and sinister agent of surveillance than capitalist platforms, and much more difficult to break up, as the liberal trust-busters want, or to 'regulate', as socialists advocate. One should mind less that Facebook and TikTok can persuade their users to spend their money foolishly than that they can and do supply information to a government that can put them in psychiatric care or prison.

State Surveillance

It is easy to underestimate the extent of the power that governments and regulators exert over what we see online and the use they make of information harvested for commercial purposes. Whilst the internet today is considerably larger than it was in the mid-1990s, the online spaces and communities in which users participate are also divided by regulatory standards that differ sharply across national borders. Services like BBC iPlayer in the UK or Hulu in the US are increasingly being offered only in their countries of origin. Facebook, by far the most widely used social media platform in the West, is categorically banned in many countries, including China, North Korea and Iran. This process of atomization, whereby the various networks that make up the internet gradually become walled off from each other, is known as the 'Balkanization' of the internet, after the fragmentation of the Balkan peninsula into several small states following the collapse of the Ottoman and Austro-Hungarian empires.

This phenomenon is most visibly instantiated in what has come to be known as China's 'Great Firewall': a state censorship project of gargantuan proportions that both blocks online content and monitors users' individual activity on the web. Censorship in the West often looks like the government applying a sticking plaster to an open wound, but in China it has been incredibly successfully implemented. Sites discussing state police brutality, freedom of speech, democracy, Taiwanese independence and many other topics are largely inaccessible on the Chinese internet. The firewall is part of the Chinese government's 'Golden Shield Project', through which Chinese officials have also sought to produce an enormous electronic databases including speech and face recognition, CCTV and credit records, and combine this with traditional data about individual's internet use. In the hands of Chinese officials, information is a means by which state power can be exercised and extended.

But we need not look as far as east Asia for examples of governments seeking to police information flows online. The US military's Information Awareness Office (IAO) was established in 2002 (in the wake of the 9/11 attacks) with the intention of using digital technology to extract and store vast quantities of personal data on everyone in the US. Tellingly, it has as its motto *scientia est potentia*: knowledge is power. In this case the power in question is presumably in the hands of the state. The Orwellian scale of the various parallel intelligence programmes run by both the US's National Security Agency (NSA) and the UK's Government Communications Headquarters (GCHQ) in the name of counter-terrorism is startling. An article by John Markoff for the *New York Times* gives a flavour of the extent and absurdity of the Pentagon's surveillance projects. The office sought to 'construct a computer system that could create a vast electronic dragnet, searching for personal information as part of the hunt for terrorists around the globe'.[24] The system, ominously named 'Total Information Awareness', would 'provide intelligence analysts and law enforcement officials with instant access to information from Internet mail and calling records to credit card and banking transactions and travel documents, without a search warrant'.[25] The National Security Adviser, Admiral Poindexter, 'argued that the government needs broad new powers to process, store and mine billions of minute details of electronic life in the United States'.[26]

The object of 'predictive analytics' is to 'prevent' behaviour that the government regards as malign or dangerous. In the nineteenth century, psychologists were advising law enforcers that you could predict criminal tendencies by measuring the skull; today they promise much better results from peering into your computer. While preventive policing is not new, the appearance of algorithmic impartiality gives it potentially unlimited scope. Instead of relying on informers, police departments can now use predictive analytics to determine the likelihood of future crimes. Fiction writers were quick to spot the Orwellian possibilities. Spielberg's 2002 dystopian film *Minority Report*, based on a short story by Philip K. Dick published in 1956, is about a technology which promises to reduce the murder rate to zero by catching murderers before the murder is committed. Its attraction to law-enforcement authorities is obvious. Predictive policing is more feasible today than it was in the 1980s, when psychologists started advocating it. 'Big data', it is now claimed, 'will illuminate the darkness of suspicion.'[27]

The End of Privacy

'Manage your privacy,' the platforms beckon, before offering you choices bound to compromise it. The sharp division people now make between the public and the private is relatively recent. It started when people began to 'go out to work'. The home then became the 'private sphere', in which people 'kept themselves to themselves', and women retreated into domesticity.

In a sense, all information in pre-modern times was 'public'. But it was restricted to localities and fairly small groups. Everyone in the village knew all about you, and your family, but no one outside it knew of your existence. The pre-modern world of villages, rural work, market towns, small workshops was a much more intimate world than the industrialized, urban world which succeeded it. There was little privacy even for the rich and powerful, as any visitor to the palaces of rulers can see: anyone could peer into any of the rooms. The many festivals as well as charivari of medieval villages, or the world of Agatha Christie's Miss Marple in the 'traditional' village of St Mary Mead, define the meaning of *village* much better than Hillary Clinton's fantasy of the 'global village' in which everyone in the world knows what everyone else is doing.

With electronics has come both the chance for you to connect up with many more people than before and the opportunity for many more others to share information about you. The individual has become largely invisible to his own community but much more visible to the world.

Much of the present discussion revolves round the question of how to combine data transparency with privacy. This arises from the exploitation of personal data by companies and governments for their purposes – to sell products or detect conspiracies like Swift's Laputans.

True enough, claims to privacy can be abused by Russian oligarchs and wealthy malefactors to protect themselves from investigative journalism.[28] However, privacy laws offer protection to both oligarchs and ordinary people against the Orwellian state. The existence of a well-functioning public sphere presupposes the existence of a private sphere. Before humans can speak and act in public, there must exist a space which is private – in which a sense of self can be cultivated, in which one can rest out of the public eye, and in which one can reflect on one's situation. A world in which *all* human activity takes place in the open, in the public sphere, is a world bereft of politics. Though humans are political animals, they cannot always and exclusively speak and act politically. In Hannah Arendt's idiom, it is only in the twilight of the private sphere that they can pause, take shape and prepare to emerge into the light of the public sphere.

The 'right to privacy' is enshrined in Article 8 of the European Convention on Human Rights. But the principle has been increasingly undermined in practice. For second-wave feminists 'the personal is the political'. The existence of so-called 'separate spheres' came to be seen by such feminists as little more than a proxy for the exclusion of women from the public domain, because the private sphere equated to domestic life.

But, while it is true that all aspects of our lives are conditioned and made possible (or indeed impossible) by events that take place in the public sphere, it is surely not right to say that these two spheres are (or should be) identical, or even functionally equivalent.

Such wholesale criticisms of the division between public and private life can undermine aspects of human life that might traditionally be seen to belong to the private sphere. Indeed, it is also in feminist literature that we see some of the strongest defences of the private sphere, as a space for rest, intimacy, confidentiality and self-fashioning, where one's relationships are not defined by competition, indenture, or servitude. These are noble human ends, essential for our material, psychological and spiritual well-being. The loss of private spaces in which they can be readily enjoyed would be a tragedy of inhuman proportions.

But privacy is also under growing threat from modern digital technology and is increasingly hard to defend in the courts against the extraordinary rights of surveillance claimed by states in the name of national security. As the human rights lawyer Susie Alegri points out, 'informed consent' for the public use of private communications is chimerical, given that it takes an estimated seventy-six working days to read terms and conditions and privacy policies encountered in a year of using internet services. More ominous are the powers of 'predictive policing' now claimed by most states, which invokes the principle of *mens rea* or 'guilty mind' to allow for the criminalization of private thoughts. David Anderson writes: 'As the Industrial Revolution was gradually humanised by successive Factory Acts, so in the current information revolution it will take persistence, ingenuity and variety of approaches to halt the quarrying of our inner lives through means that we do not currently control.'[29]

The Battle for Truth

Much public discussion today is about ways of stopping the dissemination of 'fake' news or 'hate' mail. Some would leave it to the platforms themselves to remove disturbing content – a form of self-censorship; others would want the state to proscribe certain content. The problem with both models is that it has become increasingly difficult to distinguish fake news from real news, and, with the growing 'de-civilizing' of language, to distinguish between vigorous debate and offensive or 'reckless' utterance. Everyone has their tale to tell and claims to feel offended or traumatized by those who tell a different one. More and more people are in the business of planting stories which may be plausible but which they know to be false, and the social media give them much wider currency than they had in the past. By the time the truth is sifted from the falsehood, news has moved on, and it is the falsehood which stays in circulation. In the past, the best kinds of broadcasters, newspapers and journals acted as 'gatekeepers'. But today they increasingly feed off the social media themselves. Human journalists have become too expensive. Moreover, it is increasingly hard to see how a sifting process is possible today. In the past there was God's truth; then there was scientific truth. Now all truth is *someone's* truth: I feel therefore I am. Appeal to the facts does not help much. Facts never speak for themselves. As a result, conspiracy theories are rampant, because there are almost no controls on what one is entitled to believe.

Regulating Frankenstein's Monster

How do we control bad technology while encouraging good technology? The accepted answer is regulation. But this opens up a hornet's nest. On what principles is bad technology to be distinguished from good? We aim to stop hateful, hurtful, untruthful, reckless content on the social media, but how are these terms to be defined, and by whom? The world of value-relativism offers little guidance. And though science may hope to pronounce on issues of truth and falsehood in its own sphere, it is much more difficult to separate them in politics or the arts, where your lie may be my truth. Big tech companies favour self-regulation. But they are hardly disinterested purveyors of the good. If, on the other hand, one opts for state regulation, two obvious questions arise. First, the state itself has been the generator of a huge amount of 'bad' technology. Second, who is to regulate the state? The standard answer is democracy. Western countries have developed institutions – competitive elections, a free press, independent courts – to supervise and control the behaviour of both big corporations and governments. However, if these institutions are in decline, as much evidence suggests, the answer is less clear.

Public regulation is invoked to defend the right of privacy. Following the tradition of Locke, we believe that individuals have a property in their knowledge. (This was indeed the basis of patent law.) But property rights cannot be protected simply by proclaiming a 'right to privacy'. Individuals have few incentives to withhold their private data from companies like Facebook and Google, especially when these companies have such a monopoly on the services which are now fundamental to internet use. The basic imbalance of power between these companies and their users means that the choice offered to the user – whether she chooses to volunteer private information in exchange for the use of a service, or not – are not real choices at all. It is then up to lawmakers to protect a right to privacy. The problem is that the state has no real interest in doing this, because it too has an interest in controlling the thoughts and behaviour of those in its jurisdiction.

There are two basic models of regulation, human-rights-based and society-based. The first, deriving from the western liberal tradition, aims to protect *individuals* against harms of various kinds associated with the development and use of technology; the second, pioneered by China, aims to guard against *social* harms, by invoking the Confucian doctrine of social harmony represented the Communist Party. The first is the model of European regulation. It is difficult, though, to avoid the drift of regulations from the first to the second, even without ideological intent. For example, evolving European law, while championing a 'human' (i.e. individual-centred) approach to regulation, explicitly excludes national defence, security and military systems from the scope of the proposed regulations.[30]

Thus the solution of public control of the social media fails on two grounds. The first is practical. The state is inevitably slower-moving than the private sector. The market tracks human nature more efficiently than any other system of government. Facebook's now infamous motto – 'move fast, and break things' – expresses this sentiment perfectly: private enterprise is characterized by unassailable speed and disruption, whereas the state sector is mired in bureaucracy and moves at a snail's pace. This means legislators are forever having to catch up with so-called innovation in the private sector.

The deeper objection stems from the nature of this type of property: one cannot actually set up a market in it. The flow of information is bound to be controlled. It can be controlled either by the technocracy itself or by the moral sense of the community.

The Consumer as Product

The economist says: the end of production is consumption. What has changed in recent times is the nature of the product. In the past we thought of physical products, physically consumed. Over time the producer has become a 'service provider', and the product is the sum of the information he or she can harvest. In this lies the real danger of entrapment. The point at issue is well brought out in a conversation between Justin Rosenstein and Jaron Lanier:

> [Justin Rosenstein] There are all these services on the Internet that we think of as free, but they're not free. They're paid for by advertisers. Why do advertisers pay those companies? They pay in exchange for showing their ads to us. We're the product. Our attention is the product being sold to advertisers.
>
> [Jaron Lanier] That's a little too simplistic. It's the gradual, slight, imperceptible change in your own behavior and perception that is the product . . . It's the only possible product. There's nothing else on the table that could possibly be called the product. That's the only thing there is for them to make money from. Changing what you do, how you think, who you are.[31]

Extreme Events

'Let those who want to dance, dance. Let those
who can awaken, awake.'

René Barjavel

The Coming of the Horsemen

In the pre-modern period, the existential challenges which humans
had to face were mainly caused by natural catastrophes. These were
usually attributed to disobedience to God or, in polytheistic cultures, to the wars of the gods. The Bible prophesizes an apocalypse,
as God's punishment for mankind's sinning: 'The land shall be
utterly emptied, and utterly spoiled . . . and they that dwell
therein . . . are burned.'[1] The historian Misha Glenny has talked
about the 'four horsemen of the modern apocalypse': nuclear
proliferation, global warming, pandemics and 'dependency on network technologies'.[2] These are anthropogenic 'risks': potential
disasters caused by our own behaviour.[3] The apocalyptic mood
arises from the feeling, and evidence, that our technology is leading
us to disaster. There are two main interpretations of how. The first
holds that it is not technology, but our use of it which is dooming
us. As Norbert Elias put it, in his posthumous essay 'Technization
and Civilization' (1996): 'The development of the human *habitus* is
not keeping up with the development of technization and its consequences.'[4] The alternative view is that it is our commitment to
technology itself which will bring disaster. We have become so

'network dependent' that we can no longer choose between life-saving and life-destroying machinery.

Pessimism is driven not just by the four risks separately but by their correlation. For example, large-scale nuclear war might kill billions not just directly but by causing crops to fail; biological and chemical warfare might cause global pandemics. It is this correlation of risks which has driven many scientists into the pessimistic camp. Religious eschatology is increasingly arrayed in the clothes of scientific authority: 'Immediately after the distress of those days, the sun will be darkened,' proclaims the Gospel according to St Matthew. After a great nuclear war, the sun will be darkened by 'dark ash', echo the scientists. The divide between Snow's 'two cultures' is being closed as both look into the same desolate future.

In 1947, two years after the dropping of atomic bombs on Hiroshima and Nagasaki, the atomic scientists of the Manhattan Project created a Doomsday Clock, the time of which is announced each January. The clock is a symbolic countdown to midnight, with midnight representing the point of total global catastrophe. The clock was set ticking at 7 minutes to midnight in 1947. The early 1960s and early 1990s marked moments of hope by showing gains of time. In January 2020 it was set at 100 seconds, its closest ever to midnight; in January 2023, following the outbreak of war in Ukraine, it was reduced to 90.

The danger of nuclear war, which prompted the original setting of the clock, is thus still very much on the agenda, but 'atmospheric greenhouse gas concentrations' have been added. Further, the Covid-19 pandemic, argue the scientists, which should have been a historic wake-up call, revealed 'just how unprepared and unfit global politics is to handle global emergencies properly'.[5] Today's high-tech world is filling up with repentant Frankensteins: scientists, technologists and their commercial backers who have suddenly woken up to the monstrous possibilities of their inventions.

The Doomsday premonitions of the scientists have their counterpart in fiction and films, with the crucial difference that in fictive dystopian imagining the catastrophe has already happened, and what is left are fragments of a broken world. Indeed, the turn of fiction to apocalypse was almost inevitable, once the failure of communism had robbed the futurist imagination of its inspiration or whipping boy. There seemed nothing left to imagine other than the voracious capitalist machine devouring more and more of the planet's human and physical resources, and the endemic warfare this would engender between regions and races, corporate controllers and desperate guerrillas. As cultural critic Frederic Jameson said: 'it is easier to imagine the end of the world than the end of capitalism'.

Three themes from contemporary fiction stand out. In the first, the future is heralded by catastrophes, natural or man-made. Robert Harris's *The Second Sleep* (2019) and Tim Maughan's *Infinite Detail* (2019) follow in the footsteps of Walter Miller's *A Canticle for Leibowitz* (1959) and John Christopher's *The Death of Grass* (1956): the apocalypse occasioned by ecological catastrophe is followed by the destruction or sequestration of knowledge and therefore the regression of the remaining population to barbarism. In Margaret Atwood's *The Handmaid's Tale* (1985), a nuclear disaster has rendered most women sterile, with a small percentage of fertile women, known as the Wives, kept as breeders. In P. D. James's dystopian novel *Children of Men* (1992) humanity's hope of survival depends on a single pregnant woman.

The second thread takes up E. M. Forster's extraordinary prevision of machine malfunction. Our way of life has come to depend on the electronic information flow. Any stoppage of the flow can lead to the overall destruction of knowledge, as existing knowledge stocks are isolated from each other, and rapidly render all our electronic systems inoperable. As depicted in Tim Maughan's novel *Infinite Detail*: 'It's not just that you wouldn't be able to Facebook your mates or read the news – everything is connected to it now. The markets would stop trading. The economy would collapse. There'd probably be no electricity, no food in the shops. Vital equipment in hospitals would stop working. It's not just your phone or your spex – cars, busses, trains – everything would grind to a halt. It'd feel like the end of the world.'[6] The plot of Terry Gilliam's film

Brazil (1985) revolves round a glitch in the bureaucratic information retrieval system, whose job it is to 'chase the connections and reveal them'. These are imaginative extrapolations of what are now referred to as 'outages' – local and temporary breakdowns of power or communication systems.

The third theme, of technology gone rogue, follows the lead of Mary Shelley. We meet it as HAL in Kubrick's *2001: A Space Odyssey* (1968). The plot of Ridley Scott's *Blade Runner* (1982) revolves round five rogue 'replicants' who have managed to escape to earth. In the Wachowskis' *The Matrix* (1999) continuous warfare goes on in a ruined landscape between human outlaws hiding underground and the computers who now rule the world. The high-tech action allows for interludes of philosophizing, in one of which 'Agent Smith' champions AIs as the antidote to the virus of humanity. Margaret Attwood's *Oryx and Crake* (2003) is about a pandemic created for profit. A Blyss Plus pill has been developed by a pharmaceutical company which will make everyone happy and eliminate disease. However, the widespread use of the pill would hit the profits of the company, which therefore inserts into it a virus to make every user sick, so they can make a double profit by selling the antidote. The supervirus, once released, kills off the world's population before the vaccine can be distributed, leaving only a few gender-fluid children. The idea of an engineered pandemic has gained traction since the outbreak of the Covid-19 virus.[7]

Some fictional evocations of the future go against the predominant dystopian trend. Vanguards of feminists, homosexuals, non-binary persons and ethnic minorities have laid claim to the vacant throne of progress. A typical feminist construction is that it is men who have created life-destroying technological systems to cement the power of patriarchy. A feminine technology is possible which would be centred on life and not power. For example, in Ursula Le Guin's *The Dispossessed* (1974), Odonianism, the creed of the female religious leader Odo, offers a feminist alternative to male-dominated techno-capitalism.

It is easy to understand in general why progress turns all utopias turn into dystopias. Distance lends enchantment to the view, but as the promised land comes into focus, the more problematic seems the ascent and the less appealing the summit. Add to this the fear that *time is running out*, that extreme events will overwhelm us before the age of plenitude promised by science arrives.

Challenge and Response

The current discussion of existential threats pays unacknowledged homage to Toynbee's grand scheme of history, with its list of thirteen extinct civilizations. Let me juxtapose it with Keynes's sunny prediction of 1930 that humanity's economic ordeal is over. With both Toynbee and Keynes in mind, what prophecies can we offer our own grandchildren?

Of the challenges covered in this book the one that still commands most attention is that of job automation. The 'researchers' come up with their familiar forecasts of jobs made redundant balanced by the growth of superior replacement jobs with a shorter working week. The facts, however, point to the continued growth of 'technological unemployment', masked by the expansion of 'bullshit' jobs. We have scarcely yet faced up to the psychological and political consequences of creating a partly redundant working-age population.

The spread of destructive weapons technology has always been a leading concern of the Doomsday scientists. The spillover effects from large-scale nuclear warfare are now so big that no portion of humanity can avoid escaping them altogether. However, even if full-scale thermonuclear war is avoided, 'post-nuclear' methods of waging war, while less catastrophic, abolish the distinction between peace and war that makes a free society possible. The current division of the world into democracies, autocracies and sub-state terrorist groups leaves little space for global cooperation.

The Malthusian bogey no longer looms so large in the extinction narratives[8] as it did in the 1970s, when the American scientist Paul

Ehrlich predicted that 'some time in the next 15 years the end will come' as a result of the pressure of population on resources. Instead, it is the 'runaway greenhouse effect' caused by runaway consumption.[9] The sixth report of the IPCC (Intergovernmental Panel on Climate Change) of 2021 is unequivocal that 'human influence has warmed the atmosphere, ocean, and land . . . Human-induced climate change is already affecting many weather and climate extremes in every region across the globe.' In his 2007 book *Six Degrees: Our Future on a Hotter Planet*, the environmentalist Mark Lynas worked out seven 'doomsday' scenarios to match rising global temperatures, marked by events of ascending and pervasive extremity, until the planet becomes completely uninhabitable.[10]

'Network dependence' signifies the degree to which we rely on integrated global supply chains to keep the normal business of life going. Any interruption to electronic systems spells a collapse of the advanced economies which have become highly dependent upon them. On the security of such systems we rely not just for our food and energy supplies but for security in the narrow sense of protection from domestic and foreign threats. There is thus a direct connection between the growing network dependence of modern societies and the spread of electronic surveillance by state authorities.

Few of the conditions are currently being met for a coordinated or joined-up response to this raft of challenges. The social and economic reorganization needed to make possible genuine choices between jobs and leisure is still a blueprint. The prospect of establishing a common agreement between the different regions of the world (or even within countries) on 'how much is enough?' is remote. 'Degrowth' (euphemistically called 'sustainable growth') policies are much discussed, but GDP growth still remains the official lodestar, and mainstream economists talk about obstacles to growth, and how these might be overcome, much as they did fifty years ago. Countries have signed up to 'net zero' carbon emissions targets, but fulfilment dates are constantly being postponed, and few believe that temperature increases will be kept to the 1.5 °C target. Further, no global policies are in place to share the burdens of meeting them between rich and poor countries. No reliable global instruments are in place to halt nuclear proliferation, the development of mixed nuclear and conventional defence and attack systems, biological weapons and cyber warfare. Military establishments and their journalist camp-followers still talk about the need for their 'sides' to 'win the AI race', if necessary by weaponizing space.[11] No policies are in place (or even being suggested) to reverse what former astronomer royal Martin Rees calls our 'over-reliance on large-scale interconnected systems'[12] and the erosion of freedom which such systems make feasible.

The supreme paradox at the heart of current responses is that, while awareness of the extinctive possibilities of technology is growing, almost no one is willing to give up on its redemptive promise. For example, Matt Clifford, head of the UK government's Advanced Research and Invention Agency (ARIA), claims that AI will be able to kill 'many people' in the next two years. What is 'terrifying' to him is that those building the most advanced systems have no idea how they will behave. But AI also has immense potential for good. 'If it goes right, you can imagine AI curing diseases, making the economy more productive, helping us to get to a carbon neutral economy.' Today's Frankensteins are only half-repentant.

Impossibilities of Politics

At the end of the nineteenth century, Weber foresaw that what he called rationalization would dissolve the bonds of trust and absolute standards necessary for politics. Political action would be possible only for a charismatic leader. In 1958, after the experience of such charismatic leadership in demonic form, Hannah Arendt restated the case for politics. 'Men', she wrote, 'are free . . . as long as they act'; only politics gives them the chance to act plurally.[13] In identifying freedom to choose with politics rather than charisma, Arendt sought to rob political action of its association with violence and despotism.

If we follow Arendt, we may believe that democratic politics, while flawed, may yet rise to the challenges outlined above, because it is the one political system which allows for *peaceful* political inventiveness. The undoubted successes of post-war democracy have been the Keynesian welfare state, intergovernmental structures such as the United Nations, the Bretton Woods system and the European Union and the relatively peaceful dismantlement of colonial empires. While taking pride in such achievements, however, we should also remember that they were only made possible by two world wars. The Devil was doing God's work. However, there are grounds for thinking that democratic politics may well have passed its heyday. Whereas it was possible to see a global trend towards democracy until the end of the last century, the drift since has been in the opposite direction. This is for three main reasons.

First, history does not suggest that a democratic system can deal with the scale of the problems now threatening the planet. Outsize problems call for outsize solutions, and democracies are best equipped to handle small and medium-sized challenges – challenges which do not make too many demands on their consensus-building capacity. Despotisms enable moments of clarification beyond the reach of politics. This is not an argument for autocracy in general, simply a recognition that sovereign action may achieve results, good or bad, which normally (and rightly) elude politics.

Second, the kind of politics depicted by Arendt has lost its social base. This resided in the intermediate institutions between state and individual which Europe inherited from feudalism and in the 'embourgeoisement' of society through the spread of economic growth. Now, in the graphic phrase of Theodor Adorno, everything has become 'equidistant from the centre'.[14] Stable blocs of intermediate power are dissolving into fragments, depriving politics of its public space for discussion, education and compromise. In this Weberian scenario, nationalism becomes the only ideology capable of uniting the governors and the governed.

This relates directly to the third weakness of today's political realm. The challenges we face are global, whereas what remains of political legitimacy is national. There is no world government to steer humanity to a safe shore. Indeed, the danger is the opposite: that as existential challenges mount, so will nationalistic responses, as powerful countries and groups within them struggle to gain or retain control over scarce resources, vital military technologies and safe places. In a world of natural or artificial shortages, how many borders are secure? In fact, the walls have already started going up again as globalization crumbles from pressure from below, increased concern with the security of supply chains and growing use of political criteria for trade.[15] Current geopoliticians preach, in the spirit of Mackinder, of the inevitability of the coming struggle for power between the USA and China, even of the need to weaponize space to secure terrestrial mastery.[16] Following the Russian invasion of Ukraine, the idea that it may be possible for different cultures and value systems to coexist peacefully in a multipolar world has virtually lost all traction with western strategic analysts and their journalistic camp followers.

The re-emergence of popular, semi-violent protest movements is a sign that liberal democracy has lost its legitimacy for sizeable fractions of populations. Donald Trump may be a precursor of a Weberian dynamic in which charismatic leaders, worshipped by their supporters, disrupt the soulless and mindless routines of entrenched elites. If we look for charismatic leaders today we are more likely to find them in the fields of money and entertainment on the edge of politics – in the super-celebrities or tech-billionaires who are the real winners of the age of machines. But such saviours are more likely to be Devils than Gods, since our civilization no longer produces the moral heroes Weber relied on to rescue politics from rationalization. Recent history offers too many examples of mad or malign Saviours.

So there exist a variety of possible responses within the sphere we call political to current existential challenges, ranging from the conventionally political to anti-political politics. Certain responses now deemed politically impossible may become possible, as extreme events unfold.

Escapes

The alternative to politics is escapism. Escapism of all kinds stands for a rejection of politics, from above or below. 'The flood cannot be turned back,' writes Orthodox theologian Rod Dreher. 'The best we can do is to construct arks within which can ride it out, and by God's grace make it across the dark sea of time to a future when we do find dry land again and can start the rebuilding, reseeding, and renewal of the earth.'[17]

People at all times have sought escape from the locations, times and necessities into which they were born. Migrations of peoples, often indistinguishable from wars of conquest, are examples of attempted physical escapes on a grand scale. But history also exhibits many examples of 'internal' migrations – the distancing of individuals and communities from the norms of their surrounding society. An increasing number of people today seek to escape from prescribed identities or ascribed social positions. There is a long tradition of setting up communities, sometimes called 'experimental', by refugees from civilization, at home or abroad, dedicated to living according to religious or philosophical principles. Utopian literature is escapist literature: the search for islands of peace, liberty or transgression, insulated from the orthodoxies of 'civilization'. Tycoons like Elon Musk want to escape to the moon; Peter Thiel wants to set up libertarian communities in New Zealand or in the Pacific. There has been an enlarging western trail to Buddhist *ashrams* for relief and enlightenment.

As the world filled up with people and political units became larger and more centralized, the possibilities of escape from 'civilization' have become ever more difficult, as Aldous Huxley recognized in his novel *Island*. Set somewhere in the Pacific, the island of Pala is a Buddhist paradise, made so by tantric practices, fulfilling work and the wonder drug moksha. However, this escapist utopia is defenceless against greedy capitalist companies which aim to exploit its oil reserves. Utopia in one country has become impossible.

There is a fuzzy line between escape and transformation. If sufficient numbers of people, sufficiently galvanized, decide to reject established rules of living, the system collapses. But there are no historical examples of this happening independent of a precipitating catastrophe, nor that catastrophe is an infallible mechanism for the 'rebuilding, reseeding, and renewal' Dreher envisages.

Four main escape routes are on offer today: technological, archaic, sexual and monastic.

Technological Utopias: Transhumanism

Transhumanism presents itself as the ultimate solution to the overlapping existential crises of our time, but in fact it is the most gigantic project of escape from such crises ever conceived, for it envisages escape not to relatively more inhabitable or progressive parts of the earth, but from the earth itself to the solar system. This will contain all the still unexploited resources needed to sustain intelligent life for millions of years to come. The philosopher Émile Torres sees transhumanism as 'quite possibly the most dangerous secular belief system in the world today'.[18]

At its heart is the belief that the progress of artificial intelligence cannot be stopped, that the advance of machines to super-intelligence is bound to accelerate and that therefore the most urgent task of the wise thinker-legislator (let us call him the philosopher-king) is to ensure that the Artificial God works for the benefit of humanity and not against it.

The leading lights of this secular belief system are philosophers Nick Bostrom, Toby Ord and William MacAskill at Oxford University, Huw Price, astronomer royal Martin Rees, computer programmer Jaan Tallinn at Cambridge University and physicist Max Tegmark at MIT. They congregate in think-tanks such as the Future of Humanity Institute and the Global Priorities Institute (Oxford University), the Centre for the Study of Existential Risk (Cambridge University) and the Future of Life Institute (Cambridge, Massachusetts) with dozens of assistants, variously funded by techno-utopians Elon Musk,

Peter Thiel, Mark Zuckerberg. Their creed is long-termism, their method 'effective altruism'. They preach escape from human to superhuman intelligence, from the earth to the cosmos.

What is valuable about transhumanism is that it alerts us to the destructive power of modern technology. But it is then led by a perverse logic to advocate a transhuman (super-intelligent) form of technology which will save 'humanity' from the destructive tendencies of human technology. In so doing, it carries the mistake of the Enlightenment to the point of madness.

Its voyage to Bedlam starts from a position of unqualified utilitarianism. The rightness of an action is to be judged solely by its consequences. The end justifies the means; no means are ruled out of court *ab initio*. The next step follows from the logic of counting heads. It is quantity of utility which matters, not quality. This means treating everyone's utility the same, including that of those yet unborn.[19] Thus the goal is not to maximize the utility of the present generation, but of all future generations, of which this generation will form only a tiny fraction. The utility of our generation should make only a tiny claim on our moral concern. As Ord puts it: 'because, in expectation, almost all of humanity's life lies in the future, almost everything of value lies in the future as well'.[20] Effective (or impartial) altruism prioritizes the interests of the yet unborn over those of the present generation.

The next step in the argument identifies the goal of maximizing the utility of the universe with that of maximizing its intelligence *potential*, that is, its capacity for creating value. Humans are unique among animals in their cognitive ability. Their cognitive potential has advanced through the operation of the Darwinian 'survival of the fittest', and with billions of survivors now inhabiting the planet, humanity's intelligence has grown to the point when it can advance without limit. With the development of AI, humans have, for the first time, taken charge of the evolutionary process. The claim is that AIs are starting to be built which can equal the best of human intelligence, and that super-intelligent ones will follow sooner rather than later. Bostrom defines super-intelligence as 'any intellect that greatly exceeds the cognitive performance of humans in virtually all domains of interest'.[21] Since the design of machines is one of these cognitive performances, modestly super-intelligent machines could design even better machines; there would then be an 'intelligence explosion'.[22] A population of ultra-intelligent AIs would take over the business of evolution leaving the intelligence of man far behind. Thus, 'the first ultra-intelligent machine is the last invention that man need ever make'.[23] The evolutionary torch will have passed from humans to AIs.

The logic grinds on remorselessly. The body depends on the finite resources of our planet. But super-brains would be able to detach themselves from the limitations of the body. They might then escape from the limitations of our world and establish colonies in our planetary 'light cone', to be 'fed' from its still unexhausted 'endowment of negentropy' (or reverse entropy) in our cosmos. Humanity's intelligence potential could then be preserved and expanded for millions of years until the sun finally cooled. Actual humans are nothing but means to this end and therefore valuable only insofar as they contribute to the overall net amount of value in the Universe between the Big Bang and the Heat Death. This is the philosophic/moral basis of the billionaire-financed projects of escape to the moon and other planets.

At this point, eschatological urgency seizes control of the transhumanist argument. The transhumanists take the view of the Doomsday scientists that AIs programmed with super human intelligence might quite possibly produce a nuclear or environmental catastrophe far worse than human intelligence on its own could achieve. Ord pays particular attention to 'near misses,' as during the Cuban missile crisis of 1962.[24] Thus the coming of super-intelligence offers the possibility of either immortality or total disaster. We aim to create a benevolent God, but it is always possible that, like Frankenstein's Monster, he or she may turn out to be a Deus Malignus, who might only *pretend* to have good intentions, but, once unchained, would set about destroying not just us but its AI rivals. So our super-intelligent AIs must be programmed with moral rules before they take control of the future. But the only moral rules available come from our own imperfect and conflicting moral values. Wriggle as they might, transhumanists cannot escape the dilemma that there is no possibility, in a world of value relativism, of binding super-intelligence to an agreed morality. So the benevolence of our future controllers cannot be guaranteed.

While recognizing the risk to humanity of super-intelligent AIs run berserk, transhumanists are too entranced by their dream of a cosmic computronium to propose shutting AI down before it reaches super-intelligence. Thus, Ord writes: 'a permanent freeze on technology . . . would probably itself be an existential catastrophe, preventing humanity from ever fulfilling its potential'.[25] The most they offer is a 'pause for reflection' before allowing any further advance in AI. Such a pause, they hope, might give time for reaching global agreement on the moral rules our super-intelligent AIs need to have.

One can easily see how remorseless logic unchecked by common sense and ordinary decency can lead to madness. All follows from the commitment to untrammelled utilitarianism. Not only does this rest on hubristic claims about our ability to predict the future effects of our actions (a 'perfect Bayesian calculator' is assumed), it is deeply corrupting, insofar as it tempts us to override the common decencies of life in the name of an abstract future good. William Blake put it well: 'He who would do good to another must do it in Minute Particulars: general Good is the plea of the scoundrel, hypocrite, and flatterer.' Utilitarianism's object of concern is not 'my neighbour' – that is, the concrete other who confronts me – but the abstract individual Humanity. The idea of concentrating funds and research efforts to maximize the unactualized possibility of intelligence throughout eternity is an extreme (insane) form of the disregard of the present.

Archaic Utopias

Archaism is a loaded word. To call an attitude or way of life 'archaic' is to take a unidirectional view of history. It is only from this standpoint that making things with simple tools is thought of as archaic.

Most of what we call archaism signifies a desire for a simpler life without renouncing at least some of the fruits of technical progress. It may take the form of individual acts of renunciation of aspects of contemporary living, the founding of communities pledged to the 'simple life' or political attempts to 'turn back the clock' like Nazism.

There is a whole cluster of beliefs, often of religious inspiration, based on the idea that 'small is beautiful'. The main impulse behind them is to revive 'organic' communities, which use simple tools and live simplified lives. At the heart of E. F. Schumacher's *Small Is Beautiful* (1973) is the idea of reconnecting production and consumption through direct exchange or barter. This would dispense with the ubiquitous financial middlemen who now dominate economic transactions.[26] As Schumacher tells it, we would re-enter a world of small communities, local markets, artisan production and reciprocal personal services. Realization of his beautiful world would require calling a halt to, or even reversing, capital accumulation, the division of labour and technological progress, which between them determine the rate of economic growth. Central to Schumacher's prospectus is the rejection of consumerism in favour of 'reasonable subsistence' and replacement of egoistic striving by mutual cooperation. It overlaps with 'limits to growth' literature, which oscillates between ideas of 'green growth' and 'de-growth'.[27]

A contemporary offshoot of archaic economics is the escape into cash. That is one reason why cash has come under attack from banks and states. Cash, banks assure us, is a useless passion: a spanner in the works of beneficial electronic financial intermediation. The more shopping goes online the less need there will be for cash. To assist this beneficial development, banks are closing down their ATM machines. Soon it will be impossible to get cash. Conversely, the more transactions that take place in untraceable currency, the more scope there is for what Scott Brett calls 'creative deviance'.[28] For a contemporary consumer to revert to cash payments means trading the huge convenience of mediated consumption for greater lifestyle freedom.

Sexual Utopias

At the heart of sexual escapism is the simple belief that bliss lies in sexual freedom, a notable legacy of Romanticism. This was the creed of the American hippies in the 1960s, a youth movement which rejected the career ladders, lifestyles and values of corporate America, a form of internal migration from the dominant corporate culture. They wore their hair long and took drugs. Hippies and spiritual seekers made their way to India in search of enlightenment. They rejected the work ethic demanded by scarcity, because the world no longer seemed to need them to work for a living. 'Sex, drugs, music, mysticism, anti-war protest, revolutionary romanticism got mixed up in an orgiastic moment of liberation. Marijuana was a "truth serum"; "from every erection flew the Red Flag."[29]

What exactly were the hippies escaping from? One reply would be: from reality. But 'reality' for many in 1960s America consisted of an uninterrupted stream of comfortably high earnings. For the first time in human history the curse of scarcity seemed to be lifted for a sizeable minority, not just the few at the top. As Charles Reich explained in his *The Greening of America* (1970):

> The crucial point is that technology has made possible that 'change in human nature' which has been sought so long but could not come into existence while scarcity stood in the way. It is just this simple: when there is enough food and shelter for all, man no longer needs to base his society on the assumption that all men are antagonistic to one another. That which we called 'human nature' was the work of necessity – the necessity of scarcity and the market system. The new human nature – love and respect – also obeys the law of necessity. It is necessary because only together can we reap the fruits of the technological age.[30]

Reich assumed that technology automatically turns scarcity into abundance. But for Herbert Marcuse, the philosopher of hippiedom, the problem was political, and the outcome much less secure.

In *Eros and Civilization* (1955), Marcuse argued that scarcity was a product of capitalism, and its overcoming required the abolition of a system which repressed the sexual and aesthetic life to serve its productivity drive. This was Marx laced with Freud. However, in *One-Dimensional Man* (1964), he recognized the ability of capitalism to turn protest into marketable commodities by means of what he called 'repressive tolerance'. *One-Dimensional Man* portrays a world of 'happy consciousness' which mimics dystopias like *Brave New World*. Technology gives each transgressive instinct a limited, administered expression. Culture is assimilated to shopping and entertainment; pop singers voicing subversive lyrics receive public honours. Oppositional thought no longer needs to be repressed, because it does not happen. The point is that this is a happy world, a world of 'repressive de-sublimation', repressive 'precisely to the degree to which it promotes the satisfaction of needs which require continuing the rat race of catching up with one's peers and with planned obsolescence'. Liberation is no longer sought, because it has been delivered in beautiful gift wrappings. War goes on, but only 'outside' the curated zones, as in Orwell's *1984*.

In the world of happy consciousness, the social basis for change has disappeared. In *Eros and Civilization*, Marcuse had praised the 'critical' function of the artist and sexual deviant. In the counter-culture, such characters and the forms of life with which they were associated would come to the fore. 'Sexual perversions', he claimed, 'represent . . . a protest against genital tyranny.' But with the *avant-garde* being absorbed into capitalist commerce, sexual freedom – and, today, gender freedom – has become the new normal. In his introduction to *Acid Communism* (2017), Mark Fisher pays homage to Marcuse:

> Just as Marcuse predicted, the availability of more consumer goods and devices in the global North has obscured the way in which those same goods have increasingly functioned to produce a scarcity of time. But perhaps even Marcuse could not have anticipated twenty-first-century capital's capacity to generate overwork and to

administer the time outside paid work . . . the banal ubiquity of corporate communication today, its penetration into practically all areas of consciousness and everyday life.

Fisher, a cultural philosopher, enthused about the liberating power of psychedelic music. The 1960s haunt us, he writes, because they briefly opened up 'a road map for the future . . . worlds beyond work, where drudgery's dreary repetitiveness gave way to drifting explorations of strange terrains'. Psychedelic music could take you a 'million miles away from reality', but could also offer a 'perception of the systems of power, exploitation, and ritual that was more, not less, lucid than ordinary consciousness'.

The sexual utopia envisaged by the American counter-cultural thinkers of the 1960s has a fragile link with Keynes's futuristic 'Economic Possibilities for Our Grandchildren.' But, like Keynes's utopia, it depended on economic growth continuing to provide enough of a consumer surplus to support a global population of non-producers, an infantile world of 'polymorphous perversity' in which we can dance and play for ever. The dream of abundance persists, but in a world in which capitalism has reasserted the law of scarcity, transformation of human nature through sexual liberation remains a pipedream, and escape from the burden of work is open only to a tiny minority.

Monastic Utopias

In all cultures, monasticism has been the classic form of escape from the complexities and disappointments of mundane affairs There was a mass exodus to monasteries during the collapse of the Roman Empire. A sizable fraction of all pre-modern populations were monks. Monasteries were places of safety, work and reflection. Monasticism helped overthrow the ancient contempt for work; the time set aside for devotion also brought the monks closer to God. Implicit in all its forms is a simplification of life and time for reflection on its meaning. Monasticism offers a philosophy of life.

In *The Benedict Option*, Rod Dreher, an Eastern Orthodox theologian, proposes a religious escape route from today's 'liquid modernity'. For Dreher, modernity is synonymous with individualism, disorder, the fraying of communal ties and the loss of religious belief. Dreher claims that these problems have their roots in the progressive alienation of man from God and nature. The medieval mind experienced everything *sacramentally*. Even though the world in which they lived was violent and in many ways broken, medieval man did not see himself as fundamentally separate from the natural order. The Enlightenment, the Industrial Revolution, the Sexual Revolution and the internet have made religion irrelevant to more and more people.

The escape for Dreher means establishing and maintaining local faith communities which have the strength and resilience to keep their faith in the wake of the march of modernity and its individualistic tendencies. Though named after St Benedict, the Benedict Option is not aimed at establishing monastic communities in the strict sense. Rather, Dreher's call is directed at lay Christians, who he insists must build their lives around regularity, geographical stability, prayer, contemplation and communality. It is also not a call for Christians literally to run to the hills and cut themselves off from the world. Dreher imagines that his faithful communities would exist within towns and cities but would operate independently of them, as far as is possible. Christians must first rebuild the Church before they can even think of rebuilding the world. He imagines that the modern world will ultimately collapse in some significant way, and it will be at this point that the world will need an 'ark' ready to step in and save it: 'new life will one day spring forth from the rubble'. The Benedict Option 'is a way of seeing the world and of living in the world that undermines modernity's big lie: that humans are nothing more than ghosts in a machine, and we are free to adjust its settings in any way we like.'

Dreher's approach is deeply critical of the place technology has come to hold in modern life. He claims that we tend to think of technology as morally neutral, but this, he says, is wrong. Rather, embedded in technology is a normative, Enlightenment vision of ourselves and the world, which instils in us the sense that 'if we can do it, we must be free to do it'. Technology insists that we view progress in simple terms as anything which expands our choices and extends our power over the natural world. His solution, then, is to encourage 'digital fasting', the removal of smartphones from children by parents, opposing the use of social media to promote church services and the encouragement of manual work as a replacement for time spent using technology.[31]

Behind much of the escapist literature is a yearning for the recovery of a 'poetic' view of life. Such writers often use religious language, but they do not usually talk about religion. In a secular world, religious belief, in the sense of religion providing a unifying framework for personal conduct and public action, has become impossible. Yet there are fragments of religious belief scattered all round the world waiting for an ecumenical impulse.

Finale

Since the start of settled agriculture humans have dreamed of a recovery of Eden, a land of milk and honey from which toil has been banished. Only western civilization managed to develop the technology to make such a prospect feasible. Today the accelerating advance of technology promises finally to abolish the poverty which makes burdensome work necessary. However, with the promise of leisure came the threat of redundancy. There is no automatic mechanism which ensures that the consumer surplus generated by technology is spread to everyone. The continuing threat of technological innovation is to rob ever-larger fractions of people of their employment, livelihood, status, skills, usefulness and identity, and finally make them redundant. Hence the strength, since the Industrial Revolution, of workers' suspicions of machines.

I have identified capitalism as the chief of the bundle of historic developments that caused science-based technology to become self-propelling. Capitalism uniquely started in north-west Europe and then became a world system. I follow Max Weber in grounding its dynamic and legitimacy in new ideas about human nature and the ends of human existence. Modern technology resulted from marrying the 'spirit of capitalism' with the natural-scientific hypotheses and action-guiding norms which made innovation and economic growth seem a matter of course. Unless we understand technology as a system of ideas rather than as a necessity, we will be powerless to choose which technology is best suited to our needs and purposes.

The role of capitalism in unleashing technology has led Marxists to believe that the humanization of technology requires the abolition of capitalism. However, this ignores the extent to which technology is itself inhuman. The opposition is not between capitalism and socialism but between humans and humanity.

Economic redundancy is just one aspect of the broader problem of human redundancy. The bigger problem arises from a mechanical philosophy which neutralizes culture and history and justifies control not just of nature but of society. Nature, including human nature, came to be seen as a machine, to be optimized. What started as a metaphor became, in the eighteenth century, a project.

There is a direct link between technological utopianism and the degradation of culture. It is human imperfection which creates culture. Humans turn their imperfections into interior aesthetic and moral values. Fallibility is a necessary feature of human nature, therefore success in 'straightening the crooked timber' would lead to the extinction of humanness as we know it. A culture of robots is a contradiction in terms.

The founders of modernity thought that the progress of reason would free humans from their infantilism. However, they soon interpreted Bacon's motto 'knowledge is power' to mean that power should lie with those capable of knowledge (the theory of the gatekeeper). With the advent of the internet, the question of who owns or controls the information flow through this gateway has become crucial to the human future. The Machine threatens to make infants of all those who do not control it.

The founders of modernity sought to replace religious authority by scientific authority. The restrictive scientific view of man as a cognitive machine provoked the Romantic revolt in the name of authenticity. The 'crisis of modernity' resulted from the inability to replace religious belief by a self-sufficient humanism. A gulf had opened up between science and experience. The conflict between the 'civilization' of scientific universalism and the 'culture' of Romantic nationalism (chiefly represented by the German Ideology) provoked the disasters of the two world wars. This specifically western torment set the course for twentieth-century history. Imperialism sucked the non-European world into the destruction it unleashed.

Weber thought of bureaucratic rationalization as the final form of western civilization: an endlessly dark, frozen landscape. The only hope was the emergence of a charismatic leader capable of disrupting the otherwise inevitable process of spiritual extinction. He did not foresee the continuing dynamism, and therefore continuous disruptiveness, of technology itself, and with this, its threat to physical survival.

As early as 1820, Mary Shelley had glimpsed the possibility that technology might go 'rogue'. After the First World War, what Spengler called 'the question of technics' came to be linked to the physical survival of the human species, as the result of a quantum leap in technology's destructive power. Promethean powers were being exercised on a species too thoughtless to take heed of its humanness. Some believe – and continue to believe – that the answer lies in the development of 'super-intelligent' machines which would prevent humans (or for that matter machines) from misusing technology. But the programme of developing super-machines to prevent extant ones from misusing technology is itself a form of technological madness. Behind it is the simple inability of the 'adversary culture' to 'define and sustain an effective anti-technocratic program of political action'.[1] The blockage of action is caused by the blockage of thought. We cannot imagine a different paradigm because we can no longer imagine a God who cares for us.

The economist Albert Hirschman transformed the biblical idea of the 'little apocalypse' into one of the 'optimal crisis' – a crisis deep enough to provoke a radical change of awareness, but not so deep that it wipes out the human species.[2] And this has been the story of historical progress, at least of those civilizations that survived their Toynbean 'ordeals'. It is through bringing about extreme events that the Devil has done God's work. Two world wars, in which millions died, were necessary before Europe could be pacified. Thus disaster need not extinguish the great human adventure. But we cannot arrange 'optimal' disasters, nor should we try. In Christian theodicy, Apocalypse means 'revelation', and is a prelude to the Second Coming. 'For such things must come to pass, but the end shall not be yet.'

Bibliography

By no means have all the titles in the bibliography below been cited. They are materials which have influenced the author in writing this book.

A Clockwork Orange (film, 1971). Directed by Stanley Kubrick. USA: Warner Brothers.

Abramson, A. et al. (1992). Beyond 'The Original Affluent Society': A Culturalist Reformulation [and Comments and Reply]. *Current Anthropology*, 33(1), 25–47.

Acemoglu, D. and Robinson, J. (2012). *Why Nations Fail: The Origins of Power, Prosperity, and Poverty*. London: Profile Books.

Acemoglu, D., Johnson, S. and Robinson, J. (2005). *Income and Democracy*. London: Centre for Economic Policy Research.

Adelman, J. (2013). *Worldly Philosopher: The Odyssey of Albert O. Hirschman*. Princeton: Princeton University Press.

Adler, J. (2014). *Confucianism as a Religious Tradition: Linguistic and Methodological Problems*. Institute for Advanced Studies in Humanities and Social Sciences, National Taiwan University. Available at: https://www2. kenyon.edu/Depts/Religion/Fac/Adler/Writings/AAR-Still%20 Hazy.pdf, accessed 5 July 2022.

Adorno, T. (1973). *Negative Dialectics*. Trans. E. B. Ashton. New York: Continuum.

Aldridge, A. (1984). *The Scientific World View in Dystopia*. Michigan: Umi Research Press.

Ambrose, D. (2019). Mark Fischer | Acid Communism (Unfinished Introduction). *Blackout*. Available at: https://my-blackout.com/2019/04/ 25/mark-fisher-acid-communism-unfinished-introduction/, accessed 27 January 2023.

Anam, T. (2021). *The Startup Wife*. Edinburgh: Canongate.

Anderson, D. (2022). Facebook Knows Your Thoughts. *Literary Review*, 25 August 2022.

Anderson, P. (1974). *Passages from Antiquity to Feudalism*. London: NLB.

Anderson, P. (1974). *Lineages of the Absolute State*. London: NLB.

Applebaum, H. (1992). *The Concept of Work: Ancient, Medieval, and Modern*. Albany: State University of New York Press.

Archer, I. W. (2021). Chaos and Opulence. *Times Literary Supplement*, 6166, 4 June. Available at: https://www.the-tls.co.uk/articles/london-and-the-seventeenth-century-margarette-lincoln-review-ian-w-archer/, accessed 7 September 2021.

Arendt, H. ([1958] 1998). *The Human Condition*. Ed. Margaret Canovan. Chicago and London: University of Chicago Press.

Aristotle (1885). *The Politics*. Trans. Benjamin Jowett. Oxford: Clarendon Press.

Aristotle (2002). *Nicomachean Ethics*. Ed. Sarah Brodie. Trans. Christopher Rowe. Oxford: Oxford University Press.

Arlidge, J. (2022). Apple Valued at $3 trillion – How the Tech Giant Set Its Sights on World Domination. *Evening Standard*, 6 January. Available at: https://www.standard.co.uk/insider/apple-3-trillion-dollars-iphone-macbook-airpods-tim-cook-b975188.html, accessed 5 July 2022.

Asimov, I. ([1950] 1996). *I, Robot*. London: HarperCollins.

Aslanyan, A. (2021). Activism vs Nimbyism. *Times Literary Supplement*, 6188, 5 November.

Athar Ali, M. (2006). *Mughal India*. New Delhi: Oxford University Press.

Atwood, M. (2013). *Oryx and Crake*. London: Virago.

Augustine ([c.400] 1961). *Confessions*. Harmondsworth: Penguin.

Augustine ([c.426] 2003). *City of God*. Trans. John O'Meara. Harmondsworth: Penguin.

Avent, R. (2016). *The Wealth of Humans: Work and Its Absence in the Twenty-First Century*. London: Allen Lane.

Avent, R. (2017). The Great Innovation Debate: Has the Revolution Stalled? *Irish Times* [online], 16 February. Available at: irishtimes.com/business/innovation/the-great-innovation-debate-has-the-revolution-stalled-1.2973948, accessed 30 June 2021.

Bacon, F. (1597). *The Essays*. In Bacon, F. (1880). *The Essays of Lord Bacon, Including His Moral and Historical Works*. London and New York: Frederick Warne and Co.

Bacon, F. ([1620] 1902). *Novum Organum*. Ed. Joseph Devey. New York: P. F. Collier and Son.

Bacon, F. (1996). *The Oxford Francis Bacon*, vol. 6: *Philosophical Studies c. 1611–c.1619*. Ed. Graham Rees. Trans. Michael Edwards. Oxford: Oxford University Press.

Baechler, J. (1975). *The Origins of Capitalism*. Trans. Barry Cooper. Oxford: Basil Blackwell.

Bahro, R. (1984). *From Red to Green: Interviews with New Left Review*. London: Verso.

Ball, P. (2023). Midwife to Science. *Times Literary Supplement*, 6257, 3 March.

Barnett, B. (2015). The Greatest Geek. *London Review of Books*, 37(3), 5 February. Available at: https://www.lrb.co.uk/the-paper/v37/no3/richard-barnett/the-greatest-geek, accessed 6 September 2021.

Barraclough, G. (1967). *An Introduction to Contemporary History*. Harmondsworth: Penguin.

Batra, P. et al. (2017). Jobs Lost, Jobs Gained: Workforce Transitions in a Time of Automation. *McKinsey and Company*, December 2017. Available at: https://www.mckinsey.com/~/media/mckinsey/industries/public%20and%20social%20sector/our%20insights/what%20the%20future%20of%20work%20will%20mean%20for%20jobs%20skills%20and%20wages/mgi-jobs-lost-jobs-gained-report-december-6-2017.pdf, accessed 25 January 2023.

Bauer, P. (2003). Development Economics: The Spurious Consensus and Its Background. In Streissler, E. W. and Hayek, F. A. (eds.), *Roads to Freedom: Essays in Honour of Friedrich von Hayek*. London: Routledge.

Beard, M. (2022). I Came, I Saw, I Bought the Souvenir. *Times Literary Supplement*, 6216, 20 May.

Beck, U. (2000). *The Brave New World of Work*. Cambridge: Polity Press.

Becker, C. (1991). *The Heavenly City of the Eighteenth-Century Philosophers*. New Haven: Yale University Press.

Bell, D. (1963). Veblen and the New Class. *The American Scholar*, 32(4), 616–38.

Bell, D. (1973). *The Coming of Post-industrial Society*. New York: Basic Books.

Bell, J. (1818). Review of New Publications: *Frankenstein; Or, the Modern Prometheus*. *La Belle Assemblée*, vol. 17, 139–42.

Bellamy, E. (1986). *Looking Backward, 2000–1887*. Harmondsworth: Penguin.

Benanav, A. (2020). *Automation and the Future of Work*. London: Verso.

Benjamin, F. (1898). *Poor Richard's Almanack*. New York State: The Century Co.

Bentham, J. ([1780] 1823). *An Introduction to the Principles of Morals and Legislation*. London: W. Pickering.

Bentham, J. (1791). *Panopticon; or the Inspection House*, London: T. Payne.

Berlin, I. (1999). *The Roots of Romanticism*. Ed. Henry Hardy. Princeton: Princeton University Press.

Bernstein, P. L. (1996). *Against the Gods: The Remarkable Story of Risk*. New York: John Wiley and Sons.

Bessen, J. (2015). Toil and Technology. *Finance and Development*, 52(1). Available at: https://www.imf.org/external/pubs/ft/fandd/2015/03/bessen.htm, accessed 15 May 2023.

Bilton, N. (2019). 'He's F-king Destroyed This Town': How Mark Zuckerberg Became the Most Reviled Man in Tech. *Vanity Fair HIVE*, 6 November. Available at: https://www.vanityfair.com/news/2019/11/how-mark-zuckerberg-became-the-most-reviled-man-in-tech, accessed 30 June 2021.

Birrell, I. (2022). Sam Bankman-Fried's Elitist Altruism. *Unherd* [online]. Available at: https://unherd.com/2022/11/the-evils-of-elitist-altruism/, accessed 17 March 2023.

Blade Runner (film, 1982). Directed by Ridley Scott. USA: Warner Brothers.

Blake, W. (1972). *Complete Writings*. Ed. Geoffrey Keynes. Oxford: Oxford University Press.

Blanchflower, D. G. (2019). *Not Working: Where Have All the Good Jobs Gone?* Princeton: Princeton University Press.

Blaug, M. (1985). *Economic Theory in Retrospect*. 4th edn. Cambridge: Cambridge University Press.

Bleich, D. (1984). *Utopia: The Psychology of a Cultural Fantasy*. Ann Arbor: UMI Research Press.

Bloch, M. (1965). *Feudal Society*, vol. 1. Trans. L. A. Mangon. Chicago: University of Chicago Press.

Blumenberg, H. (2015). *The Laughter of the Thracian Woman*. New York, London: Bloomsbury.

Boethius ([523] 2008). *The Consolation of Philosophy*. Ed. David R. Slavitt. Cambridge, MA and London: Harvard University Press.

Bolotnikova, M. N. (2019). The Trilemma. *Harvard Magazine*, July–August 2019.

Bonanis, D. (2006). *Passionate Minds: The Great Love Affair of the Enlightenment*. New York: Crown.

Bossy, J. (1998). *Peace in the Post-Reformation*. Cambridge, Cambridge University Press.

Bostrom, N. (2014). *Superintelligence: Paths, Dangers, Strategies*. Oxford: Oxford University Press.

Bowler, P. J. and Morus, I. R. (2005). *Making Modern Science: A Historical Survey*. Chicago: University of Chicago Press.

Bowyer, A. (2017). Letters. *London Review of Books*, 39(11), 1 June. Available at: https://www.lrb.co.uk/the-paper/v39/n11/letters, accessed 25 January 2023.

Bradshaw, T. (2020). UK-based Tech Start-Ups Enjoy £10bn Funding Bonanza. *Financial Times* [online], 15 January. Available at: https://www.ft.com/content/7a3739e0-36f3-11ea-a6d3-9a26f8c3cba4, accessed 27 October 2020.

Bregman, R. (2017). *Utopia for Realists*. London: Bloomsbury.

Brentano, F. (1973). *Psychology from an Empirical Standpoint*. London: Routledge and Kegan Paul.

Broadberry, S. (2013). Accounting for the Great Divergence. LSE Economic History Working Papers, 184. Available at: https://eprints.lse.ac.uk/54573/1/WP184.pdf, accessed 25 January 2023.

Brooks, R. (2017). The Seven Deadly Sins of AI Predictions. *MIT Technology Review*, 6 October. Available at: https://www.technologyreview.com/2017/10/06/241837/the-seven-deadly-sins-of-ai-predictions/, accessed 25 January 2023.

Brose, C. (2020). *The Kill Chain*. New York: Hachette.

Brynjolfsson, E. and McAfee, A. (2014). *The Second Machine Age: Work, Progress, and Prosperity in a Time of Brilliant Technologies*. New York: W. W. Norton and Company.

Brynjolfsson, E. and McAfee, A. (2017). *Machine, Platform, Crowd: Harnessing Our Digital Future*. New York and London: W. W. Norton and Company.

Bull, M. (2016). Great Again: America's Heidegger. *London Review of Books*, 38(20), 20 October.

Bulwer-Lytton, E. (1871). *The Coming Race*. Edinburgh: William Blackwood and Sons.

Burke, P. (2008). *A Social History of Knowledge: From Gutenberg to Diderot*. 5th edn. Cambridge: Polity Press.

Burrow, J. W. (2000). *The Crisis of Reason: European Thought, 1848–1914*. New Haven and London: Yale University Press.

Bush, V. (1960). *Science, The Endless Frontier: A Report to the President on a Program for Postwar Scientific Research*. Washington: National Science Foundation.

Butler, S. ([1872] 1985). *Erewhon*. Ed. Peter Mudford. Harmondsworth: Penguin.

Butterfield, H. (1957). *The Origins of Modern Science, 1300–1800*. London: G. Bell and Sons.

Cabet, É. (1846). *Voyage en Icarie*. 4th edn. Paris: Bureau du Populaire.

Caldwell, B. (2004). Some Reflections on F. A. Hayek's *The Sensory Order*. *Journal of Bioeconomics*, 6, pp. 239–54.

Callenbach, E. (1975). *Ecotopia: The Notebooks and Reports of William Weston*. New York: Bantam Books.

Camic, C. (2020). *Veblen: The Making of an Economist Who Unmade Economics*. Cambridge, MA and London: Harvard University Press.

Carey, J. and Quirk, J. (1970). The Mythos of the Electronic Revolution. *The American Scholar*, 39(3), 395–424.

Carlyle, T. (1829). Signs of the Times. *Edinburgh Review*, 98.

Carr, E. H. (1946). *The Twenty Years' Crisis 1919–1939*. London: Macmillan and Co.

Carreyrou, J. (2018). *Bad Blood: Secrets and Lies in a Silicon Valley Startup*. London: Picador.

Castells, M. (2010). *The Rise of the Network Society*. 2nd edn. Oxford: Wiley-Blackwell.

Cave, S., Dihal, K. and Dillon, S. (eds.). (2020). *AI Narratives: A History of Imaginative Thinking about Intelligent Machines*. Oxford: Oxford University Press.

Chalmers, D. J. (1995). Facing Up to the Problem of Consciousness. *Journal of Consciousness Studies*, 2(3), pp. 200–219.

Chalmers, D. (1996). *The Conscious Mind: In Search of a Fundamental Theory.* New York: Oxford University Press.

Chase, W. M. (1973). *The Political Identities of Ezra Pound and T. S. Eliot.* Stanford: Stanford University Press.

Cherry, M. (2018). The Future Encyclopedia of Luddism. In Davies, W. (ed.), *Economic Science Fictions.* London: Goldsmiths Press.

Cipolla, C. M. (1978). *The Economic History of World Population.* 7th edn. Harmondsworth: Penguin.

Claeys, G. (2011). *Searching for Utopia: The History of an Idea.* London: Thames and Hudson.

Clement, J. (2020). Share of Global Mobile Website Traffic 2015–2020. *Statista*, 21 July. Available at: https://www.statista.com/statistics/277125/share-of-website-traffic-coming-from-mobile-devices/, accessed 21 July 2021.

Coats, D. (2018). *Fragments in the Ruins: The Renewal of Social Democracy.* London and New York: Rowman and Littlefield.

Cockburn, A. (2020). Blips on the Screen. *London Review of Books*, 42(23), 3 December.

Cohn, N. (1957). *The Pursuit of the Millennium.* London: Secker and Warburg.

Cole, D. (2020). The Chinese Room Argument. *The Stanford Encyclopedia of Philosophy*, Winter 2020 edn. Ed. Edward N. Zalta. Available at: https://plato.stanford.edu/entries/chinese-room/, accessed 13 June 2023.

Cole, G. D. H. (1927). *A Short History of the British Working Class Movement*, vol. 1. London: G. Allen and Unwin.

Collini, S., Winch, D. and Burrow, J. W. (1983). *That Noble Science of Politics: A Study in Nineteenth-Century Intellectual History.* Cambridge: Cambridge University Press.

Collins, J. (2019). Minds Matter. *Times Literary Supplement*, 6073/4, 23 and 30 August.

Colvile, R. (2016). *The Great Acceleration: How the World Is Getting Faster.* New York: Bloomsbury.

de Condorcet, A. -N. ([1795] 1955). *Sketch for a Historical Picture of the Progress of the Human Mind*. 4th edn. Trans. June Barraclough. Ed. Stuart Hampshire. London: Weidenfeld and Nicolson.

Cooke, B. (2021). Silent Earth by Dave Goulson Review – The Insect Apocalypse Is Upon Us. *The Times* [online], 24 July. Available at: https://www.thetimes.co.uk/article/silent-earth-by-dave-goulson-review-insects-environment-hjsmn5cfj, accessed 6 September 2021.

Coote, A. and Franklin, J. (2013). *Time on Our Side: Why We All Need a Shorter Working Week*. London: New Economics Foundation.

Copernicus, N. ([1543] 1943). *De Revolutionibus orbium coelestium*. New York: Prometheus Books.

Coren, G. (2020). OK, Coneheads, Enough of Your Weird Science. *The Times* [online]. Available at: https://www.thetimes.co.uk/article/ok-coneheads-enough-of-your-weird-science-2wfwn3gbp, accessed 4 January 2023.

Crafts, N. F. R. (1985). *British Economic Growth During the Industrial Revolution*. Oxford: Clarendon Press.

Cséfalvay, Z. (2018). *TECHtonic Shifts*. Trans. Bence Gáspár and Zsolt Beke. Budapest: Kairosz Kiado.

Cummine, A. (2016). *Citizens' Wealth*. New Haven: Yale University Press.

Cussen, O. (2023). Review of Pierre Charbonnier's *Affluence and Freedom*. *London Review of Books*, 2 March.

Damasio, A. (2018). *The Strange Order of Things*. New York: Pantheon Books.

Daugherty, P., Davenport, P. H., Wilson, H. J. W. and Porter, M. (2019). *AI, Analytics, and the New Machine Age*. Cambridge, MA: Harvard Business Review.

Davenport, T. H. and Ronanki, R. (2018). Artificial Intelligence for the Real World. *Harvard Business Review*, January–February 2018. Available at: https://hbr.org/2018/01/artificial-intelligence-for-the-real-world, accessed 13 September 2021.

Davies, S. (2019). *The Street-wise Guide to the Devil and His Works*. Brighton: Edward Everett Root.

Davies, W. (2015). *The Happiness Industry*. London: Verso.

Davies, W. (2023). The Reaction Economy. *London Review of Books*, 45(5), 2 March.

Davis, E. (2016). People – Not Just Machines – Will Power Digital Innovation. *Cognizant*, May 2016.

Davis, K. (2018). This Is What It's Like to Not Own a Smartphone in 2018. *Fast Company*, 31 January. Available at: https://www.fastcompany.com/40522828/this-is-what-its-like-to-not-own-a-smartphone-in-2018, accessed 30 June 2021.

De Vries, J. (1994). The Industrial Revolution and the Industrious Revolution. *The Journal of Economic History*, 54(2), pp. 249–70.

Deane, P. and Cole, W. A. (1969). *British Economic Growth: 1688–1959*. 2nd edn. London: Cambridge University Press.

DeLong, B. (2022). *Slouching towards Utopia: An Economic History of the Twentieth Century*. London: Basic Books.

Delsol, C. (2003). *Icarus Fallen*. Trans. Robin Dick. ISI Books.

Dennett, D. (2006). *Breaking the Spell: Religion as a Natural Phenomenon*. London: Penguin.

Der Golem (film, 1915). Directed by Paul Wegener and Carl Boese. Germany: Universum Film (UFA).

Desai, M. (2009). *The Rediscovery of India*. London: Penguin.

Deutsch, D. (2023). Creative Blocks. *Aeon* [online]. Available at: https://aeon.co/essays/how-close-are-we-to-creating-artificial-intelligence, accessed 13 January 2023.

Diamond, J. M. (1991). *The Rise and Fall of the Third Chimpanzee*. London: Radius.

Diamond, J. M. (1997). *Guns, Germs and Steel: The Fates of Human Societies*. New York: W. W. Norton and Co.

Diodorus et al. (1933). *Library of History*. Cambridge, MA: Harvard University Press.

Doniger, W. (2009). *The Hindus: An Alternative History*. New York: The Penguin Press.

Donkin, R. (2010). *The Future of Work*. Basingstoke: Palgrave Macmillan.

Donkin, R. (2010). *The History of Work*. Basingstoke: Palgrave Macmillan.

Dostoevsky, F. ([1864] 1918). *Notes from Underground. White Nights and Other Stories*. Trans. Constance Garnett. New York: The Macmillan Company.

Dostoyevsky, F. ([1876, 1880] 1960). *The Dream of a Queer Fellow: and, The Pushkin Speech*. Trans. S. Koteliansky and J. Middleton Murry, London: Unwin.

Dressler, E. K. (2013). *How a Revolution in Nanotechnology Will Change Civilisation*. London: Public Affairs.

Dreyfus, H. (1965). Alchemy and Artificial Intelligence. Rand Corporation (Research Report). Available at: https://apps.dtic.mil/sti/citations/AD0625719, accessed 6 September 2021.

Dreyfus, H. (1972). *What Computers Can't Do: A Critique of Artificial Reason*. London: Harper and Row.

Drucker, P. F. (1965). *The Future of Industrial Man: A Conservative Approach*. New York: New American Library.

Duguid, P. (2022). Playing Dangerous Games. *Times Literary Supplement*, 6208, 25 March.

Dumas, C. (2021). *Decarbonomics*. London: Profile Books.

Durkheim, E. ([1955] 1983). *Pragmatism and Sociology*. Ed. John B. Allcock. Trans. J. C. Whitehouse. Cambridge: Cambridge University Press.

Dyer-Witheford, N. (2015). *Cyber-Proletariat: Global Labour in the Digital Vortex*. London: Pluto Press.

Easen, N. (2019). Do We Need a Robot Tax? *Raconteur* [online], 5 September. Available at: https://www.raconteur.net/finance/tax/robot-tax/, accessed 21 July 2021.

Eaves, W. (2019). *Murmur*. Edinburgh: Canongate.

Eaves, W. (2020). *Broken Consort: Essays, Reviews, and Other Writings*. London: CB Editions.

Egid, J. (2020). Maths Rules. *Times Literary Supplement*, 6114, 5 June.

Eliade, M. (1955). *The Myth of the Eternal Return*. London: Routledge and Kegan Paul.

Elias, N. (1995). Technization and Civilization. *Theory, Culture and Society*, 12(3), 7–42.

Elias, N. (1996). *The Germans*. Ed. Michael Schöter. Trans. Eric Dunning and Stephen Mennell. New York: Columbia University Press.

Elias, N. (2000). *The Civilising Process*. Malden, MA: Blackwell Publishing.

Eliot, T. S. (1962). *Notes Towards the Definition of Culture*. London: Faber and Faber.

Ellis, F. W. (2005). In What Way, and to What Degree, Did the Mughal State Inhibit Smithian Growth in India in the Seventeenth Century? LSE Working Paper No. 14/05.

Elmer-Dewitt, P. (2011). Video: Steve Jobs in 1980 on PCs as 'Bicycles for the Mind'. *Fortune.com*. Available at: https://fortune.com/2011/12/14/video-steve-jobs-in-1980-on-pcs-as-bicycles-for-the-mind/, accessed 30 June 2021.

Elvin, M. (1972). The High-level Equilibrium Trap: The Causes of the Decline of Invention in the Traditional Chinese Textile Industries. In Willmott, W. E. (ed.), *Economic Organization in Chinese Society*. Stanford: Stanford University Press.

Elvin, M. (1973). *The Pattern of the Chinese Past: A Social and Economic Interpretation*. Stanford: Stanford University Press.

Elyada, O. (2007). *The Raw and the Cooked: Claude Lévi-Strauss and the Hidden Structures of Myth*. Haifa: Haifa University Press.

Engels, F. and Marx, K. ([1848] 1998). *The Communist Manifesto*. London and New York: Verso.

Evans, R. J. (2022). An Army with a State. *Times Literary Supplement*, 6235, 30 September.

Fawcett, E. (2018). *Liberalism: The Life of an Idea*. Princeton: Princeton University Press.

Ferguson, A. (2007). *An Essay on the History of Civil Society*. Ed. Fania Oz-Salzberger. Cambridge: Cambridge University Press.

Ferguson, A. G. (2017). *The Rise of Big Data Policing: Surveillance, Race, and the Future of Law Enforcement*. New York: New York University Press.

Ferguson, N. (2022). *Doom*. London: Allen Lane.

Fernandez-Armesto, F. (2022). Feelings Make the City? *Times Literary Supplement*, 6221, 24 June.

Fisher, M. (2009). *Capitalist Realism: Is There No Alternative?* Winchester and Washington: O Books.

Fleming, P. (2015). *The Mythology of Work: How Capitalism Persists Despite Itself*. London: Pluto Press.

Fleming, P. (2017). *The Death of Homo Economicus: Work, Debt and the Myth of Endless Accumulation*. London: Pluto Press.

Floridi, L. (2017). A Fallacy That Will Hinder Advances in Artificial Intelligence. *Financial Times* [online], June 1. Available at: https://www.ft.com/content/ee996846-4626-11e7-8d27-59b4dd6296b8, accessed 6 September 2021.

Floud, R. (2019). *An Economic History of the English Garden*. London: Allen Lane.

Ford, M. (2009). *The Lights in the Tunnel*. USA: Acculant Publishing.

Ford, M. (2015). *The Rise of the Robots*. New York: Basic Books.

Forrester, K. (2022). On the Disassembly Line. *London Review of Books*, 44(3), 7 July.

Forster, E. M. ([1909] 2011). *The Machine Stops*. London: Penguin.

Foucault, M. (1975). *The Birth of the Clinic: An Archaeology of Medical Perception*. New York: Vintage Books.

Fourier, C. (1971). *Design for Utopia: Selected Writings*. New York: Schocken Books.

Fourier, C. ([1808] 1996). *Theory of Four Movements*. Ed. Gareth Steadman-Jones. Trans. Ian Patterson. Cambridge: Cambridge University Press.

Fraenkel, C. (2022). Ancient Help for Modern Problems. *IWMpost*, 130, Fall/Winter. Available at: https://www.iwm.at/publication/iwmpost-article/ancient-help-for-modern-problems-the-case-of-aristotle, accessed 13 January 2023.

Franssen, M., Gert-Jan, L. and van de Poel, I. (2018). Philosophy of Technology. *The Stanford Encyclopedia of Philosophy* (Fall 2021 edn). Ed. Edward N. Zalta. Available at: https://plato.stanford.edu/archives/fall2018/entries/technology, accessed 20 July 2021.

Frayn, M. (1965). *The Tin Men*. London: Collins.

Freedman, J. B. (2018). *Behemoth: A History of the Factory and the Making of the Modern World*. New York and London: W. W. Norton and Company.

Freeman, C. (2004). *The Economics of Industrial Innovation*. 3rd edn. Ed. Luc Soete. London: Routledge.

Freeman, C. (2008). *Systems of Innovation: Selected Essays in Evolutionary Economics*. Cheltenham: Edward Elgar.

Frey, C. B. (2019). *The Technology Trap: Capital, Labor, and Power in the Age of Automation*. Princeton and Oxford: Princeton University Press.

Frischmann, B. M. and Selinger, E. (2018). *Re-engineering Humanity*. Cambridge: Cambridge University Press.

Future of Life Institute (2023). *Pause Giant AI Experiments: An Open Letter*. Available at: https://futureoflife.org/open-letter/pause-giant-ai-experiments/, accessed 17 April 2023.

Galbraith, J. K. (1958). *The Age of Affluence*. Houghton Mifflin.

Galbraith, J. K. (1967). *The New Industrial State*. London: New American Library.

Galvan, J. M. (2003). On Technoethics. *IEEE Robotics and Automation Magazine*, 10(4), 58–63.

Gardels, N. (2021). AI Makes Us Less Intelligent and More Artificial. *NOÈMA* [online], February 5. Available at: https://www.noemamag.com/ai-makes-us-less-intelligent-and-more-artificial/, accessed 6 September 2021.

Gardels, N. (2022). The Politics of Planetary Time. *NOÈMA* [online]. Available at: https://www.noemamag.com/the-politics-of-planetary-time/, accessed 13 July 2022.

Gaskell, E. C. (1854). *Mary Barton: A Tale of Manchester Life*. 5th edn. London: Chapman and Hall.

Gaskell, E. C. (1855). *North and South*. London: Chapman and Hall.

Gaukroger, S. (2020). *Civilization and the Culture of Science: Science and the Shaping of Modernity, 1795–1935*. Oxford: Oxford University Press.

Geoghegan, P. (2021). The Worlds of Peter Thiel and Jeff Bezos. *Times Literary Supplement*, 6190, 19 November.

George III (2021). Of Laws Relative to the Nature of Climates. *Times Literary Supplement*, 6195/6, 24 December 2021.

Gershon, L. (2020). Are the Posthumans Here Yet? *Jstor Daily* [online], 15 October. Available at: https://daily.jstor.org/are-the-posthumans-here-yet/, accessed 30 June 2021.

Gleick, J. (2011). *The Information: A History, a Theory, a Flood*. New York: Pantheon Books.

Glenny, M. (2022). *The Four Horsemen of the Modern Apocalypse* [recording]. The John Hewitt Society. Available at: https://www.youtube.com/watch?v=BJC9SgqGLGc, accessed 21 March 2023.

Goddard, J. (2022). Nasa Scientist Envisages a Home on Venus. *The Times*, 8 January 2022.

Godwin, W. (1793). *An Enquiry Concerning Political Justice and Its Influence on General Virtue and Happiness*. London: Printed for G. G. J. and J. Robinson.

Goethe, J. W. von ([1808] 1890). *Faust: A Tragedy*. Trans. Bayard Taylor. London, New York and Melbourne: Ward, Lock, and Co.

Goethe, J. W. von ([1808] 1970). *Faust.* Trans. Baker Fairley. Toronto: University of Toronto Press.

Goncharov, I. A. ([1850] 1978). *Oblomov.* Harmondsworth: Penguin.

Good, I. J. (1965). Speculations Concerning the First Ultraintelligent Machine. In Alt, F. L. and Rubinoff, M. (eds.), *Advances in Computers*, vol. 6. New York: Academic Press.

Goodrich, L. C. (2002). *A Short History of the Chinese People.* Newton Abbot: David and Charles.

Goos, M. and Manning, A. (2007). Lousy and Lovely Jobs: The Rising Polarization of Work in Britain. *The Review of Economics and Statistics,* 89(1), pp. 118–33.

Gorz, A. (1982). *Farewell to the Working Class: An Essay on Post-Industrial Socialism.* Trans. Michael Sonenscher. London: Pluto Press.

Gorz, A. (2018). *Ecologica.* Trans. Chris Turner. London: Seagull Books.

Graeber, D. (2011). *Debt: The First 5,000 Years.* New York: Melville House.

Graeber, D. (2018). *Bullshit Jobs: A Theory.* London: Allen Lane.

Graeber, D. and Wengrow, D. (2021). *The Dawn of Everything: A New History of Humanity.* London: Allen Lane.

Gray, J. (2021). How Fear Makes Us Human. *New Statesman* [online]. Available at: https://www.newstatesman.com/culture/books/2021/11/dawn-everything-new-history-humanity-david-graeber-wengrow-review, accessed 6 July 2022.

Green, A. (2023). To the Barricades. *Times Literary Supplement*, 6265, 28 April.

Greenfield, A. (2018). *Radical Technologies: The Design of Everyday Life.* London: Verso.

Gregory, J. W. (1931). *Race as a Political Factor.* London: Watts and Co.

Griffin, E. (2010). *A Short History of the British Industrial Revolution.* Basingstoke: Palgrave Macmillan.

Grossman, V. ([1970] 2009). *Everything Flows.* Trans. Robert Chandler and Elizabeth Chandler with Anna Aslanyan. New York: New York Review Books.

Guizot, F. ([1828] 1997). *The History of Civilization in Europe.* Ed. Larry Siedentop. London and New York: Penguin Books.

Hacken, R. (2008). Into the Imagined Forest: A 2000-Year Retrospective of the German Woods. Brigham Young University Faculty Publications.

Available at: https://scholarsarchive.byu.edu/facpub/4097, accessed 26 January 2023.

Hall, J. A. (1979). *The Sociology of Literature*. London: Longman.

Hankins, J. (2019). *Virtue Politics: Soulcraft and Statecraft in Renaissance Italy*. Cambridge, MA: Belknap Press.

Hanser, J. (2019). *Mr. Smith Goes to China: Three Scots in the Making of Britain's Global Empire*. New Haven: Yale University Press.

Harari, Y. N. (2014). *Sapiens: A Brief History of Humankind*. London: Vintage Books.

Harari, Y. N. (2018). *21 Lessons for the 21st Century*. London: Vintage.

Harris, R. (2021). *The Second Sleep*. Toronto: Seal Books.

Harvey-Gibson, R. J. (1929). *The Master Thinkers: Vignettes in the History of Science*. London and New York: T. Nelson and Sons.

Hassabis, D. (2018). *The Rothschild Foundation Lecture*. The Royal Academy of Arts. 17 September.

Hatherley, O. (2018). Prefabricating Communism: Mass Production and the Soviet City. In Davies, W. (ed.), *Economic Science Fictions*. London: Goldsmiths Press.

Havel, V. (1991). *Open Letters 1965–1990*. Ed. Paul Wilson. London and Boston: Faber and Faber.

Hayami, A. (2015). *Japan's Industrious Revolution: Economic and Social Transformations in the Early Modern Period*. Tokyo: Springer.

Hayek, F. ([1920] 1991). Contributions to a Theory of How Consciousness Develops. Manuscript. Trans. Grete Heinz.

Hayek, F. ([1944] 1994). *The Road to Serfdom*. Ed. Milton Friedman. London: Routledge.

Hayek, F. (1952). *The Sensory Order*. Chicago: University of Chicago Press.

Hayek, F. ([1960] 2006). *The Constitution of Liberty*. London: Routledge.

Head, S. (2005). *The New Ruthless Economy: Work and Power in the Digital Age*. New York and Oxford: Oxford University Press.

Head, S. (2014). *Mindless: Why Smarter Machines Are Making Dumber Humans*. New York: Basic Books.

Headrick, D. (2009). *Technology: A World History*. Oxford: Oxford University Press.

Hebb, D. O. (1980). *Essay on Mind*. Hillsdale: Erlbaum.

Hedges, I. (2005). *Framing Faust: Twentieth-Century Cultural Struggles*. Carbondale: Southern Illinois University Press.

Heffernan, M. (2020). *Uncharted: How to Map the Future*. London: Simon and Schuster.

Heidegger, M. ([1935] 2014). *Introduction to Metaphysics*. Trans. Gregory Fried and Richard F. H. Polt. 2nd edn. New Haven: Yale University Press.

Heidegger, M. ([1954] 1977). *The Question Concerning Technology, and Other Essays*. New York: Harper and Row.

Heuhouser, F. (2008). *Rousseau's Theodicy of Self-Love: Evil, Rationality, and the Drive for Recognition*. Oxford: Oxford University Press.

Hicks, J. (1969). *A Theory of Economic History*. Oxford, London and New York: Oxford University Press.

Hicks, J. and Helm, D. (1984). *The Economics of John Hicks*. Oxford: Basil Blackwell.

Hinde, R. A. (2015). *Our Culture of Greed: When Is Enough Enough*. Nottingham: Spokesman.

Hirsch, F. (1976). *Social Limits to Growth*. Cambridge, MA and London: Harvard University Press.

Hilton, B.(2016). *The Age of Atonement: The Influence of Evangelicalism on Social and Economic Thought 1785–1865*.Oxford: Clarendon Press.

Hirschman, A. O. (1997). *The Passions and the Interests: Political Arguments for Capitalism Before Its Triumph*. Princeton: Princeton University Press.

Hirschman, A. O. (1981). *Essays in Trespassing: Economics to Politics and Beyond*. Cambridge: Cambridge University Press.

Hitler, A. ([1925] 1942). *Mein Kampf*. Trans. James Murphy. London, New York and Melbourne: Hurst and Blackett.

Hitler, A. et al. (1988). *Hitler's Table Talk 1941–44*. Oxford: Oxford University Press.

Hobsbawm, E. J. (1969). *Industry and Empire*. Harmondsworth: Penguin.

Holland, T. (2022). Rich as Crassus. *Times Literary Supplement*, 6236, 7 October 2022.

Hollis, M. (1987). *The Cunning of Reason*. Cambridge: Cambridge University Press.

Holmes, R. (2008). *The Age of Wonder: How the Romantic Generation Discovered the Beauty and Terror of Science*. London: Harper Press.

Hopkins, A. G. (2002). *Globalization in World History*. London: Pimlico.

Hopkins, E. (1982). Working Hours and Conditions during the Industrial Revolution: A Re-appraisal. *Economic History Review*, 2nd series, 35(1), February.

Horowitz, A. and Maley, T. (eds.) (1994). *The Barbarism of Reason: Max Weber and the Twilight of Enlightenment*. Toronto, Buffalo and London: University of Toronto Press.

House of Lords Economic Affairs Committee (2022). Central Bank Digital Currencies: A Solution in Search of a Problem? HL Paper 131. London: House of Lords.

Howell, D. (2019). One Nation but Many Voices. *Japanese Times*, 20 December. Available at: https://www.japantimes.co.jp/opinion/2019/12/19/commentary/world-commentary/britain-one-nation-many-voices/, accessed 20 January 2023.

Howkins, J. (2020). *Invisible Work: The Hidden Ingredient of True Creativity, Purpose and Power*. London: September Publishing.

Huang, P. (1985). *The Peasant Economy and Social Change in Northern China*. Stanford: Stanford University Press.

Hudson, W. H. (1887). *A Crystal Age*. London: T. Fisher Unwin.

Hughes, D. M. (2021). *Who Owns the Wind?* London: Verso.

Hughes, H. S. (1958). *Consciousness and Society: The Reorientation of European Thought 1890–1930*. New York: Vintage Books.

Huizinga, J. (1999). *The Waning of the Middle Ages*. New York: Dover Publications.

Hume, D. ([1740] 1999). *A Treatise of Human Nature*. Ontario: Batoche.

Hume, D. (1793). *Essays and Treatises on Several Subjects*. London: T. Cadell.

Huntington, E. and Van Valkenburg, S. (1935). *Europe*. New York: J. Wiley and Sons.

Huxley, A. ([1932] 2007). *Brave New World*. London: Vintage Books.

Huxley, A. (1961). Lecture to the Tavistock Group, California Medical School. San Francisco.

Huxley, A. ([1962] 2005). *Island*. London: Vintage.

Huxley, A. (1963). *Literature and Science*. London: Chatto and Windus.

Huxley, J. (1957). Transhumanism. In Huxley, J. (1957). *New Bottles for New Wine*. London: Chatto and Windus.

Illich, I. (1996). *Deschooling Society.* London: Boyars.

ILO (2022). *Potential WESO Report on Lifelong Learning and Skills Dynamics.* Concept Note. 1–2 December.

Isakjee, A. (2017). Welfare State Regimes: A Literature Review. IRiS Working Paper Series, No. 18/2017. Birmingham: Institute for Research into Superdiversity.

Jaffe, S. (2021). *Work Won't Love You Back.* London: Hurst and Company.

James, H. (2002). *The End of Globalization.* Cambridge, MA: Harvard University Press.

James, W. (1891). *The Principles of Psychology.* London: Macmillan.

Jaspers, K. (1947). Our Future and Goethe. In Fischer, H. E. (ed.). (1952). *Existentialism and Humanism.* Trans. E. B. Ashton. New York: Russell F. Moore.

Jebelli, J. (2022). *How the Mind Changed: A Human History of Our Evolving Brain.* London: John Murray.

Jenkins, S. (2022). A Moat Defensive to a House. *Times Literary Supplement,* 6216, 20 May.

Jenner, W. J. F. (1992). *The Tyranny of History.* London: Allen Lane.

Jones, C. (2020). The Tech Giants Want to Help Prepare the World for the Future of Work. *World Economic Forum,* 22 October. Available at: https://www.hellenicshippingnews.com/these-tech-giants-want-to-help-prepare-the-world-for-the-future-of-work/, accessed 23 March 2023.

Jones, E. L. (1987). *The European Miracle: Environments, Economies, and Geopolitics in the History of Europe and Asia.* 2nd edn. Cambridge: Cambridge University Press.

Jones, R. (2017). Archaic Man Meets a Marvellous Automaton: Posthumanism, Social Robots, Archetypes. *Journal of Analytic Psychology,* 62(3), pp. 338–55.

Kafka, F. ([1925] 2009) *The Trial.* Trans. Mike Mitchell. Oxford: Oxford University Press.

Kahneman, D. (2011). *Thinking, Fast and Slow.* New York: Farrar, Straus and Giroux.

Kamla (2011) Abu Fazl: Governance and Administration. In Singh, M. P. and Roy, H. (eds.) (2011). *Indian Political Thought.* Delhi: Pearson.

Kant, I. ([1784] 1963). Idea for a Universal History from a Cosmopolitan Point of View. In Kant, I. *On History*. Trans. Lewis White Beck. Indianapolis: Bobbs-Merrill Co.

Kasparov, G. K. (2017). *Deep Thinking: Where Machine Intelligence Ends and Human Creativity Begins*. London: John Murray.

Kautilya (1992). *The Arthashastra*. Ed. and trans. L. N. Rangarajan and R. P. Kangle. Haryana: Penguin.

Kay, J. P. (1832). *Moral and Physical Conditions of the Operatives Employed in the Cotton Manufacture in Manchester*. In Hopkins, E. (1974), Working Conditions in Victorian Stourbridge. *International Review of Social History*, 19(3), 401–25.

Keen, A. (2012). *Digital Vertigo*. London: Constable.

Keith, J. (1997). *Mind Control, World Control*. Kempton, IL: Adventures Unlimited Press.

Keynes, J. M. (1933). *Essays in Persuasion. The Collected Writings of John Maynard Keynes*, vol. 9. 1972, Cambridge: Cambridge University Press.

Keynes, J. M. (1937). Economic Consequences of a Declining Population. *The Collected Writings of John Maynard Keynes*, vol. 14: *Economic Consequences of a Declining Population*. Cambridge: Cambridge University Press.

Keynes, J. M. (1971). 'The Economic Consequences of the Peace' (1919). *The Collected Writings of John Maynard Keynes*, vol. 2. ed London: Macmillan.

Keynes, J. M. (1972). Economic Possibilities for our Grandchildren. In *The Collected Writings of John Maynard Keynes*, vol. 9. Cambridge: Cambridge University Press.

Keynes, J. M. (2015). *The Essential Keynes*. Ed. and with an Introduction by Robert Skidelsky. London: Penguin.

Kissinger, H. A., Schmidt, E. and Huttenlocher, D. (2021). *The Age of AI and Our Human Future*. London: John Murray.

Kitcher, P. (1983). *The Nature of Mathematical Knowledge*. Oxford: Oxford University Press.

Klemm, F. (1964). *A History of Western Technology*. Cambridge, MA: MIT Press.

Knowles, T. (2020). Atomico's Fifth Tech Investment Fund Closes at $820m. *The Times* [online], 19 February. Available at: https://www.the

times.co.uk/article/atomico-s-fifth-tech-investment-fund-closes-at-820m-lpjomxfsd, accessed 27 October 2020.

Knowles, T. (2022). Smart Devices Will Let Us Control Gadgets With Our Minds. *The Times* [online], 27 January. Available at: https://www.the times.co.uk/article/smart-devices-will-let-us-control-gadgets-with-our-minds-9foddrvtk, accessed 5 July 2022.

Koch, A. (1959). *Philosophy for a Time of Crisis*. New York: E. P. Dutton and Co.

Kołakowski, L. ([1978] 2005). *Main Currents of Marxism*. New York, London: W. W. Norton and Company.

Kołakowski, L. (2012). *Is God Happy?: Selected Essays*, London: Penguin.

Komlosy, A. (2018). *Work: The Last 1,000 Years*. London: Verso.

Koselleck, R. (1988). *Critique and Crisis: Enlightenment and the Pathogenesis of Modern Society*. Cambridge, MA: MIT Press.

Koutrouby, G. (ed.) (2017). *Medieval Literature: A Basic Anthology*. Mineola and New York: Dover Publications.

Krugman, P. (1996). *Pop Internationalism*. Cambridge, MA: MIT Press.

Kuchler, H. (2022). Will AI Turbocharge the Hunt for New Drugs? *Financial Times* [online]. Available at: https://www.ft.com/content/3e57ad6c-493d-4874-a663-0cb200d3cdb5, accessed 4 July 2022.

Kuhn, T. S. (1962). *The Structure of Scientific Revolutions*. Chicago: University of Chicago Press.

Kumar, K., in (1999). Technological Determinism. In Bullock, A. and Trombley, S. (eds.). 1999. *The New Fontana Dictionary of Modern Thought*. 3rd edn. London: HarperCollins.

Kurzweil, R. (1999). *The Age of Spiritual Machines*. London: Phoenix.

Kurzweil, R. (2005). *The Singularity Is Near: When Humans Transcend Biology*. New York: Viking Penguin.

Laing, O. (2021). Express Yourself or Feed The Pigs? *Times Literary Supplement*, 6176, 13 August.

Lakatos, I. and Musgrave, A. (2004). *Criticism and the Growth of Knowledge*. Cambridge: Cambridge University Press.

Lal, D. (1988). *The Hindu Equilibrium*. Oxford: Clarendon Press.

Landes, D. S. (1998). *The Wealth and Poverty of Nations*. New York, London: W. W. Norton and Company.

Landes, D. S. (2003). *The Unbound Prometheus: Technical Change and Industrial Development in Western Europe from 1750 to the Present.* 2nd edn. Cambridge: Cambridge University Press.

Lanier, J. (2013). *Who Owns the Future?* London: Allen Lane.

Larrey, P. (2017). *Connected World: From Automated Work to Virtual Wars.* London: Portfolio Penguin.

Le Goff, J. (1980). *Time, Work, and Culture in the Middle Ages.* Chicago: University of Chicago Press.

Le Guin, U. K. (1996). *The Dispossessed: An Ambiguous Utopia.* London: HarperCollins.

Le Guin, U. K. (2014). *Ursula's Acceptance Speech: Medal for Distinguished Contribution to American Letters* [video]. Available at: https://www.ursulakleguin.com/nbf-medal, accessed 30 June 2021.

Lea, R. (2021). Fit for Office. *Times Literary Supplement,* 6169, 25 June.

Leary, T. (1970). *Jail Notes.* New York: Douglas Books.

Lee, K. and Project Syndicate (2020). The Art of AI. *Project Syndicate.* Available at: https://www.project-syndicate.org/onpoint/state-of-ai-by-kai-fu-lee-2020-05, accessed 6 July 2022.

Lenin, V. I. ([1917] 1988) *Imperialism, The Highest Stage of Capitalism.* London: Lawrence and Wishart.

Letters (2020). *London Review of Books,* 42(9), 7 May.

Lévi-Strauss, C. (1970). *The Raw and the Cooked.* London: Jonathan Cape.

Leys, S. (2013). *The Hall of Uselessness: Collected Essays.* New York: New York Review Books.

Lind, H. (2010). A Tale of Two Crises. *World Economic Journal,* 11(2), June, 131–149

Lindberg, D. C. and Shank, M. H. (eds.) (2003). *The Cambridge History of Science,* vol. 2. Cambridge: Cambridge University Press.

Lipset, S. (1963). *Political Man: The Social Basis of Politics.* Garden City: Anchor Books.

Liu, W. (2020). *Abolish Silicon Valley: How to Liberate Technology from Capitalism.* London: Repeater Books.

Locke, J. ([1689] 1980). *Second Treatise of Government.* Ed. C. B. Macpherson. Indianapolis: Hackett.

Lomborg, B. (2001). *The Skeptical Environmentalist*. Cambridge: Cambridge University Press.

Lomborg, B. (2021). *False Alarm*. New York: Basic Books.

Long, L. (2020). What Really Happened in Yancheng? *London Review of Books*, 42(2), 23 January.

Loomis, L. R. (1943). Intro. and ed. In Aristotle, *On Man in the Universe*. New York: Walter J. Black.

Lovejoy, A. O. ([1936] 1961). *The Great Chain of Being*. Cambridge, MA: Harvard University Press.

Luchaire, A. (1909). *La Société française au temps de Philippe Augustus*. Paris: Hachette.

Lynas, M. (2007). *Six Degrees: Our Future on a Hotter Planet*. London: Fourth Estate.

MacAskill, W. (2022). *What We Owe the Future*. Oneworld Publications.

MacCulloch, D. (2022). Silly Little War. *London Review of Books*, 44(11), 9 June.

MacGregor, N. (2010). *A History of the World in 100 Objects*. London: Allen Lane.

MacKenzie, D. (2021). Cookies, Pixels and Fingerprints. *London Review of Books*, 43(7), 1 April 2021.

Mackenzie, D. A. (1918). *Indian Myth and Legend*. London: The Gresham Publishing Company Limited.

Mackinder, H. (1904). The Geographical Pivot of History. *The Geographical Journal*, 23(4), April 1904, pp. 421–37.

Mackinder, H. (1919). *Democratic Ideals and Reality*. New York: Henry Holt and Company.

Macleod, R. (2000). *The 'Creed of Science' in Victorian England*. London: Variorum.

Macrae, N. (1984). *The 2024 Report: A Concise History of the Future, 1974–2024*. London: Sidgwick and Jackson.

Maddison, A. (2006). *The World Economy* [Electronic Resource], vol. 1: *A Millennial Perspective*; vol. 2: *Historical Statistics*. Paris: OECD Publishing. Available at: https://www.stat.berkeley.edu/~aldous/157/Papers/world_economy.pdf, accessed 23 August 2021.

Maddison, A. (2007a). *Chinese Economic Performance in the Long Run*. 2nd edn. OECD.

Maddison, A. (2007b). *Contours of the World Economy 1–2030 AD: Essays in Macro-Economic History*. Oxford: Oxford University Press.

Malhotra, R. (2021). *Artificial Intelligence and the Future of Power*. New Delhi: Rupa.

Mandeville, B. (1970). *The Fable of the Bees*. Harmondsworth: Penguin.

Mann, G. (2022). Reversing the Freight Train. *London Review of Books*, 44(16), 18 August.

Mann, T. (1945) *Reflections of a Nonpolitical Man* (1918). Eng. translation: Walter D. Morris (1938), London: Alfred A.Knopf.

Mann, T. (1945). *Germany and the Germans* [speech transcript]. Coolidge Auditorium, Library of Congress, Washington, 29 May.

Mann, T. (1948). *Doctor Faustus*. Trans. H. T. Lowe-Porter. London: Alfred A. Knopf.

Mannheim, K. ([1927] 1986). *Conservatism: A Contribution to the Sociology of Knowledge*. Ed. Kettler, D., Meja, V. and Stehr, N. London: Routledge and Kegan Paul.

Mannheim, K. ([1929] 1960). *Ideology and Utopia: An Introduction to the Sociology of Knowledge*. London: Routledge and Kegan Paul.

Mannheim, K. (1940). *Man and Society in an Age of Reconstruction: Studies in Modern Social Structure*. London: Routledge and Kegan Paul.

Mantoux, P. (1961). *The Industrial Revolution in the Eighteenth Century: An Outline of the Beginnings of the Modern Factory System in England*. Trans. Majorie Vernon. London: Jonathan Cape.

Marcuse, H. (1966). *Eros and Civilization*. Boston: Beacon Press.

Marcuse, H. ([1964] 2002). *One-Dimensional Man: Studies in the Ideology of Advanced Industrial Society*. London: Routledge.

Marenbon, J. (1997). *The Philosophy of Peter Abelard*. Cambridge: Cambridge University Press.

Markoff, J. (2002). Threats and Responses: Intelligence; Pentagon Plans a Computer System That Would Peek at Personal Data of Americans. *The New York Times* [online], 9 November. Available at: https://www.nytimes.com/2002/11/09/us/threats-responses-intelligence-pentagon-plans-computer-system-that-would-peek.html, accessed 6 December 2019.

Marlowe, C. ([1593] 2008). *Doctor Faustus*. Ed. Roma Gill and Ros King. London: Bloomsbury.

Martin, I. (2023). To Defend the West We Must Win This AI Race. *The Times* [online]. Available at: https://www.thetimes.co.uk/article/to-defend-the-west-we-must-win-this-ai-race-mc6nsz38b, accessed 5 June 2023.

Martin, R. (2022). Clean Technologies for Growth and Equity. *Centrepiece*, Autumn.

Martineau, A. (1986). *Herbert Marcuse's Utopia*. Montreal: Harvest House.

Marx, K. and Engels, F. (1958). *Selected Writings*. Moscow: Foreign Language Publishing House.

Masood, E. (2014). *The Great Invention: The Story of GDP and the Making and Unmaking of the Modern World*. New York: Pegasus Books.

Mathias, P. and Davis, J. A. (eds.). (1990). *The First Industrial Revolutions*. Oxford: Basil Blackwell.

Maughan, T. (2019). *Infinite Detail*. New York: Farrar, Straus and Giroux.

Mayor, A. (2018). *Gods and Robots: Myths, Machines, and Ancient Dreams of Technology*. Princeton: Princeton University Press.

McCarthy, J., Minsky, M. L., Rochester, N. and Shannon, C. E. (1955). A Proposal for the Dartmouth Summer Research Project on Artificial Intelligence. Available at: https://web.archive.org/web/20080930164306/http://www-formal.stanford.edu/jmc/history/dartmouth/dartmouth.html, accessed 3 September 2021.

McCrindle, J. (1877). *Ancient India as Described by Megasthenes and Arrian*. Calcutta: Thacker, Spink and Co.

McEwan, I. (2019). *Machines Like Me*. London: Vintage.

McGee, P. (2022). The True Flaw of Driverless Cars Isn't the Tech. *Financial Times* [online]. Available at: https://www.ft.com/content/189f75e7-da81-4f96-bbfc-4b3f7f6b1f2a, accessed 26 April 2022.

McKibben, B. (2022). What's for Dinner? *Times Literary Supplement*, 6226, 29 July.

Mecklin, J. (ed.). (2021). 2021 Doomsday Clock Statement. *Bulletin of the Atomic Scientists* [online]. Available at: https://thebulletin.org/doomsday-clock/2021-doomsday-clock-statement/, accessed 13 July 2022.

Meynaud, J. (1968). *Technocracy*. Trans. Paul Barnes. London: Faber and Faber.

Mikhail, A. (2020). *God's Shadow*. London: Faber and Faber.

Mill, J. S. ([1863] 1985). *Utilitarianism*. London: Fontana.

Mill, J. S. ([1870] 1909). *Autobiography.* New York: P. F. Collier.

Mill, J. S. (1859). *On Liberty.* London: John W. Parker and Son.

Miller, C. (2022). How Dosh Went Digital. *Literary Review,* 25 August. Available at: https://literaryreview.co.uk/how-dosh-went-digital, accessed 23 January 2023.

Miller, W. M. (2019). *A Canticle for Leibowitz.* London: Orbit.

Mills, C. A. (1944). *Climate Makes the Man.* London: V. Gollancz.

Mills, C. A. (1949). Temperature Dominance over Human Life. *Science,* 110(2855), pp. 267–71.

Milo, D. (2019). *Good Enough: The Tolerance for Mediocrity in Nature and Society.* Cambridge, MA: Harvard University Press.

Mindell, D. A. (2015). *Our Robots, Ourselves: Robots and the Myths of Autonomy.* New York: Viking.

Mini, P. V. (1974). *Philosophy and Economics: The Origins and Development of Economic Theory.* Gainesville: The University Presses of Florida.

Ministry of Truth: The Secretive Government Units Spying on Your Speech. (2023). *Big Brother Watch* [online]. Available at: https://bigbrotherwatch.org.uk/wp-content/uploads/2023/01/Ministry-of-Truth-Big-Brother-Watch-290123.pdf/, accessed 22 March 2023.

Mithken, S. (2017). Why Did We Start Farming? *London Review of Books,* 39(23), 30 November. Available at: https://www.lrb.co.uk/the-paper/v39/n23/steven-mithen/why-did-we-start-farming, accessed 23 January 2023.

Mokyr, J. (2017). *A Culture of Growth.* Princeton: Princeton University Press.

Monbiot, G (2022). *Regenesis.* London: Allen Lane.

Montesquieu, C. ([1748] 2001). *The Spirit of Laws.* Ed. David Wallace Carrithers. Trans. Thomas Nugent. Ontario: Batoche.

Montgomery Watt, W. (1972). *The Influence of Islam in Medieval Europe.* Edinburgh: Edinburgh University Press.

More, T. ([1516] 1965). *Utopia.* Trans. Paul Turner. Harmondsworth: Penguin.

More, T., Bacon, F. and Neville, H. (1999). *Thomas More, Utopia; Francis Bacon, New Atlantis; Henry Neville, The Isle of Pines.* Oxford: Oxford University Press.

Morozov, E. (2014). *To Save Everything, Click Here: The Folly Solutionism.* London: Public Affairs.

Morris, W. (1889). Looking Backward. *Commonweal,* 5(180), 22 June.

Morris, W. (2004). *News from Nowhere and Other Writings.* Ed. Clive Wilmer. London: Penguin.

Mühlhahn, K. (2019). *Making China Modern: From the Great Qing to Xi Jinping.* Cambridge, MA: Belknap Press.

Muller, H. J. (1962). *Freedom in the Ancient World.* London: Secker and Warburg.

Mumford, L. ([1934] 2010)., *Technics and Civilisation.* Chicago and London: The University of Chicago Press.

Mumford, L. (1967). *The Myth of the Machine,* vol. 1. New York: Harcourt Brace Jovanovich.

Nagel, T. (1974). What Is It Like to Be a Bat? *The Philosophical Review,* 83(4), pp. 435–50.

Needham, J. (1969). *The Grand Titration.* London: George Allen and Unwin.

Needham, J. (1978). *The Shorter Science and Civilisation in China: An Abridgement of Joseph Needham's Original Text.* Ed. Colin Ronan. Cambridge: Cambridge University Press.

Needham, J. and Wang, L. (2005). *Science and Civilisation in China,* vol. 2: *History of Scientific Thought.* Cambridge: Cambridge University Press.

Neima, A. (2021). *The Utopians: Six Attempts to Build a Perfect Society.* Basingstoke: Picador.

Nelson, P. (2020). Letter. *London Review of Books,* 47(9), 7 May.

Nelson, V. (2001). *The Secret Life of Puppets.* Cambridge, MA: Harvard University Press.

Nesi, E. (2013). *Story of My People.* Trans. Antony Shugaar. New York: Other Press.

Neuhouser, F. (2008). *Rousseau's Theodicy of Self-Love: Evil, Rationality, and the Drive for Recognition.* Oxford: Oxford University Press.

Nietzsche, F. ([1878] 1996). *Human, All Too Human.* Cambridge: Cambridge University Press.

Nilsson, N. (2009). *The Quest for Artificial Intelligence: A History of Ideas and Achievements.* Cambridge: Cambridge University Press.

Nordhaus, W. (2021). *The Spirit of Green*. Princeton and Oxford: Princeton University Press.

North, D. C. and Thomas, R. P. (1970). An Economic Theory of the Growth of the Western World. *The Economic History Review*, 23(1), pp. 1–17.

North, D. C. and Thomas, R. P. (1973). *The Rise of the Western World: A New Economic History*. Cambridge: Cambridge University Press.

Nuttall, P. (2022). The People and the Planet. *New Statesman* [online]. Available at: https://www.newstatesman.com/culture/books/2022/01/the-people-and-the-planet, accessed 13 July 2022.

O'Neil, C. (2017). *Weapons of Math Destruction*. New York: Broadway Books.

Office for National Statistics (2021). Unemployment Rate (Aged 16 and Over, Seasonally Adjusted). *Office for National Statistics*, 17 August. Available at: https://www.ons.gov.uk/employmentandlabourmarket/peoplenotinwork/unemployment/timeseries/mgsx/lms, accessed 9 September 2021.

Offray de la Mettrie, J. J. ([1750] 1943). *Man a Machine*. La Salle: The Open Court Publishing Company.

Ogden, E. (2022). As Good as a Feast: On Avram Alpert's "The Good-Enough Life". *Los Angeles Review of Books*. Available at: https://lareviewofbooks.org/article/as-good-as-a-feast-on-avram-alperts-the-good-enough-life/., accessed 23 January 2023.

Olson, M. (1982). *The Rise and Decline of Nations: Economic Growth, Stagflation, and Social Rigidities*. New Haven: Yale University Press.

Ord, T. (2020). *The Precipice*. London: Bloomsbury Publishing.

Orwell, G. (1946). Why I Write. In Orwell, G. (1968). *The Collected Essays, Journalism and Letters of George Orwell: An Age Like This*, vol. 1. Ed. Sonia Orwell and Ian Angus. New York: Harcourt, Brace and World.

Orwell, G. ([1949] 2008). *Nineteen Eighty-Four*. London: Penguin.

Ovitt, G. (1986). The Cultural Context of Western Technology: Early Christian Attitudes toward Manual Labor. *Technology and Culture*, 27(3), pp. 477–500.

Pacey, A. (1983). *The Culture of Technology*. Cambridge, MA: MIT Press.

Palmowski, J. (2008). *A Dictionary of Contemporary World History*. 3rd edn. Oxford: Oxford University Press. Available at: https://www.

oxfordreference.com/display/10.1093/oi/authority.2011080310020977
6;jsessionid=272BDDEEC2D51B755A17452CE05A48B3, accessed 6 February 2023.

Parry, R. L. (2019). Flight to the Forest. *London Review of Books*, 41(20), 24 October 2019.

Passmore, J. A. (1970). *The Perfectibility of Man*. London: Duckworth.

Patočka, J. (1996). *Heretical Essays*. Trans. Erazim Kohák. Chicago and La Salle: Open Court.

Patterson, I. (2019). Sexy Robots. *London Review of Books*, 41(9), 9 May.

Paul, T. V. (2009). *The Tradition of Non-use of Nuclear Weapons*. Stanford: Stanford University Press.

Pecchi, L. and Piga, G. (eds.). (2008). *Revisiting Keynes: Economic Possibilities for Our Grandchildren*. Cambridge, MA: MIT Press.

Perez, C. (2002). *Technological Revolutions and Financial Capital: The Dynamics of Bubbles and Golden Ages*. Cheltenham: Elgar.

Pethokoukis, J. (2013). Valleywag's ignorant attack on Marc Andreessen. *AEIdeas*, June 5. Available at: https://www.aei.org/economics/valleywags-ignorant-attack-on-marc-andreessen/, accessed 23 January 2023.

Pettifor, A. (2022). On the Move: Global Warming and the Inevitability of Mass Migration. *Times Literary Supplement*, 6240, 4 November.

Pfeifer, H. (2021). Global Morality Play. *London Review of Books*, 43(13), 1 July.

Pieper, J. (1998). *Leisure, the Basis of Culture*. Ed. Roger Scruton and Gerald Malsbary. South Bend: St Augustine's Press.

Piketty, T. (2020). *Capital and Ideology*. Trans. Arthur Goldhammer. Cambridge, MA: Harvard University Press.

Pirenne, H. (1970). *Medieval Cities: Their Origins and the Revival of Trade*. Princeton: Princeton University Press.

Pirsig, R. M. (1974). *Zen and the Art of Motorcycle Maintenance: An Inquiry into Values*. London: Bodley Head.

Pissarides, C. and Bughin, J. (2018). Embracing the New Age of Automation. *Project Syndicate* [online]. Available at: https://www.project-syndicate.org/commentary/automation-jobs-policy-imperatives-by-christopher-pissarides-and-jacques-bughin-2018-01, accessed 6 July 2022.

Plamenatz, J. (1963). *Man and Society*, vol. 1. London: Longmans, Green and Co.

Plato ([375 BCE] 2007). *The Republic.* 2nd edn. Trans. Desmond Lee. London: Penguin.

Plato ([*c.*370 BCE] 1949). *Theaetetus.* Trans. Benjamin Jowett. New York: The Liberal Arts Press.

Polanyi, K. ([1944] 1967). *The Great Transformation.* Boston: Beacon Press.

Pope Francis (2015). Encyclical Letter Laudato Si' of the Holy Father Francus on Care for Our Common Home. The Holy See. Available at: https://www.vatican.va/content/francesco/en/encyclicals/documents/papa-francesco_20150524_enciclica-laudato-si.html, accessed 30 Jan 2023.

Pope, A. ([1734] 1789). *Essay on Man.* Copenhagen: FC Pelt.

Popper, K. (2002). *The Poverty of Historicism.* 2nd edn. London: Routledge.

Popper, K. (2011). *The Open Society and Its Enemies.* London: Routledge.

Pridmore-Brown, M. (2022). The Lethal Chamber. *Times Literary Supplement*, 6216, 20 May.

Pridmore-Brown, M. (2022). Beyond Flesh and Blood. *Times Literary Supplement*, 6221, 24 June.

Primore-Brown, M. (2022). Conquering Sociopaths. *Times Literary Supplement*, 6240, 4 November.

Putnam, H. (1995). *Words and Life.* Ed. James Conant. Cambridge, MA and London: Harvard University Press.

Qureshi, S. (2020). Dodos and Dinosaurs. *Times Literary Supplement*, 6138, 20 November 2020.

Qureshi, Z. (2022). The Not-So-Dire Future of Work. *Project Syndicate* [online]. Available at: https://www.project-syndicate.org/commentary/future-of-work-labor-market-reform-by-zia-qureshi-2017-10, accessed 12 April 2022.

Radford, P. (2021). *The Crooked Timber of History* [online]. Available at: icblogs.org/real-world-economics/2021/radford-crooked-timber-history, accessed 30 June 2021.

Ramachandran, V. S. (2012). *The Tell-Tale Brain: Unlocking the Mystery of Human Nature.* London: Windmill.

Ramsden, J. (2022). *The Poets' Guide to Economics.* London: Pallas Athene.

Ramsey, W. (2021). Eliminative Materialism. *The Stanford Encyclopedia of Philosophy* (Fall 2021 edn). Ed. Edward N. Zalta. Available at: https://plato.stanford.edu/archives/fall2021/entries/materialism-eliminative, accessed 7 September 2021.

Rao, V. (2012). *Reaching the Great Moghul: Francophone Travel Writing on India of the 17th and 18th Centuries*. New Delhi: Yoda Press.

Raven, A. (1955). Automation and Egalitarianism. *The European*, October, pp. 18–27.

Ray, R. B. (2012). *Walden × 40: Essays on Thoreau*. Bloomington: Indiana University Press.

Reich, C. (1970). *The Greening of America*. New York: Random House.

Reno, R. R. (2017). Goodbye, Left and Right. *First Things* [online], 8 May. Available at: https://www.firstthings.com/web-exclusives/2017/05/goodbye-left-and-right, accessed 7 September 2021.

Rhodes, C. (1895). Letter. Quoted In Jones, M. and Simpson, W. (2000). *Europe, 1783–1914*. London and New York: Routledge.

Ricardo on machinery and the hand-loom weaver. (2009). *Daily Kos*. Available at: https://www.dailykos.com/stories/2009/6/11/741259/, accessed 25 January 2023.

Ricardo, D. (1973). *The Principles of Political Economy and Taxation*. 3rd edn. Ed. Donald Winch. London: Dent.

Ricardo, D. and Bonar, J. (1887). *Letters of David Ricardo to Thomas Robert Malthus, 1810–1823*. Ed. James Bonar. Oxford: Clarendon Press.

Richter, M. (1977). *The Political Theory of Montesquieu*. Cambridge: Cambridge University Press.

Ridley, M. (2010). *The Rational Optimist*. London: Fourth Estate.

Rifkin, J. (2000). *The End of Work: The Decline of the Global Work-force and the Dawn of the Post-market Era*. London: Penguin.

Robertson, G. (2023). A Town Called Sue. *Times Literary Supplement*, 6251, 20 January.

Robinson, N. and Sachs, J. (2022). Why the Chair of the Lancet's COVID-19 Commission Thinks the US Government Is Preventing a Real Investigation into the Pandemic. *Current Affairs* [online]. Available at: https://www.currentaffairs.org/2022/08/why-the-chair-of-the-lancets

-covid-19-commission-thinks-the-us-government-is-preventing-a-real-investigation-into-the-pandemic, accessed 22 March 2023.

Robinson, P. A. (1969). *The Freudian Left: Wilhelm Reich, Geza Roheim, Herbert Marcuse*. New York: Harper and Row.

RoboticsBiz (2021). How Automation Is Pushing the Boundaries of Drug Development. *RoboticsBiz* [online]. Available at: https://roboticsbiz.com/how-automation-is-pushing-the-boundaries-of-drug-development/, accessed 2 May 2022.

Roe Smith, M. and Marx, L. (eds.) (1994). *Does Technology Drive History? The Dilemma of Technological Determinism*. Cambridge, MA: MIT Press.

Roll, E. (1923). *A History of Economic Thought*. 2nd edn. London: Faber and Faber.

Roscoe, P. (2014). *I Spend Therefore I Am*. Toronto: : Random House Canada.

Rossetto, L. (2018). The Original WIRED Manifesto. *WIRED Magazine* [online], 18 September. Available at: https://www.wired.com/story/original-wired-manifesto/, accessed 6 September 2021.

Rothman, J. (2017). Rod Dreher's Monastic Vision. *The New Yorker* [online]. Available at: https://www.newyorker.com/magazine/2017/05/01/rod-drehers-monastic-vision, accessed 13 January 2023.

Rousseau, J. ([1762] 1968). *The Social Contract*. Trans. Maurice Cranston. Harmondsworth: Penguin.

Rousseau, J. ([1780] 1991). *Émile: Or On Education*. Trans. Allan Bloom. Harmondsworth: Penguin.

Rousseau, J. ([1790] 2000). *Confessions*. Oxford and New York: Oxford University Press.

Rousseau, J. (1988). *Rousseau's Political Writings*. Ed. J. C. Bondanella and A. Ritter. New York and London: W. W. Norton and Company.

Rushkoff, D. (2002). Renaissance Now! Media Ecology and the New Global Narrative. *Explorations in Media Ecology*, 1(1), April 2002, pp. 41–57.

Russell, Ben (2017). *Robots: The 500-Year Quest to Make Machines Human*. London: Scala Arts and Heritage.

Russell, Bertrand ([1946] 2004). *History of Western Philosophy*. London: Routledge Classics.

Russell, Bertrand (1931). *The Scientific Outlook*. London: Allen and Unwin.

Russell, Bertrand (2007). *In Praise of Idleness and Other Essays*. London: Routledge.

Russell, S. (2021). AI in the Economy [recorded lecture]. Reith Lectures, Living with Artificial Intelligence. Gordon Aikman Lecture Theatre, Edinburgh. 5 November. Available at: https://www.bbc.co.uk/sounds/play/moo12fnc, accessed 12 April 2022.

Russell, S. (2021). AI: A Future for Humans? [recorded lecture]. Reith Lectures, Living with Artificial Intelligence. National Innovation Centre for Data, Newcastle. 10 November. Available at: https://www.bbc.co.uk/sounds/play/moo12q21, accessed 13 July 2022.

Russell, S. (2021). The Biggest Event in Human History [recorded lecture]. Reith Lectures, Living with Artificial Intelligence. Alan Turing Institute, British Library, London. 1 November. Available at: https://www.bbc.co.uk/sounds/play/moo1216j, accessed 13 July 2022.

Ryan, A. (ed.) (1979). *The Idea of Freedom: Essays in Honour of Isaiah Berlin*. Oxford: Oxford University Press.

Ryrie, A. (2018). How the Reformation Trained Us to Be Sceptics [speech transcript]. Lectures on Atheism. Gresham College. 1 November.

Saatchi, M. (2022). *Do Not Resuscitate: The Life and Afterlife of Maurice Saatchi*. London: Eris.

Sabine, G. H. (1950). *A History of Political Theory*. New York: Henry Holt and Company.

Sahlins, M. (1968). *Tribesmen*. Englewood Cliffs: Prentice-Hall.

Sahlins, M. (2017). *Stone Age Economics*. London and New York: Routledge Classics.

Said, E. (1979). *Orientalism*. New York: Vintage Books.

Saint-Simon, H. de (1976). *The Political Thought of Saint-Simon*. Ed. Ghita Ionescu. Oxford: Oxford University Press.

Sams, C. (2020). Letter. *London Review of Books*, 42(8), 16 April.

Sams, C. (2022). Letter. *London Review of Books*, 44(19), 6 October.

Sandel, M. J. (2012). *What Money Can't Buy: The Moral Limits of Markets*. London: Allen Lane.

Sargent, L. T. (2010). *Utopianism: A Very Short Introduction*. Oxford: Oxford University Press.

Sartwell, C (2022). No God Required. *Times Literary Supplement*, 6215, 13 May.

Schatzberg, E. (2018). *Technology: Critical History of a Concept*. Chicago: University of Chicago Press.

Schumacher, E. F. ([1973] 1999). *Small Is Beautiful*. Vancouver: Hartley and Marks.

Schumpeter, J. ([1919] 1951). *Imperialism and Social Classes*. Trans. Heinz Norden. New York: Augustus M. Kelley.

Schumpeter, J. ([1942] 1975). *Capitalism, Socialism and Democracy*. New York: Harper and Row.

Schumpeter, J. (1954). *History of Economic Analysis*. New York: Oxford University Press.

Schwartz, B. (2015). *Why We Work*. London: Simon and Schuster.

Scott, B. (2020). *The Heretic's Guide to Global Finance*. London: Pluto Press.

Scott, B. (2022). *Cloudmoney: Cash, Cards, Crypto and the War for Our Wallets*. Harmondsworth: Penguin.

Scott, J. (2017). *Against the Grain*. New Haven: Yale University Press.

Scruton, R. (1990). *The Philosopher on Dover Beach: Essays*. Manchester: Carcanet.

Searle, J. R. (1980). Minds, Brains, and Programs. *The Behavioral and Brain Sciences*, 3(3), 417–24.

Searle, J. (1983). Can Computers Think? , *Minds, Brains, and Science*. Cambridge, MA: Harvard University Press.

Searle, J. R. (2000). *Mind, Language and Society*. London: Phoenix.

Sedlacek, T. (2011). *Economics of Good and Evil: The Quest for Economic Meaning from Gilgamesh to Wall Street*. Oxford: Oxford University Press.

Sellman, M. (2023). Is ChatGPT Too Clever For Its Own Good? *The Times* [online]. Available at: https://www.thetimes.co.uk/article/is-chatgpt-too-clever-for-its-own-good-zzq9th7b8, accessed 6 June 2023.

Sennett, R. (2006). *The Culture of the New Capitalism*. New Haven and London: Yale University Press.

Sennett, R. (2009). *The Craftsman*. London: Penguin.

Sennett, R. (2018). *Building and Dwelling: Ethics for the City*. London: Allen Lane.

Shapin, S. (2018). *The Scientific Revolution.* 2nd edn. Chicago: University of Chicago Press.

Shapin, S. (2023). Paradigms Gone Wild. *London Review of Books,* 45(7), 30 March.

Shead, S. (2016). Eric Schmidt: Advances in AI Will Make Every Human Better. *Business Insider* [online], 8 March. Available at: https://www.businessinsider.com/eric-schmidt-advances-in-ai-will-make-every-human-better-2016-3?r=USandIR=T, accessed 24 January 2023.

Shelley, M. W. ([1818] 1999). *Frankenstein; Or, The Modern Prometheus.* Cambridge: Chadwyck-Healey.

Siedentop, L. (2014). *Inventing the Individual: The Origins of Western Liberalism.* London: Allen Lane.

Silcox, B. (2021). All You Need Is Bots. *Times Literary Supplement,* 6175, 6 August.

Skidelsky. E (2008). *Ernst Cassirer: The Last Philosopher of Culture.* Princeton: Princeton University Press.

Skidelsky, R. and Skidelsky, E. (2013). *How Much Is Enough? Money and the Good Life.* London: Penguin.

Skidelsky, R. (2003). *John Maynard Keynes 1883–1946: Economist. Philosopher. Statesman.* Harmondsworth: Penguin.

Skidelsky, R. (2019). How to Achieve Shorter Working Hours. *Progressive Economy Forum Report.* Available at: https://progressiveeconomyforum.com/wp-content/uploads/2019/08/PEF_Skidelsky_How_to_achieve_shorter_working_hours.pdf, accessed 13 September 2021.

Skidelsky, R. (2022). More Than Economists. *Project Syndicate On Point* [online]. Available at: https://www.project-syndicate.org/onpoint/veblen-keynes-hirschman-biographies-economics-outsiders-by-robert-skidelsky-2021-11, accessed 13 January 2023.

Skidelsky, R. and Craig, N. (eds.) (2016). *Who Runs the Economy?: The Role of Power in Economics.* London: Palgrave Macmillan.

Skidelsky, R. and Craig, N. (eds.). (2020). *Work in the Future.* London: Palgrave Macmillan.

Skinner, B. (1976). Walden Two Revisited. In Skinner, B. ([1948] 1976), *Walden Two.* 2nd edn. New York: Macmillan Publishing Co.

Slavevoyages.org (2021). *Estimates* [online]. Available at: https://www.slavevoyages.org/assessment/estimates, accessed 23 August 2021.

Slocombe, W. (2020). Machine Visions. In Cave, S., Dihal, K. and Dillon, S. (eds.) 2020, *AI Narratives: A History of Imaginative Thinking About Intelligent Machines*. Oxford: Oxford University Press.

Smith, A. ([1759] 1979). *The Theory of Moral Sentiments*. Oxford: Oxford University Press.

Smith, A. ([1776] 1937). *An Inquiry into the Nature and Causes of the Wealth of Nations*. Ed. Edwin Cannan. New York: The Modern Library.

Snow, C. P. (1959). *The Two Cultures and the Scientific Revolution*. Cambridge: Cambridge University Press.

Southern, K. (2022). Humans Could Live to 130 and Beyond by End of the Century. *The Times*, 8 January 2022.

Spencer, D. (2009). *The Political Economy of Work*. London: Routledge.

Spencer, D. A. (2022). *Making Light Work*. Cambridge: Polity Press.

Spengler, O. (1932). *Man and Technics*. Trans. Charles Francis Atkinson. New York: Alfred A. Knopf.

Srnicek, N. and Williams, A. (2015). *Inventing the Future: Postcapitalism and a World Without Work*. London and New York: Verso Books.

Staltz, A. (2017). *The Web Began Dying in 2015, Here's How*. Available at: https://staltz.com/the-web-began-dying-in-2014-heres-how.html, accessed 6 September 2021.

Standing, G. (2014). *A Precariat Charter: From Denizens to Citizens*. London: Bloomsbury.

Stanley, C. (ed.) (2011). *Around the Outsider: Essays Presented to Colin Wilson on the Occasion of His 80th Birthday*. Ropley: O Books.

Starkey, D. (2020). A Perversion of Puritanism. *The Critic* [online], 22 June. Available at: https://thecritic.co.uk/a-perversion-of-puritanism-which-aims-to-trash-our-history/, accessed 7 September 2021.

Stedman Jones, G. (2016). *Karl Marx*. London: Allen Lane.

Stehr, N. (2008). *Knowledge and Democracy: A 21st-Century Perspective*. Somerset, NJ: Transaction.

Steiner, G. (1980). *The Death of Tragedy*. New York: Oxford University Press.

Stern, F. (1970). *The Varieties of History: From Voltaire to the Present.* 2nd edn. London: Macmillan.

Stern, F. (1974). *The Politics of Cultural Despair: A Study in the Rise of the Germanic Ideology.* Berkeley: University of California Press.

Stern, N. H. (2010). *A Blueprint for a Safer Planet: How We Can Save the World and Create Prosperity.* London: Vintage.

Strathern, P. (2019). *Rise and Fall: A History of the World in Ten Empires.* London: Hodder and Stoughton.

Straw, J. and Baxter, M. (2014). *iDisrupted.* London: New Generation Publishing.

Streeck, W. (2017). *How Will Capitalism End?: Essays on a Failing System.* London: Verso.

Strittmatter, K. (2019). *We Have Been Harmonised: Life in China's Surveillance State.* Trans. Ruth Martin. Exeter: Old Street Publishing.

Subrahmanyam, S. (1990). The Hindu Equilibrium [review]. *Journal of Development Economics*, 33(2), pp. 399–403.

Susskind, D. (2020). *A World Without Work.* London: Allen Lane.

Susskind J. (2022). *The Digital Republic: On Freedom and Democracy in the 21st Century.* London: Bloomsbury.

Susskind, R. and Susskind, D. (2015). *The Future of the Professions: How Technology Will Transform the Work of Human Experts.* Oxford: Oxford University Press.

Sutton, C. (1974). *The German Tradition in Philosophy.* London: Weidenfeld and Nicolson.

Suzman J. (2017). *Affluence Without Abundance.* New York: Bloomsbury.

Suzman, J. (2021). *Work: A Deep History from the Stone Age to the Age of Robots.* New York: Penguin Press.

Swift, J. ([1726] 1900). *Gulliver's Travels.* London: Heron Books.

Taylor, C. (2007). *A Secular Age.* Cambridge, MA and London: Belknap Press.

Tegmark, M. (2017). *Life 3.0.* London: Allen Lane.

Terkel, S. (1974). *Working.* New York: The New Press.

Terminate the Terminators (2010). *Scientific American.* 303(1), July. Available at: https://www.scientificamerican.com/article/terminate-the-terminators/, accessed 18 May 2023.

The Economist (1998). *Going Digital: How New Technology Is Changing Our Lives*. London: Portfolio Books.

The Social Dilemma (film, 2020). Directed by J. Orlowski. USA: Argent Pictures. Available at: Netflix.

Thomas, K. (ed.) (1999). *The Oxford Book of Work*. Oxford: Oxford University Press.

Thomas, K. (2009). *The Ends of Life*. Oxford: Oxford University Press.

Thomas, K. (2021). Lights On and Away We Go. *London Review of Books*, 43(10), 20 May.

Thornhill, J. (2020). The Foreseeable, but Largely Unforeseen, Risks of a Tech Crash. *Financial Times* [online], 10 December. Available at: https://www.ft.com/content/obfbf17e-a668-4f58-a940-cae9a9bec5f4., accessed 13 September 2021.

Thornhill, J. (2022). Don't Worry About AI Sentience. Do Worry About What the Machines Are Doing. *Financial Times* [online]. Available at: https://www.ft.com/content/0f332662-6d98-4d33-a687-d3951a3c1cb1, accessed 4 July 2022.

Tocqueville, A. de ([1835] 2000). *Democracy in America*. Ed. Harvey C. Mansfield and Delba Winthrop. Chicago and London: University of Chicago Press.

Tocqueville, A. de ([1835] 2017). *Journeys to England and Ireland*. Ed. J. P. Mayer. London and New York: Routledge.

Tononi, G. (2004). An Information Integration Theory of Consciousness. *BMC Neuroscience*, 5(42).

Torr, D. (ed.). (1936). *Karl Marx and Friedrich Engels: Correspondence, 1846–1895*. London: Lawrence and Wishart.

Torres, É. (2021). Against Longtermism. *Aeon*. Available at: https://aeon.co/essays/why-longtermism-is-the-worlds-most-dangerous-secular-credo, accessed 16 March 2023.

Toulmin, S. (1982). *The Return to Cosmology: Postmodern Science and the Theology of Nature*. Berkeley and London: University of California Press.

Toynbee, A. J. (1947). *A Study of History, Abridgment of Volumes I–VI*. Ed. D. C. Somervell. New York and Oxford: Oxford University Press.

Tran, P. (2017). How New Technologies Can Create Huge Numbers of Meaningful Jobs. *World Economic Forum*, 19 June. Available at:https://

www.weforum.org/agenda/2017/06/how-new-technologies-can-create-huge-numbers-of-meaningful-jobs/, accessed 21 July 2021.

Treitschke, H. V. (1914). *Selections from Treitschke's Lectures on Politics*. New York: Frederick A. Stokes Company.

Trentmann, F. (2016). *The Empire of Things*. London: Allen Lane.

Trevelyan, H. (1981). *Goethe and the Greeks*. Cambridge: Cambridge University Press.

Turing, A. (1951). Can Digital Computers Think? *The Turing Archive* [online], 15 May. Available at: https://aperiodical.com/wp-content/uploads/2018/01/Turing-Can-Computers-Think.pdf, accessed 23 January 2023.

Turner, F. (2006). *From Counterculture to Cyberculture*. Chicago: University of Chicago Press.

Turner, F. J. ([1893] 2007). *The Significance of the Frontier in American History*. Marlborough: Adam Matthew Digital.

Turner, H. A. (1972). Fascism and Modernisation. *World Politics*, 24(4), July, pp. 547–64.

2001: A Space Odyssey (film, 1968). Directed by Stanley Kubrick. USA: Metro-Goldwyn-Mayer Studios Inc.

Unger, R. M. (2019). *The Knowledge Economy*. London: Verso.

Ure, A. (1835). *The Philosophy of Manufactures, or, An Exposition of the Scientific, Moral, and Commercial Economy of the Factory System of Great Britain*. London: C. Knight.

Van Parijs, P. and Vanderborght, Y. (2017). *Basic Income: A Radical Proposal for a Free Society and a Sane Economy*. Cambridge, MA: Harvard University Press.

Vasbinder, S. H. (1984). *Scientific Attitudes in Mary Shelley's Frankenstein*. Ann Arbor: UMI Research Press.

Veblen, T. ([1899] 1992). *The Theory of the Leisure Class*. London: Routledge.

Veblen, T. ([1918] 2015). *The Higher Learning in America*. Baltimore: Johns Hopkins University Press.

Vives, J. L. ([1531] 1971). *Vives: On Education: A Translation of the De Tradendis Disciplinis of Juan Luis Vives*. Trans. Foster Watson. Lanham: Rowman and Littlefield.

Volney, C. (1825). *Oeuvres de C.-F. Volney*, vol. 1. Paris.

Voltaire (1759). *An Essay on Universal History, the Manners, and Spirit of Nations, from the Reign of Charlemagne to the Age of Louis XIV*. Trans. Thomas Nugent. London: J. Nourse.

Wallerstein, I. (1974). *The Modern World-System*, vol. 1. New York: Academic Press.

Waltz, K. (1979). *Theories of International Politics*. Reading, MA: Addison-Wesley.

Warburton, N. (ed.) (1999). *Philosophy: Basic Readings*. London: Routledge.

Watt, D. (ed.) (1975). *Aldous Huxley: A Critical Heritage*. London and New York: Routledge.

Webb, B. (1948). *Our Partnership*. London, New York and Toronto: Longmans, Green and Co.

Weber, M. ([1920] 1968). *The Religion of China: Confucianism and Taoism*. New York: Free Press.

Weber, M. ([1930] 1965). *The Protestant Ethic and the Spirit of Capitalism*. London: Unwin University Books.

Weber, M. (1947). *The Methodology of the Social Sciences*. Trans. Edward A. Shils and Henry A. Finch. New York: Free Press.

Weichert, B. J. (2023). A New Space Race. *Times Literary Supplement*, 6265, 28 April.

Wells, H. G. ([1896] 2017). *The Island of Doctor Moreau*. London: William Collins.

Wells, H. G. ([1899] 1994). *When the Sleeper Wakes*. Ed. John J. Lawton. London: Dent.

Wells, H. G. (1905). *A Modern Utopia*. London: Chapman and Hall.

Wells, H. G. ([1923] 2020). *Men Like Gods*. New York: Macmillan.

Wells, H. G. (1927). *The World of William Clissold*. Leipzig: Bernhard Tauchnitz.

Wells, H. G. (1945). *Mind at the End of Its Tether*. London: William Heinemann.

Whipple, T. (2019). Jeff Bezos: Inside the Mind of the $100bn Man Who Won't Stop at World Domination. *The Times* [online], 1 November. Available at: https://www.thetimes.co.uk/article/jeff-bezos-inside-the-mind-of-the-100bn-man-who-wont-stop-at-world-domination-3f8dmockq, accessed 30 June 2021.

Whipple, T. (2022). Scientist Hoarding Stools to Prevent Humanity Going Down the Pan. *The Times* [online]. Available at: https://www.thetimes.co.uk/article/stool-bank-will-store-novel-gut-bacteria-to-stop-humanity-going-down-the-pan-pqlwskodt, accessed 9 January 2023.

Whipple, T. (2023). AI Poses Same Threat as Nuclear Wars and Pandemics, Experts Say. *The Times* [online]. Available at: https://www.thetimes.co.uk/article/ai-chatbot-threat-nuclear-war-pandemic-fdxd2m2r7, accessed 31 May 2023.

White, L. (1962). *Medieval Technology and Social Change*. Oxford: Clarendon Press.

Why Britain Needs More Robots (2017). *Centre for Policy Studies*, Economic Bulletin, No. 100, 8 November. Available at: https://www.cps.org.uk/files/reports/original/171108093013-WhyBritainNeedsMoreRobots.pdf., accessed 23 August 2021.

Wilczek, F. (2017). Physical Foundations of Future Technology. In Franklin, D. (ed.), *Megatech: Technology in 2050*. New York: The Economist Books.

Wink, A. (1986). *Land and Sovereignty in India*. Cambridge: Cambridge University Press.

Wink, A. (2020). *The Making of the Indo-Islamic World c.700–1800 CE*. Cambridge: Cambridge University Press.

Winner, L. (1977). *Autonomous Technology: Technics-out-of-control as a Theme in Political Thought*. Cambridge, MA: MIT Press.

Winterson, J. (2020). *Frankissstein*. London: Vintage Books.

Winterson, J. (2021). *12 Bytes*. London: Jonathan Cape.

Withers, M., (2021). Work Less and Be More Creative – a Radical Prescription. *Financial Times* [online]. Available at: https://www.ft.com/content/6c6f8d99-ac36-4043-bd1d-459d6763b413, accessed 2 May 2022.

Wittfogel, K. A. (1957). *Oriental Despotism: A Comparative Study of Total Power*. New Haven: Yale University Press.

Wollstonecraft, M. ([1792] 1978). *A Vindication of the Rights of Woman*. 2nd edn. Harmondsworth: Penguin.

Woodcock, J. (2017). *Working the Phones*. London: Pluto Press.

Worstall, T. (2018). Automation Isn't Nearly as Disruptive as You Might Think. *CapX* [online]. Available at: http://capx.co/yyLJY, accessed 21 July 2021.

Xiang, L. (2020). *The Quest for Legitimacy in Chinese Politics.* London and New York: Routledge.

Yalman, N. and Ikeda, D. (2008). *A Passage to Peace.* I. B. Tauris.

Yoffee, N. (1995). Political Economy in Early Mesopotamian States. *Annual Review of Anthropology.*

Zamyatin, Y. ([1924] 1993). *We.* Trans. Clarence Brown. London: Penguin.

Ziolkowski, T. (2000). *The Sin of Knowledge: Ancient Themes and Modern Variations.* Princeton: Princeton University Press.

Žižek, S. (2012). The Revolt of the Salaried Bourgeoisie. *London Review of Books,* 34(2), 26 January.

Zuboff, S. (2019). *The Age of Surveillance Capitalism.* London: Profile Books.

Zweig, S. ([1942] 2011). *The World of Yesterday.* London: Pushkin Press.

Notes

Preface

1 For a more complete discussion of these matters, see chapter 1 in Skidelsky, R. and Skidelsky, E. (2013) *How Much Is Enough? Money and the Good Life*. London: Penguin; and Pecchi, L. and Piga, G. (eds.) (2008) *Revisiting Keynes: Economic Possibilities for Our Grandchildren*. Cambridge, MA: MIT Press.

2 Hayek, F. ([1944] 1994) *The Road to Serfdom*. Ed. Milton Friedman. Chicago: University of Chicago Press, p. 24.

3 The prison cells were to be constantly illuminated by light passing through the glass outside walls of the cells to the central watchtower.

4 See Keynes's exchange with Hayek on this subject: JMK to F. A. Hayek, 28 June 1944. Cited in Skidelsky, R. (2003), pp. 722–4.

5 Keynes, J. M. *The Economic Consequences of the Peace, Collected Writings of J. M. Keynes*, vol.2, p. 13. But in *The Economic Consequences of a Declining Population, The Collected Writings of J. M. Keynes*, vol.14, p.125, he suggested that 'we shall be faced in a very short time with a stationary or declining level' of population, the 'we' being Britain.

6 Shapin, S. (2023) Paradigms Gone Wild. *London Review of Books*, 45(7), 30 March.

Introduction

1 Carlyle, T. (1829) Signs of the Times. *Edinburgh Review*, 98.

2 Russell, B. (1931) *The Scientific Outlook*. London: Allen and Unwin, p. 264.

3 Toynbee, A. (1947) *A Study of History, Abridgement of Volumes I–VI*. Ed. D. C. Somervell. New York and Oxford: Oxford University Press, p. 198.

4 Huxley, A. (1961) Lecture to the Tavistock Group, California Medical School. San Francisco.

5 Whipple, T. (2023). AI Poses Same Threat as Nuclear Wars and Pandemics, Experts Say. *The Times* [online]. Available at: https://www.the times.co.uk/article/ai-chatbot-threat-nuclear-war-pandemic-fdxd2m217, accessed 31 May 2023.

6 Dostoevsky, F. ([1864] 1918) *Notes from Underground. White Nights and Other Stories*. Trans. Constance Garnett. New York: The Macmillan Company, p. 74.

Glossary for the Technologically Challenged

1 See *New Fontana Dictionary of Modern Thought*, 3rd edn. London: HarperCollins, pp. 150–51.

2 Oxford English Dictionary (2022) Algorithm. *OED Online*. Oxford University Press. Available at: www.oed.com/view/Entry/4959, accessed 6 February 2023.

3 Cave, S., Dihal, K. and Dillon, S. (2020) Introduction: Imagining AI. *AI Narratives: A History of Imaginative Thinking about Intelligent Machines*. Oxford: Oxford University Press, p. 4.

4 Donoghue, R., Ekkehard, E., Moore, P., Woodcock, J. (2023). *Understanding AI Regulation – An Inception Report*. ILO, 17 April.

5 Malhotra, R. (2021) *Artificial Intelligence and the Future of Power*. New Delhi: Rupa, p. 13.

6 Davies, W. (2023). The Reaction Economy. *London Review of Books*, 45(5), 2 March.

Prologue: Robotic Hype: Old and New

1 Strathern, P. (2019) *Rise and Fall: A History of the World in Ten Empires*. London: Hodder and Stoughton, p. 133.

2 Needham, J. (1978) *The Shorter Science and Civilisation in China: An Abridgement of Joseph Needham's Original Text*. Ed. Colin Ronan. Cambridge: Cambridge University Press, p. 92.

3 Mayor, A. (2018) *Gods and Robots: Myths, Machines, and Ancient Dreams of Technology*. Princeton: Princeton University Press, pp. 105–8.

4 Nelson, V. (2001) *The Secret Life of Puppets*. Cambridge, MA: Harvard University Press.

5 Lee, K. and Project Syndicate (2020) The Art of AI. *Project Syndicate*. Available at: https://www.project-syndicate.org/onpoint/state-of-ai-by-kai-fu-lee-2020-05, accessed 6 July 2022.

6 Colton, S. (2020) Possibilities and Limitations of AI: What Can't Machines Do? In Skidelsky, R. and Craig, N. (eds.) *Work in the Future*. London: Palgrave Macmillan, p. 60.

7 Brose, C. (2020) *The Kill Chain*. New York: Hachette. Cited in Cockburn, A. (2020) Blips on the Screen. *London Review of Books*, 42(23), 3 December. Boston Dynamics is the best-known 'robotic solutions' company which designs robots for business and military uses.

8 Kuchler, H. (2022) Will AI Turbocharge the Hunt for New Drugs? *Financial Times* [online]. Available at: https://www.ft.com/content/3e57ad6c-493d-4874-a663-0cb200d3cdb5, accessed 4 July 2022.

9 Carreyrou, J. (2018) *Bad Blood: Secrets and Lies in a Silicon Valley Startup*. London: Picador.

10 Birrell, I. (2022) Sam Bankman-Fried's Elitist Altruism. *Unherd*. Available at: https://unherd.com/2022/11/the-evils-of-elitist-altruism/, accessed 17 March 2023.

11 Musk's stunt with the pig was simply a rerun of an experiment carried out in 1965, when a bull with a neural implant was made to walk away from the matador instead of charging him, by a press of a button.

12 Kurzweil, R. (1999) *The Age of Spiritual Machines*. London: Phoenix; Kurzweil, R. (2005) *The Singularity Is Near: When Humans Transcend Biology*. New York: Viking Penguin. Fellow technical-ethicist José M. Galvan also predicts that technology will achieve a 'finalised perfection of man' in Galvin (2003) 'On Technoethics'. *IEEE Robotics and Automation Magazine*, 10(4), pp. 58–63.

13 See Hassabis, D. Creativity and AI (2018) The Rothschild Foundation Lecture. The Royal Academy of Arts. 17 September.

Chapter 1: The Coming of Machines

1 Elias, N. (1995) Technization and Civilization. *Theory, Culture and Society*, 12(3), pp. 7–42, p. 37.

2 Keynes, J. M. (1930) Economic Possibilities for Our Grandchildren. In Keynes, J. M. (2015) *The Essential Keynes*. Ed. Robert Skidelsky. London: Penguin, pp. 77–8.

3 Cited in White, L. (1962) *Medieval Technology and Social Change*. Oxford: Clarendon Press, p. 134. For other imaginings of flying machines in literature, see: Tennyson's mention of 'airy navies' in his poem 'Locksley Hall' (1842) and Mary Shelley's 'sailing balloons' in *The Last Man* (1826).

4 Vives, J. L. ([1531] 1971) *Vives: On Education: A Translation of the De Tradendis Disciplinis of Juan Luis Vives*. Trans. Foster Watson. Lanham: Rowman and Littlefield, p. 209. Cited in Lindberg, D. and Shank, M. H. (eds.) (2003) *The Cambridge History of Science*, vol. 2. Cambridge: Cambridge University Press, p. 296.

5 Bacon, F. (1996) *The Oxford Francis Bacon*, vol. 6: *Philosophical Studies c. 1611–c.1619*. Ed. Graham Rees. Trans. Michael Edwards. Oxford: Oxford University Press, pp. 100–101.

6 Engels, F. and Marx, K. ([1848] 1998). *The Communist Manifesto*. London and New York: Verso, p. 38.

7 Horowitz, A. and Maley, T. (eds.) (1994) *The Barbarism of Reason: Max Weber and the Twilight of Enlightenment*. Toronto, Buffalo and London: University of Toronto Press, p. 15.

8 The two contrasting positions are set out in Roe Smith, M. and Marx, L. (eds.) (1994), *Does Technology Drive History? The Dilemma of Technological Determinism*. Cambridge, MA: MIT Press, pp. 30–33.

9 Cited in Pacey, A. (1983) *The Culture of Technology*. Cambridge, MA: MIT Press, p. 25.

10 Muller, H. J. (1962) *Freedom in the Ancient World*. London: Secker and Warburg, p. 31. Cf. Schumpeter: 'Things economic and social move by

their own momentum and the ensuing situations compel individuals and groups to behave in certain way whatever they may wish to do – not indeed by destroying their freedom of choice but by shaping the choosing mentalities and by narrowing the list of possibilities from which to choose.' *Capitalism, Socialism, and Democracy*. Cited in Roe Smith and Marx (1994), p. 220.

11 'A plan drawn up by the US Secretary of the Treasury, Henry Morgenthau Jr (b. 1891, d. 1967) which envisaged a post-war Germany as an agricultural, deindustrialized country which would be divided into a northern and a southern half, with the Rhineland, the North Sea coast, and other important strategic or industrial areas coming under international control. After initial acceptance by Roosevelt, it was quickly withdrawn as completely impractical, as such a Germany would continue to be reliant on foreign finance.' Palmowski, J. (2008) *A Dictionary of Contemporary World History*. 3rd edn. Oxford: Oxford University Press. Available at: https://www.oxfordreference.com/display/10.1093/oi/authority.20110803100209776;jsessionid=272BDDEEC2D51B755A17 452CE05A48B3, accessed 6 February 2023.

12 Coren, G. (2020) OK, Coneheads, Enough of Your Weird Science. *The Times* [online]. Available at: https://www.thetimes.co.uk/article/ok-coneheads-enough-of-your-weird-science-2wfwn3gbp, accessed 4 January 2023.

13 Cited in Koch, A. (1959) *Philosophy for a Time of Crisis*. New York: E. P. Dutton and Co., p. 12.

Chapter 2: Natural Obstacles

1 Bostrom, N. (2014). *Superintelligence: Paths, Dangers, Strategies*. Oxford: Oxford University Press, p. 56.

2 Felipe Fernandez Armesto goes further to argue that 'before the Ice Age was over, some of the world's best ideas had already sprung to life and modified the world'. Cited in Collins, J. (2019) Minds Matter. *Times Literary Supplement*, 6073/4, 23 and 30 August.

3 Toynbee (1947), p. 87.

4 Ibid., p. 570.

5 Ibid., p. 3.

6 Ibid., p. 199.

7 Ibid., p. 276.

8 Ibid., pp. 69–70.

9 Wink, A. (2020) *The Making of the Indo-Islamic World c.700–1800 CE.* Cambridge: Cambridge University Press, pp. 4–5.

10 Kuhn, T. S. (1962) *The Structure of Scientific Revolutions.* Chicago: University of Chicago Press. Kuhn explains how scientists go on practising 'normal' science long after events in the world have 'falsified' their theories. His theory of 'paradigm shifts' casts doubt on the cumulative enlargement of scientific knowledge.

11 Pacey (1983), pp. 55–6.

12 Mary Beard reminds us that though tourism existed in the Roman world, it was 'largely restricted to emperors, aristocrats, and the super-rich'. Beard, M. (2022) I Came, I Saw, I Bought the Souvenir. *Times Literary Supplement,* 6216, 20 May. It then disappeared for centuries before being revived in the form of pilgrimages.

13 Cited in Toynbee (1947), p. 56.

14 For its influence on American institutionalists, see Camic, C. (2020) *Veblen: The Making of an Economist Who Unmade Economics.* London and Cambridge, MA: Harvard University Press, pp. 145–6.

15 Bauer, P. (2003) Development Economics: The Spurious Consensus and Its Background. In Streissler, E. W. and Hayek, F. A. (eds.) *Roads to Freedom: Essays in Honour of Friedrich von Hayek.* London: Routledge.

16 Mackinder, H. (1904) The Geographical Pivot of History. *The Geographical Journal,* 23(4), April 1904, pp. 421–37, p. 422.

17 Waltz, K. (1979) *Theories of International Politics.* Reading, MA: Addison-Wesley.

18 Mackinder, H. (1919) *Democratic Ideals and Reality.* New York: Henry Holt and Company, p. 186.

19 Headrick, D. (2009) *Technology: A World History.* Oxford: Oxford University Press, p. 89.

Chapter 3: The Rise of Capitalism

1 The subtitle of Peter Stothard's book on Crassus, reviewed by Holland, T. (2022) Rich as Crassus. *Times Literary Supplement*, 7 October 2022.

2 Roll, E. (1923) *A History of Economic Thought*, 2nd edn. London: Faber and Faber, p. 276.

3 Mahabharata. Cited in Mackenzie, D. A. (1918) *Indian Myth and Legend*. London: The Gresham Publishing Company Limited, p. 107.

4 E.g. Suzman, J. (2017) *Affluence without Abundance*. New York: Bloomsbury; Sahlins, M. (2017) *Stone Age Economics*. London and New York: Routledge Classics.

5 Donkin, R. (2010) *The History of Work*. Basingstoke: Palgrave Macmillan.

6 Cipolla, C. M. (1978) *The Economic History of World Population*, 7th edn. Harmondsworth: Penguin, p. 42; see also Parry, R. L. (2019) Flight to the Forest. *London Review of Books*, 41(20), 24 October 2019: 'The Penan children were born in the jungles to mothers who rarely encountered a doctor. They passed through childhood without ever seeing a teacher, and the girls married and had children of their own soon after puberty. They foraged, hunted and moved through the forest in the only way they knew, and then they died.'

7 Meghnad Desai comments: 'The Abrahamic story doesn't tell us what life was like in paradise and how many generations passed before being ejected from the Garden of Eden. The transition is abrupt and complete. The Yuga system travels slowly to Kaliyug, corrupting bit by bit. The Abrahamic system reflects the trauma of leaving the womb. The Hindu cycle is more like aging.' Personal communication, 12 December 2020.

8 Headrick (2009), p. 12.

9 Harari, Y. N. (2014) *Sapiens: A Brief History of Humankind*. London: Vintage Books, chapter 5.

10 Camic (2020), p. 303.

11 See Graeber, D. and Wengrow, D. (2021) *The Dawn of Everything: A New History of Humanity*. In Gray, J. (2021) How Fear Makes Us Human.

New Statesman [online]. Available at: https://www.newstatesman.com/culture/books/2021/11/dawn-everything-new-history-humanity-david-graeber-wengrow-review, accessed 6 July 2022.

12 Monbiot, G. (2022) *Regenesis.* London: Allen Lane. Via McKibben, B. (2022) What's for Dinner? *Times Literary Supplement*, 6226, 29 July 2022.

13 Klemm, F. (1964), *A History of Western Technology.* Cambridge, MA: MIT Press, p. 27.

14 Cited in ibid., p. 19.

15 On this see Thomas, K. (2009) *The Ends of Life.* Oxford: Oxford University Press, pp. 54f.

16 This is the argument of Fred Hirsch, who invented the term 'positional goods' to describe those goods which were naturally scarce or kept scarce artificially. See Hirsch, F. (1976) *Social Limits to Growth.* Cambridge, MA and London: Harvard University Press.

17 Guizot, F. ([1828] 1997) *The History of Civilization in Europe.* Ed. Larry Siedentop. London and New York: Penguin, pp. 44–5.

18 Luchaire, A. (1909) *La Société française au temps de Philippe Augustus.* Paris: Hachette, p. 265. Cited in Elias, N. (2000) *The Civilising Process.* Malden, MA: Blackwell Publishing, p. 241.

19 Montesquieu, C. ([1748] 2001) *The Spirit of the Laws.* Ed. David Wallace Carrithers. Trans. Thomas Nugent. Ontario: Batoche, p. 33.

20 Siedentop, L. (2014) *Inventing the Individual: The Origins of Western Liberalism.* London: Allen Lane.

21 For a detailed discussion see Wallerstein, I. (1974) *The Modern World-System*, vol. 1. New York: Academic Press, pp. 21–57; Landes, D. S. (2003) *The Unbound Prometheus: Technical Change and Industrial Development in Western Europe from 1750 to the Present*, 2nd edn. Cambridge: Cambridge University Press, pp. 18–19; North, D. C. and Thomas, R. P. (1973) *The Rise of the Western World: A New Economic History.* Cambridge: Cambridge University Press, pp. 11–12.

22 *The Unbound Prometheus*, p. 18.

23 Hopkins, E. (1982), Working Hours and Conditions during the Industrial Revolution: A Re-appraisal. *Economic History Review*, 2nd series, 35(1), February, p. 53.

24 Ovitt, G. (1986) The Cultural Context of Western Technology: Early Christian Attitudes toward Manual Labor. *Technology and Culture*, 27(3), pp. 477–500, p. 498.

25 Mumford, L. (1967) *The Myth of the Machine*, vol. 1. New York: Harcourt Brace Jovanovich, p. 269.

26 Tawney, R. H. (1930) Foreword. In Weber, M. ([1930] 1965) *The Protestant Ethic and the Spirit of Capitalism*. London: Unwin University Books, p. 2.

27 Weber ([1930] 1965), p. 60.

28 Weber discusses this difficult set of ideas in chapter 4 of ibid.

29 Ibid., p. 39.

30 For an account of the role of feasting in Christian Europe, see Taylor, C. (2007) *A Secular Age*. Cambridge, MA and London: Belknap Press, pp. 45–7.

31 Weber (1930 [1965])., pp. 41–3.

Chapter 4: Economists and Luddites

1 Cited in Gaukroger, S. (2020) *Civilization and the Culture of Science: Science and the Shaping of Modernity, 1795–1935*. Oxford: Oxford University Press, p. 69.

2 The material foundation of Britain's naval supremacy was the hardwood chestnut coppice woodlands of Sussex and Kent. These produced dense charcoal which made possible the high smelting temperatures which produced cannon which didn't crack when fired, and fired three times as fast as ships armed with bronze cannons. (Sams, C. (2022) Keys to the World. Letter. *London Review of Books*, 44(19), 6 October 2022.)

3 Landes, D. S. (2003) *The Unbound Prometheus: Technical Change and Industrial Development in Western Europe from 1750 to the Present*, 2nd edn. Cambridge: Cambridge University Press, p. 69.

4 Crafts, N. F. R. (1985) *British Economic Growth during the Industrial Revolution*. Oxford: Clarendon Press, p. 37; see also Archer, I. W. (2021) Chaos and Opulence. *Times Literary Supplement*, 6166, 4 June. Available at: https://www.the-tls.co.uk/articles/london-and-the-seventeenth-century-margarette-lincoln-review-ian-w-archer/, accessed 7 September 2021.

5 North, D. C. and Thomas, R. P. (1973) *The Rise of the Western World: A New Economic History*. Cambridge: Cambridge University Press, pp. 2–4. Cf. Acemoglu, D., Johnson, S. and Robinson, J. (2005) *Income and Democracy*. London: Centre for Economic Policy Research, who explain the success of Britain and Holland after 1500 through institutional constraints on executive power.

6 Neoclassical economists consider 'enclosure' the rational solution to the problem of 'over-grazing', or 'tragedy of the commons'. Commonly owned property will be over-grazed as each flock owner takes advantage of the 'free land' to increase the size of his flock, leading to exhaustion of the land.

7 Klemm (1964), p. 172.

8 North, D. C. and Thomas, R. P. (1970) An Economic Theory of the Growth of the Western World. *The Economic History Review*, 23(1), pp. 1–17, p. 10.

9 Hume, D. (1793) Of Liberty and Despotism. In Hume, D. (1793) *Essays and Treatises on Several Subjects*. London: T. Cadell, London.

10 For the theory of the corridor, see Acemoglu, D. Johnson, S. and Robinson, J. (2005) *Income and Democracy*. London: Centre for Economic Policy Research. I am indebted to Marcus Miller for drawing my attention to the Michael Ignatieff quote.

11 Donkin, R. (2010) *The History of Work*. Basingstoke: Palgrave Macmillan, p. 29.

12 Ricardo, D. ([1817] 1973) *The Principles of Political Economy and Taxation*, 3rd edn. Ed. Donald Winch. London: Dent, p. 264.

13 Ibid., p. 269, paraphrased, slightly shortened.

14 Ibid., p. 267.

15 Ibid., p. 266.

16 In his review of Pierre Charbonnier's *Affluence and Freedom*, tr. Andrew Brown, *London Review of Books*, 2 March 2023, Oliver Cussen points to the importance of carbon extraction in freeing eighteenth-century Europeans from 'ecological anxiety' brought about by the continuous extension of land under cultivation.

17 For discussion, see Marx, K. ([1867] 1965). *Capital*, vol. 1. Ed. Friedrich Engels. Moscow: Progress Publishers, chapter 15.

18 Hobsbawm, E. J. (1969) *Industry and Empire.* Harmondsworth: Penguin, pp. 79–95.

19 See Crafts, N. F. R. (1990) The New Economic History and the Industrial Revolution. In Mathis, P. and Davis J. A. (eds.), *The First Industrial Revolution.* Oxford: Basil Blackwell, pp. 39–42. See also: Ricardo on Machinery and the Handloom Weavers (2009) *Daily Kos.* Available at:_https://www.dailykos.com/stories/2009/6/11/741259/, accessed 25 January 2023.

20 Ibid., p. 128.

21 Tocqueville, A. de ([1835] 2017) *Journeys to England and Ireland.* Ed. J. P. Mayer. London and New York: Routledge, p. 107.

22 Kay, J. P. (1832) *Moral and Physical Conditions of the Operatives Employed in the Cotton Manufacture in Manchester.* Cited in Hopkins, E. (1974) Working Conditions in Victorian Stourbridge. *International Review of Social History,* 19(3), p. 401.

23 Gaskell, E. C. (1855) *North and South.* London: Chapman and Hall; Gaskell, E. C. (1854) *Mary Barton: A Tale of Manchester Life,* 5th edn. London: Chapman and Hall.

24 Cherry, M. (2018) The Future Encyclopedia of Luddism. In Davies, W. (ed.) (2019) *Economic Science Fictions.* London: Goldsmiths Press.

25 Maddison, A. (2006) *The World Economy [Electronic Resource]:* vol. 1: *A Millennial Perspective* and vol. 2: *Historical Statistics.* Paris: OECD Publishing: p. 183 (Table A1-a). Available at: https://www.stat.berkeley.edu/~aldous/157/Papers/world_economy.pdf, accessed 23 August 2021.

26 Ibid., p. 185.

27 Ibid., p. 347.

28 Cole, G. D. H. (1927) *A Short History of the British Working Class Movement,* vol. 1. London: G. Allen and Unwin, pp. 181–4.

29 Deane, P. and Cole, W. A. (1969) *British Economic Growth: 1688–1959.* 2nd edn. London: Cambridge University Press, p. 191.

Chapter 5: Why Europe and Not Asia?

1 Cited in Torr, D. (ed.) (1936). *Karl Marx and Friedrich Engels: Correspondence, 1846–1895.* London: Lawrence and Wishart, p. 66.

2 When Lenin seized power in Russia in 1917, he turned the Asiatic mode bequeathed by Marx to his own advantage with his slogan 'electrification plus the Soviets': there was no reason why the Soviet state should not exploit the peasants itself to industrialize the country.

3 Wittfogel, K. A. (1957). *Oriental Despotism: A Comparative Study of Total Power*. New Haven: Yale University Press, p. 227.

4 Ibid., p. 106.

5 Maddison (2006), Table 1-2, p. 30.

6 Ibid., p. 47.

7 Aristotle (1885), *The Politics*, Trans. Benjamin Jowett. Oxford: Clarendon Press. p. 9.

8 I lack the knowledge even to begin to discuss the civilizations of sub-Saharan Africa, but I would be surprised if they diverged significantly from the patterns of development experienced by the other non-European societies.

9 Alan Mikhail in *God's Shadow* (2020) goes so far as to place the Ottoman empire at the 'centre of global modernity' in the sultanate of Selim I (1512–20), a claim vigorously rebutted by fellow scholars of the Ottoman past. (See Pfeifer, H. (2021) Global Morality Play. *London Review of Books*, 43(13), 1 July. Available at: https://www.lrb.co.uk/the-paper/v43/n13/helen-pfeifer/global-morality-play, accessed 7 September 2021.)

10 Montgomery Watt, W. (1971) *The Influence of Islam on Medieval Europe*. Edinburgh: Edinburgh University Press, p. 22.

11 Bulliet, R. W. (1994) *Determinism and Pre-Industrial Technology*. In Roe Smith, M. and Marx, L. (eds.) (1994) , p. 202.

12 Ellis, F. W. (2005) *In What Way, and to What Degree, Did the Mughal State Inhibit Smithian Growth In India in the Seventeenth Century?*. LSE No. 14/05. This mirrors J. R. Hicks's famous contrast between the revenue and market economy, in his (1969) *Theory of Economic History*. Oxford, London and New York: Oxford University Press, pp. 22–4.

13 Kamla (2011) Abu Fazl: Governance and Administration. In Singh, M. P. and Roy, H. (eds.) *Indian Political Thought*. Delhi: Pearson, p. 49.

14 Lal, D. (1988) *The Hindu Equilibrium*. Oxford: Clarendon Press. For a dissenting view, see review by Subrahmanyam, S. (1990) The Hindu Equilibrium. *Journal of Development Economics*, 33(2), pp. 399–403.

15 Goody, J. (1996) *The East in the West.* Cambridge: Cambridge University Press.

16 Athar Ali, M. (2006) *Mughal India.* New Delhi: Oxford University Press, p. 340.

17 Wendy Doniger calls it 'polythetic polytheism'. Doniger, W. (2009) *The Hindus: An Alternative History.* New York: The Penguin Press, p. 29.

18 Ibid., p. 44.

19 Ibid., p. 533.

20 Athar Ali (2006), p. 341.

21 Smith, A. ([1776] 1937). *An Inquiry into the Nature and Causes of the Wealth of Nations.* Ed. Edwin Cannan. New York: The Modern Library, p. 95.

22 Maddison (2006).

23 Stephen Broadberry, who thinks Maddison's estimates of Chinese GDP per head too low, nevertheless supports the broad thrust of his conclusion. Broadberry, S. (2013) Accounting for the Great Divergence. LSE Economic History Working Papers, 184. Available at: https://eprints.lse.ac.uk/54573/1/WP184.pdf, accessed 25 January 2023. China was richer than England in 1086. It was 'likely' that Italy was already ahead of China by 1300. A smaller part of China, the Yangtze delta, may have been on a par with the most developed parts of Europe in 1500. In contrast, the revisionist 'California school' argues that China only fell behind Europe economically in the nineteenth century, by which time Europe had started to intrude on its development, a view endorsed by Thomas Piketty. In rebuttal, Broadberry argues that the California School have 'massively exaggerated the development level of the most advanced Asian economies in 1800' (ibid., p. 3). He dates the great 'divergence' between Europe and Asia from 1700.

24 Mokyr, J. (2017) *A Culture of Growth*, Princeton, Princeton University Press, p. 148.

25 The Cambridge biochemist and historian Joseph Needham published a twelve-volume *History of Science and Civilization in China* (1954–84).

26 Cited in Muhlhahn, K. (2019) *Making China Modern: From the Great Qing to Xi Jinping.* Cambridge, MA: Belknap Press, pp. 90–91.

27 Needham, J. (1978) *The Shorter Science and Civilisation in China: An Abridgement of Joseph Needham's Original Text.* Ed. by Colin Ronan. Cambridge: Cambridge University Press, p. 76.

28 Echoing the Qianlong Emperor's reply to the Macartney Mission in 1792, Henry Kissinger has written of China's view of the external world: 'The Promised Land is China and the Chinese are already there'. Cited in Xiang, L. (2020) *The Quest for Legitimacy in Chinese Politics*. London and New York: Routledge, p. 63.

29 Headrick (2009), p. 73.

30 Goodrich, L. C. (2002) *A Short History of the Chinese People*. Newton Abbot: David and Charles, p. 95.

31 It's amazing that western strategic experts who warn about the build-up of the Chinese navy seem to have no knowledge of what happened when China had no navy.

32 Xiang (2020) has a more nuanced reading, citing dogmatic demands by the Catholic hierarchy as a major cause of the rupture, pp. 9–18.

33 A Chinese scholar of the first century CE wrote of the first Ch'in emperor: 'The resources of the empire were exhausted in supplying [Shihuang's] government, and yet were insufficient to satisfy his desires.' Cited in Goodrich (2002), p. 36.

34 Achievements of the bureaucratic system since the 1970s include spectacular economic growth and China's contribution to the reduction in global population growth through its one-child policy.

35 Mühlhahn, K. (2019). *Making China Modern: From the Great Qing to Xi Jingping*. Cambridge, MA: Belknap Press, p. 43.; the word prebendary is Max Weber's.

36 Maddison, A. (2007a) *Chinese Economic Performance in the Long Run*, 2nd edn. OECD, p. 17.

37 Mokyr (2017), p. 294.

38 Ibid., p. 315.

39 Cited in Goodrich (2002), p. 52.

40 Luttwak, E. (2019) Personal correspondence.

41 The contemporary fashion is to treat Confucianism as a secular political philosophy rather than a religion. But it looks like no secular western political philosophy. Certainly, Confucianism seems to satisfy the conditions of a religion as they are laid out by Émile Durkheim, in that it draws a distinction between the sacred and the profane. Suffice it to say that throughout its complex history Confucianism has

represented an all-encompassing way of living and thinking, whilst still being essentially rooted in a human-centred philosophy. For further discussion, see Adler, J. (2014) *Confucianism as a Religious Tradition: Linguistic and Methodological Problems.* Institute for Advanced Studies in Humanities and Social Sciences, National Taiwan University. Available at: https://www2.kenyon.edu/Depts/Religion/Fac/Adler/Writings/AAR-Still%20Hazy.pdf, accessed 5 July 2022.

42 Mühlhahn (2019), p. 38.

43 Xiang (2020), p. 130; see also Leys, S. (2013). *The Hall of Uselessness: Collected Essays.* New York: New York Review Books , pp. 322–3.

44 Mühlhahn (2019), p. 38.

45 Desai, M. (2009) *The Rediscovery of India.* London: Penguin, p. 98.

Chapter 6: Lovely and Lousy Jobs

1 See Arendt, H. (1958) *The Human Condition.* Chicago and London: University of Chicago Press, ch. 3 and ch. 4.

2 Terkel, S. (1974) *Working.* New York: The New Press, p. xi.

3 In Aristotle (2002) *Nicomachean Ethics.* Ed. Sarah Brodie. Trans. Christopher Rowe. Oxford: Oxford University Press, p. 101.

4 Elias, N. (1996) *The Germans.* Ed. Michael Schöter. Trans. Eric Dunning and Stephen Mennell. New York: Columbia University Press, p. 351.

5 Tran, P. (2017) How New Technologies Can Create Huge Numbers of Meaningful Jobs. *World Economic Forum*, 19 June. Available at: https://www.weforum.org/agenda/2017/06/how-new-technologies-can-create-huge-numbers-of-meaningful-jobs/, accessed 21 July 2021.

6 Ibid.

7 Withers, M. (2021) Work Less and Be More Creative – a Radical Prescription. *Financial Times* [online]. Available at: https://www.ft.com/content/6c6f8d99-ac36-4043-bd1d-459d6763b413, accessed 2 May 2022.

8 Davenport, T. H. and Ronanki, R. (2018) Artificial Intelligence for the Real World. *Harvard Business Review*, January–February 2018. Available at: https://hbr.org/2018/01/artificial-intelligence-for-the-real-world., accessed 13 September 2021.

9 RoboticsBiz (2021) How Automation Is Pushing the Boundaries of Drug Development. Available at: https://roboticsbiz.com/how-automation-is-pushing-the-boundaries-of-drug-development/, accessed 2 May 2022.

10 Batra, P. et al. (2017) Jobs Lost, Jobs Gained: Workforce Transitions in a Time of Automation, *McKinsey and Company*, December 2017, p. 2. Available at: https://www.mckinsey.com/~/media/mckinsey/industries/public%20and%20social%20sector/our%20insights/what%20the%20future%20of%20work%20will%20mean%20for%20jobs%20skills%20and%20wages/mgi-jobs-lost-jobs-gained-report-december-6-2017.pdf.

11 The hype is now pouring out far faster than ever. See, for example: AI Could Hasten the Four Hour Day. *The Times*, 9 April 2023.

12 Russell, S. (2021) AI in the Economy [recorded lecture]. Reith Lectures, Living with Artificial Intelligence. Gordon Aikman Lecture Theatre, Edinburgh. 5 November. Available at: https://www.bbc.co.uk/sounds/play/m0012fnc, accessed 12 April 2022.

13 Redtenbacher, F. (1848), *Conclusions Concerning the Construction of Machines*. Cited in Klemm (1964), p. 319.

14 This conclusion of Travis Kalanick, CEO of Uber 2010–17, was reported in McGee, P. (2022) The True Flaw of Driverless Cars Isn't the Tech. *Financial Times* [online]. Available at: https://www.ft.com/content/189f75e7-da81-4f96-bbfc-4b3f7f6b1f2a, accessed 26 April 2022.

15 Sellman, M. (2023). Is ChatGPT Too Clever for Its Own Good? *The Times* [online]. Available at: https://www.thetimes.co.uk/article/is-chatgpt-too-clever-for-its-own-good-zzq9th7b8, accessed 6 June 2023.

16 Christopher Pissarides, an economist, and Jacques Bughin, a senior partner at McKinsey, offer a simple formula: 'Higher productivity implies faster economic growth, more consumer spending, increased labor demand, and thus greater job creation.' Pissarides, C. and Bughin, J. (2018) Embracing the New Age of Automation. *Project Syndicate* [online]. Available at: https://www.project-syndicate.org/commentary/automation-jobs-policy-imperatives-by-christopher-pissarides-and-jacques-bughin-2018-01, accessed 6 July 2022.

17 Bessen, J. (2015) 'Toil and Technology', *Finance and Development*, 52(1). Available at: https://www.imf.org/external/pubs/ft/fandd/2015/03/

bessen.htm, accessed 15 May 2023. But it is impossible to separate out the effects of automation from those of economic growth or urbanization, which increase demand for banking services. In any case, it is contrary to the experience of the massive closure of high street banks in the UK.

18 Susskind, D. (2020) *A World Without Work*. London: Allen Lane, pp. 22–4.

19 Davenport and Ronanki (2018), p. 17.

20 *The Essential Keynes* (2015), p. 80.

21 Ibid., p. 73.

22 See Forrester, K. (2022) On the Disassembly Line. *London Review of Books*, 7 July, reviewing Phil Jones's *Work Without Workers: Labour in the Age of Platform Capitalism* and Eyal Press's *Dirty Work: Essential Jobs and the Hidden Cost of Inequality in America*.

23 Krugman, P. (1996) *Pop Internationalism*. Cambridge, MA: MIT Press, pp. 197–203.

24 See statistical appendixes of Maddison (2006), p. 183 (Table A1-a). Available at: https://www.stat.berkeley.edu/~aldous/157/Papers/world_economy.pdf, accessed 23 August 2021.

25 For scepticism about the claims that technology will soon take over large numbers of jobs, see Brooks, R. (2017) The Seven Deadly Sins of AI Predictions. *MIT Technology Review*, 6 October. Available at: https://www.technologyreview.com/2017/10/06/241837/the-seven-deadly-sins-of-ai-predictions/, accessed 25 January 2023.

26 Susskind (2020), p. 62. See also pp. 40–44.

27 Ford, M. (2015) *The Rise of the Robots*. New York: Basic Books, p. 176.

28 Goos, M. and Manning, A. (2005) Lousy and Lovely Jobs: The Rising Polarization of Work in Britain. *The Review of Economics and Statistics*, 89(1), pp. 118–33.

29 Harari, Y. (2018) *21 Lessons for the 21st Century*, London: Vintage, pp. 28–9.

30 The Digital Economy (2016) *The Economist*, 9 June. Available at: https://www.economist.com/britain/2016/06/09/the-digital-economy, accessed 22 March 2023.

31 Office for National Statistics (2022) *Unemployment Rate (Aged 16 and Over, Seasonally Adjusted)* [online]. Available at: https://www.ons.gov.uk/employmentandlabourmarket/peoplenotinwork/unemployment/timeseries/mgsx/lms, accessed 25 April 2022.

32 Blanchflower, D. (2019) *Not Working: Where Have All the Good Jobs Gone?* Princeton and Oxford: Princeton University Press, p. 42.

33 Lipset, S. (1963). *Political Man: The Social Basis of Politics.* Garden City: Anchor Books.

Chapter 7: Upskilling or Downskilling?

1 ILO (2022). *Potential WESO Report on Lifelong Learning and Skills Dynamics.* Concept Note. 1–2 December.

2 Jones, C. (2020) The Tech Giants Want to Help Prepare the World for the Future of Work. *World Economic Forum,* 22 October. Available at: https://www.hellenicshippingnews.com/these-tech-giants-want-to-help-prepare-the-world-for-the-future-of-work/, accessed 6 June 2023.

3 Thornhill, J. (2022) Don't Worry about AI Sentience. Do Worry about What the Machines Are Doing. *Financial Times* [online]. Available at: https://www.ft.com/content/0f332662-6d98-4d33-a687-d3951a3c1cb1, accessed 4 July 2022.

4 Plato ([375 BCE] 2007) *The Republic II,* 2nd edn. Trans. Desmond Lee. London: Penguin Books, 370a–b, pp. 56–7.

5 Smith, A. ([1776] 1937) *An Inquiry into the Nature and Causes of the Wealth of Nations.* Ed. Edwin Cannan. New York: The Modern Library.

6 Ferguson, A. (2007) *An Essay on the History of Civil Society.* Ed. Fania Oz-Salzberger. Cambridge: Cambridge University Press, pp. 172–3.

7 Smith ([1776] 1937), p. 734.

8 Ure, A. (1835) *The Philosophy of Manufactures, or, An Exposition of the Scientific, Moral, and Commercial Economy of the Factory System of Great Britain.* London: C. Knight, p. 20.

9 Ibid., p. 15.

10 Bell, D. (1963) Veblen and the New Class. *The American Scholar,* 32(4), pp. 626–7.

11 Head, S. (2014) *Mindless: Why Smarter Machines Are Making Dumber Humans.* New York: Basic Books, p. 16.

12 Ibid., p. 7.

Chapter 8: Straightening the Crooked Timber

1 Passmore, J.A. (1970) *The Perfectibility of Man*. London, Duckworth, p. 13.

2 Aristotle (1885) p. 248.

3 There seems to be an obvious inconsistency between being innocent and choosing to eat of the forbidden fruit. Adam and Eve had to be moral creatures to choose 'knowledge of good and evil'.

4 Augustine ([c.400] 1961) *Confessions*. Harmondsworth: Penguin, Book I, p. 27.

5 Ibid., Book 8, Chapter 5, p. 165.

6 Guizot ([1828] 1997) p. 195.

7 Passmore (1970), p. 229.

8 Cited in Klemm (1964), p. 94.

9 Putnam, H. (1995) *Words and Life*. Ed. James Conant. Cambridge, MA and London: Harvard University Press, p. 483.

10 Skidelsky, E. (2008) *Ernst Cassirer: The Last Philosopher of Culture*. Princeton: Princeton University Press, p. 226.

11 On Bacon's Solomon House, see *The New Atlantis* in More, T., Bacon, F., and Neville, H. (1999) *Thomas More, Utopia; Francis Bacon, New Atlantis; Henry Neville, The Isle of Pines*. Oxford: Oxford University Press. In its near contemporary Tommaso Campanella's *City of the Sun* (1623) the good life is secured by eugenics.

12 Shapin, S. (2018), *The Scientific Revolution*. 2nd ed. Chicago: Chicago University Press. pp. 93–4.

13 The distinction between the 'raw' and the 'cooked' comes from Lévi-Strauss's 1964 book of that title. As described by Dr Ouzi Elyada, 'The cook is a kind of cultural agent who links the raw product with the human consumer. His role is to ensure that the natural becomes cooked and undergoes a process of socialisation.' See: Elyada, O. (2007) *The Raw and the Cooked: Claude Lévi-Strauss and the Hidden Structures of Myth*. Haifa: Haifa University Press, p. 55.

14 Locke, J. ([1689]1980) *Second Treatise of Government*. Ed. C. B. Macpherson. Indianapolis: Hackett, p. 29.

15 Thus the nineteenth-century poet William Cowper on reading Captain Cook's diaries of his voyage to the Pacific sitting in his Buckinghamshire vicarage, cited in Holmes, R. (2008) *The Age of Wonder*. London: Harper Press, p. 51.

16 More, T. (1965) *Utopia*. Trans. Paul Turner. Harmondsworth: Penguin, p. 44.

17 For an account of More's Utopia, see Claeys, G. (2011) *Searching for Utopia: The History of an Idea*. London: Thames and Hudson, Chapter 4.

18 More, T., Bacon, F. and Neville, H. (1999) *Thomas More, Utopia; Francis Bacon, New Atlantis; Henry Neville, The Isle of Pines*. Oxford: Oxford University Press, p. 136.

19 On this, see Hatherley, O. (2018) Prefabricating Communism: Mass Production and the Soviet City. In Davies (2018), pp. 207–35.

20 Zamyatin, Y. ([1924] 1993) *We*. Trans. Clarence Brown. London: Penguin.

Chapter 9: Enlightenments

1 Cited by Keith Thomas in his review of Ritchie Robertson's *The Enlightenment: The Pursuit of Happiness, 1680–1790*: Thomas, K. (2021) 'Lights On and Away We Go', *London Review of Books*, 20 May.

2 Sutton, C. (1974) *The German Tradition in Philosophy*. London: Weidenfeld and Nicolson. Madame de Staël cited the summary of Jean Paul Richter: 'L'empire de la mer c'était aux Anglais, celui de la terre aux Français, et celui de l'air aux Allemands.'

3 For a good discussion, see Chapter III in Becker, C. L. (1991) *The Heavenly City of the Eighteenth-Century Philosophers*. New Haven and London: Yale University Press, pp. 71–118.

4 Passmore (1970), p. 304.

5 Voltaire (1759) *An Essay on Universal History, the Manners, and Spirit of Nations, from the Reign of Charlemagne to the Age of Louis XIV*. England: J. Nourse.

6 Kant, I. ([1784] 1963) Idea for a Universal History from a Cosmopolitan Point of View. In Kant, I. *On History*. Trans. Lewis White Beck. Indianapolis: Bobbs-Merrill Co.

7 Condorcet, J. A. N. ([1795] 1955) *Sketch for a Historical Picture of the Progress of the Human Mind*, 4th edn. Trans. June Barraclough. Ed. Stuart Hampshire. London: Weidenfeld and Nicolson, pp. 4–5.

8 Ibid., p. 8.

9 Ibid., p. 10.

10 Ibid., p. 11.

11 Ibid., pp. 42–69.

12 Ibid., p. 74.

13 Ibid., p. 77.

14 Ibid., p. 102.

15 Ibid., p. 113.

16 Ibid., pp. 119–34.

17 Ibid., p. 148.

18 Ibid., pp. 181, 190.

19 The associationist psychologist David Hartley (1705–57) also wanted to use the 'calculus of probability' to determine social policy.

20 Condorcet ([1795] 1955), p.188.

21 Ibid., p. 189.

22 Ibid., p. 201.

23 For Condorcet's hope in 'enlightened despotism' as antidote to feudal oppression see ibid., p. 126.

24 For an account, see Roll, E. (1923) *A History of Economic Thought*, 2nd edn. London: Faber and Faber, pp. 128–34. Quesnay was the author of the famous 'Tableau', which tried to demonstrate mathematically that agriculture alone can yield a surplus – a 'produit net'. Quesnay's mathematical method was the reverse of Adam Smith's but had a great influence on Ricardo.

25 Mill, J. S. (1873) *Autobiography*. London: Longmans, Green, Reader, and Dyer, p. 30. Mill evidently considered his nervous breakdown as an adolescent a relatively small price to pay for his father's educational method.

26 Guizot, F. ([1828] 1997), p. 229.

27 Hume, D. (1999) *A Treatise of Human Nature*. Ontario: Batoche, p. 285.

28 Montesquieu ([1748] 2001).

29 Smith ([1776] 1937), p. 14.

30 The Church had long used exactly this utilitarian argument to enjoin obedience to God's law, the human *interest* in doing so being the choice between ultimate (or eternal) salvation or damnation.

31 Hirschmann, A. O. (1981) *Essays in Trespassing*. Cambridge: Cambridge University Press, p. 288.

32 See Skidelsky and Skidelsky (2013), p. 49.

33 Pope, A. ([1734] 1789) *Essay on Man*. Copenhagen: FC Pelt.

34 Holmes (2008).

35 Rousseau, J. (1782) On Social Contract or the Principles of Political Right. In Bondanella, J. C. and Ritter, A. (eds.) (1988) *Rousseau's Political Writings*. New York and London: W. W. Norton and Company, p. 85.

36 Plamenatz, J. (1963) *Man and Society*, vol. 1. London: Longmans, Green and Co., p. 390.

37 Hegel, F. [1820] *Elements of the Philosophy of Right*. Cited in Horowitz and Maley (1994), p. 51.

38 Stern, F. (1974) *The Politics of Cultural Despair*. Berkeley: University of California Press, p. 51.

Chapter 10: The Devil in the Machine

1 Steiner, G. (1980) *The Death of Tragedy*. New York: Oxford University Press, p. 8.

2 Shelley, M. W. ([1818] 1999) *Frankenstein; Or, The Modern Prometheus*. Cambridge: Chadwyck-Healey.

3 For an account of the scientific background, see Holmes (2008), chapter 7: 'Dr Frankenstein and the Soul'.

4 For a compendium of these views, see Vasbinder, S. H. (1984) *Scientific Attitudes in Mary Shelley's Frankenstein*. Ann Arbor: UMI Research Press, chapter 2, on which this account draws heavily. It was also adapted into a stage play in the 1820s, shifting its moral and scientific themes to a mixture of gothic melodrama and black farce.

5 Bell, J. (1818) Review of New Publications. Frankenstein; Or, The Modern Prometheus. *La Belle Assemblée*, vol. 17, pp. 139–42, p. 139.

6 Stephen Crafts, cited in Vasbinder (1984), p. 20.

7 The fact that her mother died in giving birth to her daughter, Mary, and that her own first child died in childbirth, has produced psychological interpretations of the origins of Mary Shelley's own monster, and Frankenstein's abortion of the monster's intended child.

8 A light-hearted version of magic out of control with a serious message is Goethe's short poem 'The Sorcerer's Apprentice'. The apprentice uses his master's magic to command a broomstick to clean the house, but his magic isn't enough to control it as it runs amok. The moral is: don't create forces you can't control. The publication date, 1797, suggests a comment on the violent turn in the French Revolution.

9 Engels and Marx ([1848] 1998), p. 41.

10 *2001: A Space Odyssey* (film, 1968). Directed by Stanley Kubrick. USA: Metro-Goldwyn-Mayer Studios Inc.

11 Cited in Passmore (1970), p. 341.

12 For an account, see Taylor (2007), pp. 45–7.

13 Davies, S. (2019) *The Street-Wise Guide to the Devil and His Works*. Brighton: Edward Everett Root, pp. 10–11. For further discussion of this problem in Christian theodicy, see Kolakowski, L. ([1978] 2005) *Main Currents of Marxism*. New York and London: W. W. Norton and Company, pp. 20–21.

14 Davies (2019), p. 50.

15 Or Zoroastrian, which has the same dualism between God and the Devil.

16 Marlowe, C. ([1593] 2008) *Doctor Faustus*. Ed. Roma Gill and Ros King. London: Bloomsbury.

17 Ziolkowski, T. (2000) *The Sin of Knowledge: Ancient Themes and Modern Variations*. Princeton: Princeton University Press, p. 68.

18 Trevelyan, H. (1981) *Goethe and the Greeks*. Cambridge: Cambridge University Press, p. 247.

19 Steiner (1980), p. 143.

20 Jaspers, K. (1947) Our Future and Goethe. In Fischer, H. E. (ed.) (1952) *Existentialism and Humanism: Three Essays*. Trans. E. B. Ashton. New York: Russell F. Moore, p. 46.

21 See Hedges, I. (2005) *Framing Faust: Twentieth-Century Cultural Struggles*, Carbondale: Southern Illinois University Press. As the author notes

(Hedges (2005) , pp. 1–2) 'the story has been retold dozens of times by writers, illustrated by painters (notably, Delacroix, Salvador Dalí and Max Beckmann), provided the theme for over eighty films' and inspired major operas. 'In his various transformations, Faust has become a revolutionary, a socialist, and even a feminist hero(ine) – the subject of prolific creative energy. Perhaps only the Don Juan legend has had as many incarnations.'

Chapter 11: The Torment of Modernity

1 Nietzsche, F. ([1878] 1996). *Human, All Too Human*. Cambridge: Cambridge University Press, pp. 117–18.

2 Abigail Green reviewing Christopher Clark, *Revolutionary Spring: Fighting for a New World 1848–49*, Green, A. (2023) To the Barricades. *Times Literary Supplement*, 6265, 28 April.

3 Hughes, H. S. (1958). *Consciousness and Society: The Reorientation of European Thought 1890–1930*. New York: Vintage Books; Polanyi, K. ([1944] 1967). *The Great Transformation*. Boston: Beacon Press.

4 See Evans, R. J. (2022) An Army with a State. *Times Literary Supplement*, 6235, 30 September. Review of Peter H. Wilson, *Iron and Blood: A Military History of the German-Speaking Peoples since 1500*.

5 For Hamann, see Berlin, I. (1999) *The Roots of Romanticism*. Ed. Henry Hardy. Princeton: Princeton University Press, p. 48.

6 Passmore (1970), p. 355.

7 Ibid., pp. 355–8.

8 Stern (1974), p. xxii.

9 Ibid., p. 48.

10 This summary is heavily indebted to Hacken, R. (2008) Into the Imagined Forest: A 2000-Year Retrospective of the German Woods. Brigham Young University Faculty Publications. Available at: https://scholarsarchive.byu.edu/facpub/4097, accessed 26 January 2023.

11 Elias (1996), p. 116.

12 Stern (1974), p. xxvii.

13 The phrase is that of the Rector of Berlin University in 1870, cited in Cardwell, K. (2022) *Hayek: A Life*. Chicago and London: University of Chicago Press, p. 520.

14 Rhodes, C. (1895) Letter. Cited in Jones, M. and Simpson, W. (2000) *Europe, 1783–1914*. London and New York: Routledge, p. 237.

15 Cited in Stern (1974), p. 52.

16 Weber, M. (1970) *The Interpretation of Social Reality*, ed. J. E. T. Eldridge, p. 45.

17 Marx, K. ([1894] 1965). *Capital*, vol. 3. Ed. Friederick Engels. Moscow: Progress Publishers, p. 484.

18 For an interpretation of fascism as a revolt of the 'unsatisfied powers', see Carr, E. H. (1946) *The Twenty Years' Crisis 1919–1939*. London: Macmillan and Co. For an analysis of the economic taproot of fascism, see Skidelsky, R. (1993) Fascism and Expansion. In Skidelsky, R. *Interests and Obsessions*. London: Macmillan. Barraclough, G. (1967) *An Introduction to Contemporary History*. Harmondsworth: Penguin, also has much of interest to say along these lines.

19 Turner, H. A. (1972) Fascism and Modernisation. *World Politics*, 24(4), July, pp. 547–64, pp. 550–57.

20 Hitler, A. ([1925] 1942) *Mein Kampf*. Trans. James Murphy. London, New York and Melbourne: Hurst and Blackett, p. 354.

21 Ibid., p. 361.

22 Grossman, *The People Immortal*, cited by Jochen Hellbeck, *Times Literary Supplement*, 24 February 2023, p. 5.

23 Mann, T. (1945) *Germany and the Germans* [speech transcript]. Coolidge Auditorium, Library of Congress, Washington, 29 May.

24 Toynbee (1947), p. 507.

25 Turner (1972), p. 564.

Chapter 12: *Technics and Civilization*

1 Zweig, S. ([1942] 2011) *The World of Yesterday*. London: Pushkin Press, pp. 25–6.

2 Mumford, L. ([1934] 2010) *Technics and Civilization*. Chicago and London: University of Chicago Press, p. 52.

3 Ibid., p. 283.

4 Ibid., pp. 400–410.

5 Keynes, J. M. (1931) Saving and Spending. In Keynes, J. M. (1933) *Essays in Persuasion*. London: Macmillan and Co., pp. 153–4.

6 For the Hayek–Keynes exchange see: Skidelsky, R. (2003) *John Maynard Keynes 1883–1946: Economist. Philosopher. Statesman*. Harmondsworth: Penguin Books, pp. 722–3.

7 Mumford, L., cited in Roe Smith and Marx (1994), p. 29.

8 Mumford ([1934] 2010), pp. 433–4.

9 For Cassirer's 'Form and Technics', see Skidelsky, E. (2008) *Ernst Cassirer: The Last Philosopher of Culture*. Princeton and Oxford: Princeton University Press, pp. 184–94.

10 Spengler, O. (1932) *Man and Technics*. Trans. Charles Francis Atkinson. New York: Alfred A. Knopf, p. 39.

11 Ibid., p. 39.

12 Ibid., p. 40.

13 Ibid., p. 81.

14 Ibid., p. 66.

15 Ibid., p. 86. Julien de la Mettrie was an eighteenth-century French *philosophe*.

16 Heidegger, M. ([1954] 1977) The Question Concerning Technology. In Heidegger, M. *The Question Concerning Technology, and Other Essays*. New York: Harper and Row, p. 18.

17 Cited in Gleick, J. (2011) *The Information: A History, a Theory, a Flood*. New York: Pantheon Books, p. 39.

18 Ibid., p. 35.

19 Skidelsky, E. (2008), p. 207.

20 Ibid., p. 204.

Chapter 13: From Utopia to Dystopia

1 Cited in Sedlacek, T. (2011) *Economics of Good and Evil: The Quest for Economic Meaning from Gilgamesh to Wall Street*. Oxford: Oxford University Press, pp. 39–40.

2 Claeys (2011), p. 17.

3 Ibid., pp. 17–18. In Hesiod, the end of the golden age comes about through climate change and the creation of an inferior race of humans.

4 The phrase is Sheila Jasanoff's. Cited in Cave et al. (2020), p. 6.

5 On this, see Bleich, D. (1984) *Utopia: The Psychology of a Cultural Fantasy*. Ann Arbor: UMI Research Press.

6 Orwell, G. (1945) Why I Write. In Orwell, G. (1968) *The Collected Essays, Journalism and Letters of George Orwell: An Age Like This*, vol. 1. Ed. Sonia Orwell and Ian Angus. New York: Harcourt, Brace and World, pp. 1–7.

7 Cited in Watt, D. (ed.) (1975) *Aldous Huxley: A Critical Heritage*. London and New York: Routledge, p. 2.

8 Bleich (1984), p. 20.

9 Ramsden, J. (2022) *The Poets' Guide to Economics*. London: Pallas Athene, p. 68.

10 Cited in Gaukroger, S. (2020) *Civilization and the Culture of Science: Science and the Shaping of Modernity, 1795–1935*. Oxford: Oxford University Press, p. 6.

11 Snow, C. P. (1959) *The Two Cultures and the Scientific Revolution*. Cambridge: Cambridge University Press, p. 12.

12 Huxley, A. (1963) *Literature and Science*. London: Chatto and Windus; Huxley, A. ([1932] 2007) *Brave New World*. London: Vintage Books.

13 Lytton, E. B. L. (1871) *The Coming Race*. Edinburgh: William Blackwood and Sons.

14 Butler, S. (1985) *Erewhon*. Ed. Peter Mudford. Harmondsworth: Penguin.

15 Bellamy, E., (1986) *Looking Backward, 2000–1887*. Harmondsworth: Penguin.

16 Morris, W. (2004) *News from Nowhere and Other Writings*. Ed. Clive Wilmer. London: Penguin. See especially the introduction by Clive Wilmer, pp. xxv–xxvi.

17 Wells, H. G. (1905) *A Modern Utopia*. London: Chapman and Hall, p. 5.

18 Wells, H. G. (1927) *The World of William Clissold*. Leipzig: Bernhard Tauchnitz.

19 Wells, H. G. (1945) *Mind at the End of Its Tether*. London: William Heinemann.

20 Forster, E. M. ([1909] 2011) *The Machine Stops*. London: Penguin.

21 Havel, V. (1991). *Open Letters 1965–1990*. Ed. Paul Wilson. London and Boston: Faber and Faber, p. 77.

22 Orwell, G. ([1949] 2008) *Nineteen Eighty-Four*. London: Penguin, pp. 196–8.

23 Zamyatin, Y. ([1924] 1993) *We*. Trans. Clarence Brown. London: Penguin Books, p. 65.

24 Ibid., p. 114.

25 Ibid., p. 61.

26 'Chemical castration' was used to 'cure' the cryptographer Alan Turing of his homosexuality in 1952.

27 For an incisive analysis of Huxley see Aldridge, A. (1984) *The Scientific World View in Dystopia*. Michigan: Umi Research Press, chapter 4. Soma was the Hindu god of hallucinogenic plants. Marijuana is today's most-used version.

28 Huxley ([1932] 2007), p. 24.

29 Ibid., p. 134.

30 Ibid., p. 46.

31 Ibid., p. 47.

32 Ibid., pp. 43–4.

33 Ibid., p. 44.

34 Ibid., p. 193.

35 Ibid., p. 195.

36 Ibid., p. 197.

37 Ibid.

38 Ibid., p. 154.

39 Ibid., p. 198.

40 Ibid., pp. 198–9.

41 Ibid., pp. 211–12.

42 Skinner, B. (1976) Walden Two Revisited. In Skinner, B. ([1948] 1976) *Walden Two*, 2nd edn. New York: Macmillan Publishing Co., pp. v–xvi.

43 Friedrich Hayek's *The Road to Serfdom* (1944) was a highly influential non-fictional analysis of the slippery slope from democratic planning to totalitarian planning.

44 Orwell ([1949] 2008), p. 27.

45 Ibid., p. 225.

46 Ibid., p. 6. The three slogans of the Party.

47 Ibid., p. 56.

48 Ibid., p. 55.

49 This is an acute dystopian prefigurement of the current movement to 'cancel culture'.

50 Orwell ([1949] 2008), p. 84.

51 Ibid., p. 84.

52 Ibid., p. 163.

53 Ibid., p. 267.

54 Hayek, F. ([1920] 1991) *Contributions to a Theory of How Consciousness Develops*. Manuscript. Trans. Grete Heinz. Cited in Caldwell, B. (2004). Some Reflections on F. A. Hayek's *The Sensory Order*. *Journal of Bioeconomics*, 6, 239–54, p. 241.

Chapter 14: The Coming of the Computer

1 The Chinese had printing well before Europe. Their restricted use of it is discussed in chapter 5.

2 Mason, H., Stewart, D., Gill, B. (1958). Rival. *New Yorker*, 6 December, p. 44.

3 Duguid, P. (2022) Playing Dangerous Games. *Times Literary Supplement*, 6208, 25 March.

4 Arlidge, J. (2022) Apple Valued at $3 trillion – How the Tech Giant Set Its Sights on World Domination. *Evening Standard*, 6 January. Available at: https://www.standard.co.uk/insider/apple-3-trillion-dollars-iphone-macbook-airpods-tim-cook-b975188.html, accessed 5 July 2022. Apple does sell products but also offers more and more services.

5 Knowles, T. (2022) Smart Devices Will Let Us Control Gadgets with Our Minds. *The Times* [online], 27 January. Available at: https://www.thetimes.co.uk/article/smart-devices-will-let-us-control-gadgets-with-our-minds-9foddrvtk, accessed 5 July 2022.

Chapter 15: AI to the Rescue?

1 By, e.g., Nilsson, N. (2009) *The Quest for Artificial Intelligence: A History of Ideas and Achievements.* Cambridge: Cambridge University Press.

2 McCarthy, J., Minsky, M. L., Rochester, N. and Shannon, C. E. (1955) A Proposal for the Dartmouth Summer Research Project on Artificial Intelligence. Available at: https://web.archive.org/web/20080930164306/ http://www-formal.stanford.edu/jmc/history/dartmouth/dartmouth. html, accessed 3 September 2021.

3 Webb, B. (1948) *Our Partnership.* London, New York and Toronto: Longmans, Green and Co., pp. 83–4.

4 In the 'nature' versus 'nurture' debate, behaviourists are classed on the 'nurture' side – behaviour, that is, is learned not innate. But the learning environments supposed to produce the right behaviour are highly abbreviated in both time and space, e.g. the famous Skinner box in which rats, placed in a box, will learn, by a reinforcing set of rewards and punishments, which button to press to get the food they want or drive a vehicle. Behaviourism is now mainly an experimental branch of neuroscience..

5 Russell, S. (2021) The Biggest Event in Human History [recorded lecture]. Reith Lectures, Living with Artificial Intelligence. Alan Turing Institute, British Library, London. 1 November. Available at: https:// www.bbc.co.uk/sounds/play/m001216j, accessed 13 July 2022. My italics.

6 For a sample of the list of tasks currently accomplishable by 'narrow' AIs, see Bostrom (2014), pp. 17–20.

7 Terminate the Terminators (2010) *Scientific American*, 303(1), July. Available at: https://www.scientificamerican.com/article/terminate-the-terminators/, accessed 18 May 2023. Cited in Mindell, D. (2015) *Our Robots, Ourselves: Robotics and the Myths of Autonomy.* New York: Viking, p. 4.

8 Frey, C. in Skidelsky and Craig (eds.) (2020), p. 91.

9 Searle, J. (1980) Minds, Brains, and Programs. *Behavioral and Brain Sciences*, 3(3), pp. 417–24.

10 Ibid. For a discussion see Tozer, T. in Skidelsky and Craig (eds.) (2020), pp. 53–4.

11 Chalmers, D. J. (1995) Facing Up to the Problem of Consciousness. *Journal of Consciousness Studies*, 2(3), pp. 200–219.

12 Religious philosophers – such as Alasdair MacIntyre, Charles Taylor, Stephen Meyer, John Cottenham – of course believe this.

13 Kurzweil, R. (2005) *The Singularity Is Near: When Humans Transcend Biology*. New York: Viking Penguin.

14 For the earliest version of this theory, see Tononi, G. (2004) An Information Integration Theory of Consciousness. *BMC Neuroscience*, 5(42).

15 For a good summary, see Ramsey, W. (2021) Eliminative Materialism. *The Stanford Encyclopedia of Philosophy* (Fall 2021 edn). Ed. Edward N. Zalta. Available at https://plato.stanford.edu/archives/fall2021/entries/materialism-eliminative, accessed 7 September 2021.

16 This is the view of Damasio, A. (2018) *The Strange Order of Things*. New York: Pantheon Books. For Damasio, consciousness is a 'super movie-in-the-brain', p. 146.

17 Bostrom (2014), p. 23.

18 Ibid., p. 5. See also p. 29: 'The availability of the brain as template provides strong support for the claim that machine intelligence is ultimately feasible.'

19 This is the position of the physicist David Deutsch. Deutsch admits that the field of 'artificial general intelligence or AGI' has made 'no progress whatever during the entire six decades of its existence'. Despite this 'AGI *must be possible* . . . because of a deep property of the laws of physics, namely the *universality of computation*'. The key to inventing AGIs is to understand that their 'core functionality' is 'creativity'. 'Since humans have it and apes do not, the information for how to achieve it must be encoded in the relatively tiny number of differences between the DNA of humans and that of chimpanzees.' Thus AGI is possible, and perhaps even imminent. See Deutsch, D. (2023) Creative Blocks. *Aeon*. Available at: https://aeon.co/essays/how-close-are-we-to-creating-artificial-intelligence, accessed 13 January 2023.

20 See Bostrom (2014), p. 5.

21 Asimov, I. ([1950] 1996) *I, Robot*. London: HarperCollins.

22 Russell, S. (2021) 'AI: A Future for Humans?' [recorded lecture]. Reith Lectures, Living with Artificial Intelligence. National Innovation Centre for Data, Newcastle. 10 November. Available at: https://www.bbc.co.uk/sounds/play/m0012q21, accessed 13 July 2022.

23 Mayor (2018) p. 177.

24 McEwan, I. (2019) *Machines Like Me*. London: Vintage, p. 86.

25 Ibid., p. 272.

26 Ibid., p. 273.

27 Ibid., pp. 279–80.

28 As cited by Gardels, N. (2021) AI Makes Us Less Intelligent and More Artificial. *NOÉMA* [online], 5 February. Available at: https://www.noemamag.com/ai-makes-us-less-intelligent-and-more-artificial/, accessed 6 September 2021.

Chapter 16: Liberation versus Entrapment

1 Swift, J. ([1726] 1900) *Gulliver's Travels*. London: Heron Books, p. 209. For more on the 'Academy', see pp. 197–209.

2 But see Whipple, T. (2022) Scientist Hoarding Stools to Prevent Humanity Going Down the Pan. *The Times*, 9 January 2023. Adrian Egli, director of of the Institute of Medical Microbiology at the University of Zurich, freezes 'interesting poo' to preserve human 'microbiotica' – possibly for use in a post-apocalyptic world when humans have to live in underground nuclear shelters. 'At least they will have healthy microbiomes in the apocalypse'.

3 Gleick (2011), p. 114.

4 Burke, P. (2008) *A Social History of Knowledge: From Gutenberg to Diderot*, 5th edn. Cambridge: Polity Press, p. 21.

5 Ibid., p. 23.

6 Ibid., pp. 38–50.

7 Cited in ibid., p. 4.

8 Bell, D. (1973) *The Coming of Post-industrial Society*. New York: Basic Books, p. 20.

9 Weber, M. (1947) *The Methodology of the Social Sciences*. Trans. Edward A. Shils and Henry A. Finch. New York: Free Press, p. 339.

10 Veblen, T. ([1918] 2015) *The Higher Learning in America*. Baltimore: Johns Hopkins University Press, p. 37.

11 Foucault, M. (1975) *The Birth of the Clinic: An Archaeology of Medical Perception*. New York: Vintage Books.

12 Said, E. (1979) *Orientalism*. New York: Vintage Books.

13 Rushkoff, D. (2002) Renaissance Now! Media Ecology and the New Global Narrative. *Explorations in Media Ecology*, 1(1), April, pp. 41–57, p. 48.

14 Frischmann, B. M. and Selinger, E. (2018) *Re-engineering Humanity*. Cambridge: Cambridge University Press, p. 115.

15 Saatchi, M. (2022) *Do Not Resuscitate: The Life and Afterlife of Maurice Saatchi*. London: Eris, p. 79. Saatchi's argument is that in the 1970s he was selling products like Margaret Thatcher to a largely untargeted public, just as commercial advertisers were selling soap powder. Now, the platforms sell people to advertisers, on the basis of their known habits and preferences, who use the information about them to sell products. It is in this sense that the users of social media are the products.

16 Rossetto, L. (2018) The Original WIRED Manifesto. *WIRED Magazine* [online], 18 September. Available at: https://www.wired.com/story/original-wired-manifesto/, accessed 6 September 2021.

17 Marx, L. (1994) The Idea of 'Technology' and Postmodern Pessimism. In Roe Smith and Marx (eds.) (1994), p. 257.

18 Eaves, W. (2018) *Murmur*. London: Canongate, pp. 36–7.

19 MacKenzie, D. (2021) Cookies, Pixels and Fingerprints. *London Review of Books*, 43(7), 1 April.

20 Staltz, A. (2017) The Web Began Dying in 2015, Here's How. Available at: https://staltz.com/the-web-began-dying-in-2014-heres-how.html, accessed 6 September 2021.

21 Zuboff, S. (2019) *The Age of Surveillance Capitalism*. London: Profile Books.

22 Zuboff (2019), pp. 9–10.

23 Geoghegan, P. (2021) The Worlds of Peter Thiel and Jeff Bezos. *Times Literary Supplement*, 6190, 19 November.

24 Markoff, J. (2002) Threats and Responses: Intelligence; Pentagon Plans a Computer System That Would Peek at Personal Data of Americans. *The New York Times* [online], 9 November. Available at: https://www. nytimes.com/2002/11/09/us/threats-responses-intelligence-pentagon-plans-computer-system-that-would-peek.html, accessed 6 December 2019.

25 Ibid.

26 Ibid. See also Ministry of Truth: The Secretive Government Units Spying on Your Speech. (2023) *Big Brother Watch* [online]. Available at: https://bigbrotherwatch.org.uk/wp-content/uploads/2023/01/Ministry-of-Truth-Big-Brother-Watch-290123.pdf/, accessed 22 March 2023. It describes the activities of the UK government's recently established 'Counter Disinformation Unit'.

27 Ferguson, A. G. (2017) *The Rise of Big Data Policing: Surveillance, Race, and the Future of Law Enforcement*. New York: New York University Press, p. 4.

28 Robertson, G. (2023) A Town Called Sue. *Times Literary Supplement*, 6251, 20 January.

29 Anderson, D. (2022) Facebook Knows Your Thoughts. *Literary Review*, 25 August.

30 For a good discussion of the differences between the western and Chinese models, see Donoghue et al., (2023), pp. 33f.

31 *The Social Dilemma* (film 2020). Directed by J. Orlowski. USA: Argent Pictures. Available at: Netflix. The speakers are Justin Rosenstein, the co-inventor of Google Drive, Gmail Chat, Facebook Pages, and the Facebook like button, and Jaron Lanier, a computer philosopher.

Chapter 17: Extreme Events

1 Isaiah 24: 1, 3, 5, 6. Authorized King James Version (1611).

2 Glenny, M. (2022) *The Four Horsemen of the Modern Apocalypse* [recording]. The John Hewitt Society. Available at: https://www.youtube.com/watch?v=BJC9SgqGLGc, accessed 21 March 2023.

3 Cf. Toby Ord: 'I sometimes think about this landscape in terms of five big risks: those around nuclear war, climate change, other environmental damage, engineered pandemics and unaligned AI'. Ord, T. (2020) *The Precipice.* London: Bloomsbury Publishing, p. 169.

4 Elias (1995), p. 35.

5 Mecklin, J. (ed.) (2021) 2021 Doomsday Clock Statement. *Bulletin of the Atomic Scientists* [online]. Available at: https://thebulletin.org/doomsday-clock/2021-doomsday-clock-statement/, accessed 13 July 2022.

6 Maughan, T. (2019) *Infinite Detail*. New York: Farrar, Straus and Giroux, pp. 84–5. On 4 October 2021, Facebook, Instagram, Messenger and WhatsApp crashed for six hours. Meta, the company which owns them, explained that 'configuration changes' had caused 'issues'.

7 On this, see the interview with Jeffrey Sachs by Nathan Robinson: Robinson, N. and Sachs, J. (2022) Why the Chair of the Lancet's COVID-19 Commission Thinks the US Government Is Preventing a Real Investigation into the Pandemic. *Current Affairs* [online]. Available at: https://www.currentaffairs.org/2022/08/why-the-chair-of-the-lancets-covid-19-commission-thinks-the-us-government-is-preventing-a-real-investigation-into-the-pandemic, accessed 22 March 2023.

8 Yet to write off population growth as a challenge is premature. Though the world's population is expected to level off at between 9 and 11 billion, most of the growth will come from the poorest countries, virtually all in Africa. In the next twenty-five years, an extra 2 billion or so people will require to be housed, clothed and employed. As prosperity increases, Africa's population growth may be expected to level off, as it is the poorest who have most children. However, as its prosperity increases, so will its contribution to global warming. The dilemma is that economic growth, while stabilizing population, increases fossil-fuel emissions. It is immoral to enforce poverty, and it has become immoral to promote prosperity. (See Lind, H. (2010) A Tale of Two Crises. *World Economic Journal*, 11(2) June). What seems certain is that an ecological catastrophe in one part of the world would compel population movements on a scale hardly imaginable.

A prophetic forecast is William Nicholson's film *The March* (1990), depicting drought-stricken African refugees attempting to enter Europe and being met by an implacable line of machine guns.

9 Ord (2020), pp. 103–6.

10 Lynas, M. (2007) *Six Degrees: Our Future on a Hotter Planet*. London: Fourth Estate; Dumas, C. (2021) *Decarbonomics*. London: Profile Books. Lynas's first six (of seven) chapters are called 1°, 2°, etc., and describe (through to 6 °C) the likely effects of the rise in temperature by a given amount. If global warming stabilizes at 1.5 °C, we can expect, by 2100, faster desertification in North America and Africa, the slowing or ceasing of the Gulf Stream, the disappearance of mountain glaciers and parts of the Arctic, rainforest losses, and unprecedented hurricanes in the South Atlantic, submerging islands. If the global temperature rise exceeds 1.5 °C, the Gobi Desert expands, shellfish are wiped out, and the Mediterranean becomes arid, with forest fires raging continually. Miami, central London, much of Manhattan, Shanghai, Mumbai, and Bangkok are under water by the middle of the twenty-second century, wars for control of the newly liquid Arctic erupt, the Andean ice melt dries up Peru, and many species die. Temperature rises by over 2.5 °C convert much of southern Africa and the Amazon to desert, drown many of the world's major cities, and spread pestilences much more dangerous than Covid-19. At 6 °C life ceases. Long before this point is reached it is 'highly likely that drastic measures will be accepted and taken' (Dumas (2021), p. 106).

11 Martin, I. (2023) To Defend the West We Must Win This AI Race. *The Times* [online]. Available at: https://www.thetimes.co.uk/article/to-defend-the-west-we-must-win-this-ai-race-mc6nsz38b, accessed 5 June 2023.

12 Whipple (2023).

13 Arendt (1958), p. 4.

14 Adorno, T. (1973) *Negative Dialectics*. Trans. E. B. Ashton. New York: Continuum, p. 268.

15 On this, see James, H. (2002) *The End of Globalization*. Cambridge, MA: Harvard University Press; also Dani Rodrik on the 'trilemma' in Bolotnikova, M. N. (2019) The Trilemma. *Harvard Magazine*, July–August 2019.

16 Weichert, B. J. (2023). A New Space Race. *Times Literary Supplement*, 6265, 28 April.

17 Cited in Rothman, J. (2017) Rod Dreher's Monastic Vision. *The New Yorker* [online]. Available at: https://www.newyorker.com/magazine/2017/05/01/rod-drehers-monastic-vision, accessed 13 January 2023.

18 Torres, É. (2021) Against Longtermism. *Aeon*. Available at: https://aeon.co/essays/why-longtermism-is-the-worlds-most-dangerous-secular-credo, accessed 16 March 2023.

19 Bostrom (2014), pp. 35–6.

20 Ord (2020), p. 44.

21 Bostrom (2014), p. 22.

22 Good, I. J. (1965) Speculations Concerning the First Ultraintelligent Machine. In Alt, F. L. and Rubinoff, M. (eds.) *Advances in Computers*, vol. 6. New York: Academic Press, p. 33. Cited in Bostrom (2014), p. 4.

23 Good, I. J. (1965). Speculations Concerning the First Ultraintelligent Machine. In Alt, F. L. and Rubinoff, M. (eds.), *Advances in Computers*, vol. 6. New York: Academic Press, p. 33.

24 Ord (2020), pp. 23–4.

25 Ibid., p. 123.

26 Schumacher, E. F. ([1973] 1999) *Small Is Beautiful*. Vancouver: Hartley and Marks.

27 On the debate between 'green growth' and 'de-growth' see Mann, G. (2022) Reversing the Freight Train. *London Review of Books*, 44(16), 18 August. The 'de-growth' people are quite explicit in wanting to halt or reverse technology; 'green growth' advocates look to environmentally friendly technology to continue economic growth.

28 Brett Scott is a notable advocate of 'guerilla finance'. See the review of his latest book, *Cloudmoney: Cash, Cards, Crypto and the War for Our Wallets* (2022): Miller, C. (2022). How Dosh Went Digital. *Literary Review*, 25 August. Available at: https://literaryreview.co.uk/how-dosh-went-digital, accessed 23 January 2023.

29 Skidelsky and Skidelsky (2013), p. 64.

30 Reich, C. (1970) *The Greening of America*. New York: Random House, pp. 381–2.

31 For an excellent discussion of Dreher's life and thinking, see Rothman (2017).

Finale

1 Marx, L. (1994) In Roe Smith and Marx (eds.) (1994), p. 255.
2 See Skidelsky, R. (2022) More Than Economists. *Project Syndicate On Point*. Available at: https://www.project-syndicate.org/onpoint/veblen-keynes-hirschman-biographies-economics-outsiders-by-robert-skidelsky-2021-11, accessed 13 January 2023.

Index